Biological Agents Index

Quality Management of Infectious Disease Intervention Programs

Achieving cost-effective outcomes using macroeconomics and microbiology, in addition to new public management concepts for implementation and evaluation of best practices in community based sanitation, health promotion, large scale antibiotics and vaccines manufacturing, and laboratory analytical platforms

THIRD EDITION (REVISED)

Author
Nze Robert Olisa, III
MPA; MS; M (ASCP); RM (NRM)

American Journal of Biological Defense ® Washington DC

ISBN 978-0-615-18918-5; 978-0-9815543-5-8 (Print, Hard Cover 251 pages Revised)
ISBN 978-0-9815543-0-3 (Online PDF, 251 pages)
ISBN 978-0-9815543-2-7; 978-0-9815543-1-0 (Software)

Publishing Headquarters
American Journal of Biological Defense Press
7362 Remcon Circle Suite 36
El Paso, Texas, USA

Editorial Board of Review
American Journal of Biological Defense
P.O Box 75650 Washington D.C, 20013

Worldwide Web

http://www.biologicalagents.com

Library of Congress Control Number: 2008926496

The Publisher offers generous price reductions on this book when ordered in bulk quantities. Please contact sales director using the address above.

PRINTED IN THE UNITED STATES OF AMERICA

Dedicated to Janine.

CONTENTS

PART II: BEST PRACTICES

CHAPTER THREE

COST EFFECTIVE PROCESS IMPLEMENTATION FOR BIOLOGY AND INFORMATION SYSTEMS

CHAPTER FOUR

PROGRAM EVALUATION OF INFECTIOUS DISEASE INTERVENTIONS

PART III: CASE STUDIES

CHAPTER FIVE

ABOUT THE AUTHOR

Nze Robert Olisa, III, is Chairman and Chief Executive Officer of BAC Pharmaceuticals, manufacturers of early cancer diagnostics, and natural immunity boosting therapeutics and supplements. He is the managing editor of the America Journal of Biological Defense. The journal publishes the Biological Agents Index. He holds graduate degrees in Public Administration, and Biological Sciences from the University of Texas and an Undergraduate Degree in Zoology from the University of Jos. In 2007 he was awarded a US patent in the area of Computational Biology. He achieved this by using a specific proteomics (Cys affinity Chromatography) technology he invented to purify microbial iron binding protein and show its use in medical technology. Additionally, in 1998 he authored the third edition of Biological Agents Index, a handbook for quality management of infectious disease intervention programs. Mr Olisa founded the Olisa Foundation in 2006. Today, the foundation is registered in the US as a Non Profit Organization. The foundations goal is to reduce threats of war, hunger, and infectious disease through the use of economic development by distributing immune boosting pharmaceuticals, and early cancer detection diagnostics. The foundation also advocates for improved rural health by promoting the use of information, and biological technologies to boost economic development. He was born in Nigeria, but immigrated to the US in 1971. He is from El Paso, Texas and serves in the United States Naval Reserves.

ACKNOWLEDGEMENTS

This book has been 19 years in the making and is the product of numerous institutional collaborations and team work. I owe a debt of gratitude to my mother, Ifeyinwa Stella Olisa, who provided some of the best practices literature in rural outreach and waste water management. I thank my father, Emeka G. Olisa, who introduced me to science; the faculty of Natural and Medical Sciences at the University of Jos, Nigeria, where my early curiosity in biotechnology and science was ignited; the United States Department of Defense where my interest in biotechnology was developed along with the skill set to subsequently develop the innovations made to the on-line algorithms used in the research and development of Biological Agents INDEX Excel Spreadsheets and the National Email Evaluation Systems for Infectious Disease Surveillance (NEMeSIS). Research into this book was entirely funded by the Olisa Foundation.

Furthermore, I would like to acknowledge the distinguished fellows, current and past board members of the Olisa Foundation specifically Peter J. Terek, and Yvonne Thelwell. Thanks to the faculty of the Graduate School of Biology, University of Texas El Paso; Graduate School of Public Health; the Open University at the San Diego State University; Minority Biomedical Research Team at the National Institutes of Health and Department of Microbiology, Graduate School of Medicine at Howard University; and Howard University Hospital for awarding me the Charles S. Ireland "first place prize" for part of the research that went into this book; Hans-Peter Fiedler and faculty of the Institute fur Mikrobiologie und Membrane Physiologie, Universitaet Tübingen, Germany, where I spent three years of study abroad to develop Olisferrol; the faculty of Biological Sciences, City College, San Diego, and Prince Georges County Community College where I developed material for teaching concepts in microbiology; the faculty of the Institute for Policy and Economic Development, University of Texas El Paso, where I developed material for teaching macroeconomics and new public management.

In addition, I would like to thank the following for providing some guideline materials, criticisms, and reviews used in preparing the manuscripts of this book: Sergo Pena, Karl Roberts, Karen Lyon, Elizabeth Dalton, and William Weaver. In addition, I would like to thank the following for their technical support or for providing some of the Multiple Drug Resistant Clinical Isolates used in the research of this book: Angela Brueggemann; Thomas Halder, and Michael Betzler. Furthermore, I would also like to acknowledge unknown contributors of the online encyclopedia Wikipedia for providing some of the definitions used in the preparation of this manuscript, in addition to Takashi Inoue for meticulously proofing algorithms in the Biological Agents Index. I would like to thank Stanly Tai, Volkmar Braun, Allen Douglas, and Elaine Fredericksen for reading all or part of the manuscript of this book. In addition, I would like to thank Elie Mavoungou and Paul F. Kahle of the Teaching Hospital, and Institut für Tropenmedizin, Universitaet Tübingen, Germany, and the Albert Schweitzer Hospital, Lambbaréné, Gabon for their input in reviewing this book.

Nze Robert Olisa
El Paso, Texas

PREFACE

Until now, this millennia has seen major and meteoric advances in socio-economic and biological sciences like, but not limited to, concepts in Game Theory; Organizational Theories like Transformation, and Computational Biology. In addition, there have been numerous discoveries that have brought increases in the understanding and links between the emergence of new and old cases of infectious disease (incidence and prevalence), economic development, and the democracy. Interestingly, these links have been drawn between outbreaks of war, famine, and infectious disease. What is known is that democracies reduce risks of wars, increase economic development, and reduce prevalence to infectious disease. Consequently, infectious disease intervention programs should contain both socio-economic and biomedical inputs and outputs in order to achieve effective outcomes.

Accordingly, to effectively manage these programs, managers should be familiar with concepts in macroeconomics, microbiology, and new public management. For the most part, origins of modern socio-economic and biology concepts date as far back as the 1950s, '60s, and '70s. The global war on terror; and increasing globalization have ably assisted in shaping the way global interventions against highly infectious disease are planned and managed. There have been numerous lessons learned. For one thing, it is more cost effective and cost beneficial to replace labor with technology (new public management). Secondly, and consequently, highly effective governments tend to outsource social and public programs and play a greater role in regulation and oversight.

Subsequently, the private sector (corporations and non-profit organizations) are increasingly participating in program implementation. Biological Agents Index (Third Edition) evolved from an earlier thesis and mathematical models developed for infectious disease surge estimation. The first edition was titled *Model and Real Time Prediction of Salmonellosis* (US Library of Congress Copyright TXu 1-068-657; 2002); the second edition was titled, *Online Algorithm for use in Biological Defense* (US Library of Congress Copyright TXu 1-101-217; 2003). This edition, the third, titled *Biological Agents Index: Quality Management of Infectious Disease Intervention Programs* has been published to demystify the synthesis of the principles and algorithms presented earlier along with the best practices associated with applying them.

Biological Agents Index has been written for performers in government agencies, public, non-profit, and private sectors and for students of management. *Biological Agents Index* stresses the need for increased reliance on information technologies for cost-effective management and discusses best practices of using bioinformatics in implementing, assessing, evaluating socio-economic and biomedical technology programs, specifically pharmaceutical, public health, and clinical laboratory diagnostics platforms. Like *Lean Six Sigma*, the Index can be used to identify constraint within infectious disease intervention processes. This information can be used to reduce threats to validity and variation when implementing specific programs. If correctly used, the index can ably assist the user in the implementation of leaner processes, and in conducting more accurate program evaluations.

During the preparation of this edition, previous and current authors and works have been cited at the end of each part. In addition, other contributors have been documented in the acknowledgement section. This edition has been written to provide the user basic skills needed to be effective in the evaluation of socio-economic and or biomedical technology intervention programs against infectious disease in urban and rural communities. In addition, this edition can supplement the user's education and experience in infectious disease healthcare management or serve as a handbook for future reference. To achieve these goals, this edition has been arranged into three parts with five chapters. The first part discusses basic concepts in macroeconomics, new public management, and microbiology. In addition, the chapters in Part One outline basic management concepts in strategic planning and attempts to demystify microbiology and its components: bacteriology, virology, biotechnology, immunology, and bioinformatics. Furthermore, suggestions are made on how concepts in Part One can be used as tools in the implementation, analysis, and evaluation associated with strategic planning concepts like inputs, outputs, and outcomes, and program assessments and analysis. Part Two of this book offers suggestions on the best way to approach managing best practices in the area of infectious diseases infection control and health promotion programs using administrative processes like outreach, rural economic development, sanitation, and laboratory quality management. Finally, Part Three delivers series of realistic synopses and a case study that places the reader in realistic management crisis situations.

Finally, this book is currently being reviewed for a fourth edition. Readers with suggestions for improvement and interested scholarly contributors can submit book chapter inputs or paper publications to: *info@biologicalagents.com.* Guidelines for submission can be downloaded at *www.biologicalagents.com/American Journal of biological defense*

Nze Robert Olisa
Editor in Chief, American Journal of Biological Defense
Washington DC

BiologicalAgents INDEX (Third Edition): Quality Management of Infectious Disease Intervention Programs
Author: Nze Robert Olisa

PART I: BASIC CONCEPTS

Chapter 1

CONCEPTS IN MACROECONOMICS AND NEW PUBLIC MANAGEMENT

1.1. MACROECONOMICS

A. INTRODUCTION

Unlike other branches of economics, macroeconomics focuses on the role price plays in resource allocation in addition to dealing with fiscal policy, performance measures, performance budgeting, and its impact on government programs and financial systems. In the context of infectious disease intervention programs, cost saving and effective public program implementation can be achieved by applying basic principles of macroeconomics since the emphasis is on the *public good,* community based income, government funding, and international trade. Furthermore, macroeconomics is a broad field of study, which is closely related to new public management.

Historically, macroeconomics can trace its roots to 1933 when the Norwegian economist Ragnar Frisch coined the term to distinguish the individual need from the community's needs. Later in the decade, the concept gained significance after the great depression when the British economist, John Maynard Keynes—father of Keynesian economics—described causes of the US great depression in economic terms. In later years, other social scientists like Dutch economist Jan Tinbergen and American economist Lawrence Klein used these definitions and explanations to develop practical economic models. In the 1970s, New Keynesian economics evolved when investigators like Robert Lucas, Jr. started to question traditional macroeconomics models not derived from assumptions on individual behavior, but rather based on past correlations between classical economics and the stochastic general equilibrium theory, which accommodate the role that time and independent events (variables) that impact human behavior like health promotion and epidemiology in addition to the impact demographics have on: economic development, disease, war, food distribution, and famine.

The traditional distinction between the two different approaches is that Keynesian economics focus on public demand, effectively giving the public a say in the outcome of public programs that are implemented by the government. Conversely, supply-side (or neo-classical) economics focus on supply that can effectively reduce public impact on fiscal policies. Neither view is typically endorsed to the complete exclusion of the other, but most schools of thought emphasize one or the other as a theoretical foundation. The significance here is that governmental and non-governmental agencies tend to appropriate fiscal and monetary policies that impact the "best practice" for implementing and evaluating international programs. These policies in turn are driven by economics. Furthermore, according to Keynesian economics, the success of these programs would depend on the "market," Since most markets in these areas are imperfect, this notion would be disastrous for governments with unpopular yet necessary policies. Therefore, the efficiency outcome of the activities and services, targeting a public good, should be unaffected by the "market," thus making supply side economics more favorable under these circumstances.

1.2. NEW PUBLIC ADMINISTRATION

A. INTRODUCTION

Public Administration can be defined as the development, implementation, and study of government policy. Furthermore, public administration accommodates non-governmental organizations that are not acting out of self-interest. In addition, the process brings scrutiny to the administration of public goods and social equity.

B. HISTORY OF PUBLIC MANAGEMENT

ERA OF THINKERS AND ADMINISTRATIVE LAW

During the pre-era of public administration, thinkers like Plato and Aristotle developed postulates that still guide the role of government and democracy in civil society. After the 18th century, King Frederick William I of Prussia initiated policies that later, in the same century and well into the 19th century would influence thinkers and legal scholars like: Max Weber, Johann Heinrich Gottlöb, and Lorenz von Stein. In later years, Von Stein would postulate theories on scientific methods needed for the implementation of public administration processes.

ERA OF THE CIVIL SERVANT

Having been influenced by the Federalist Papers, which emphasized the importance of good administration, scholars such as John A. Rohr, went on to postulate on the history behind the constitutional legitimacy of government bureaucracy. In the United States, scholars like Woodrow Wilson saw public administration as an integration of sociology, political sciences, administrative law, and public finance. He believed in the separation of politics and public administration. In an 1887 article entitled "The Study of Administration," Wilson wrote, "It is the object of administrative study to discover, first, what government can properly and successfully do, and, secondly, how it can do these proper things with the utmost possible efficiency and at the least possible cost either of money or of energy." Wilson believed in providing effective public management by training civil servants and assessing their quality. For the most part, his ideas, combined with the impacts of prohibition and the stock market pitfalls in the 1930s, initiated the era of "government agencies" in the United States.

ERA OF THE GOVERNMENT AGENCY

By 1945, after the government's role in the US increased, social scientists like Luther Gulick and Lyndall Urwick integrated the ideas of earlier theorists like Henri Fayol to create a systematic method for management using governmental organizations. The idea was to use government institutions and quasi-judiciary government agencies to implement and regulate government programs and public policy. The shift was moving slowly away from civil servants to institutions. This period also saw the return of politics in public administration. Following the United States intervention in Vietnam and the Watergate scandal, politics lost favor with American voters. Not surprisingly, academics like Louis Brownlow, a University of Chicago scholar who chaired the Hoover Commission, later founded Public Administration Service. His organization provided consulting services to government agencies at all levels in the United States and abroad, consequently igniting the birth of government outsourcing.

ERA OF FEDERAL GOVERNMENT DECENTRALIZATION AND OUTSOURCING

The decision by government to outsource services was greatly impacted by rational choice analysis in public administration. This movement was to a large extent influenced by William Niskanen, a former member of the US Council of Economic and advisor to President Reagan. In 1971 with his "budget-maximizing" model, he proposed that rational budgeting by government employees can reduce budget size and that this practice leads to strength in state growth. Consequently, governments started to privatize in the 1980s and '90s. Critics of Niskanen, like Patrick Dunleavy, proposed the bureau-shaping model which argues that bureaucrats should maximize only the parts of the budget which are spent on contractors or powerful interest groups; consequently, government agencies started to outsource. One significant problem that resulted from massive government outsourcing was how to evaluate and assess government contractors and corporations that handled government contractors. The result was the evolution of performance based management which relied heavily on information systems. Collectively, this use of information systems and performance measurements came to be known as New Public Management.

C. NEW PUBLIC MANAGEMENT

Public management should be viewed in the context of providing public goods. This process for management has been widely criticized by most western European countries. New Public Management is a form of digital era governance. The process involves the use of information technologies (IT) by government agencies to manage outsourced government vendors and their activities. Understandably, countries that fall short or lack IT capabilities would lack the resources to adopt this system. Nonetheless, highly industrialized countries and leading democracies like the United States and Japan continue to favor this system of executive governance. At its very core, a basic requirement for this system of management requires its managers to plan strategically.

1.3. STRATEGIC PLANNING

Strategic planning can be defined as an institution's process of defining its goal and direction and in managing, distributing, and assigning its resources to pursue these intended goals and human resources. Consequently, the result will be a strategic plan that can guide the managers and implementers on how to define operational and feasible plans that can include, but are not limited to, technology, human resources, logistics, communication, and policy. Before planning programs and interventions, planners should develop a "vision" which defines the institutions needs for the future and can reflect future goals. In addition, the institution needs to have a "mission" which should define the institution's direction and purpose. Finally, institutions should have values which reflect the institution's culture and priorities.

The first recommended step for planning and organizing infectious disease intervention programs is to determine and estimate the expected outcomes from the intervention. Secondly, the performer(s) should perform needs and risk assessments to determine inputs (activities) and outputs (services) needed for the program. Once these are determined, a comprehensive policy analysis should be performed on existing guidelines, regulations, and standards needed to establish criteria for future assessments, evaluations, and feedback mechanisms.

Strategic planning offers a systematic approach for planning. A major advantage is that the process provides clearly stated goals and objectives and laid out activities to meet stated benchmarks or outcomes. One disadvantage of strategic planning is that it is relatively technical and complex in comparison to a regular planning technique. The process can be composed of timelines and other restrictions and can involve complex management processes that use performance measurements. In addition, the problems for using performance measure are increased on account of the difficulties in quantifying outputs from infectious disease impacts in numerical terms. This is important because the success of quality management of biological and information technology platforms depends on "the numbers" or metrics.

In conclusion, there are several ways to plan strategically depending on whether the venture of interest is scholarly, business, educational, or military. For the purposes of healthcare planning this book will follow the sequence of developing policies, performing needs and risks assessments, identifying program objectives and activities, developing or adopting benchmarks and feedback mechanisms, and, finally, developing and initiating program evaluations and assessments. Developing strategies includes analysis of the organization and its environment as it is at this moment and how it may develop in the future. A good evaluation or analysis has to be executed at an internal level as well as an external level to identify all opportunities and threats of the new strategy. Strategic planning can be practiced either formally or informally in the decision processes and should end with clear objectives and solutions, ways to achieve those objectives, a realistic time frame and appropriate feedback mechanisms.

1.4. POLICY ANALYSIS

In a pluristic society, public policy can be defined relative to policies created by national governments. Government policy can thus be defined within the framework of the president's agenda and priorities. Most often these policies are directed to communities in the form of guidelines and protocols. In the United States, government policies are legislated by the United States Congress except for a few presidential degrees and orders. Furthermore, the executive branch of government is tasked with the implementation of policies legislated by Congress. Traditionally, legislative committees, and quasi-judiciary agencies share oversight and regulate government agencies while the United States constitution directs the judiciary to best interpret the scope and meaning of the law. Fundamentally, the balance of power in the United States government has been maintained in this way for over 200 years. Somewhere in this *iron-triangle* are advocacy groups; political action committees (PACs), and the media. Arguably, these institutions play the role of the linking communities to the government, thus they are more commonly referred to as linkage institutions. Some examples include private companies and corporations, non-profit organizations, multi-media news groups, etc. Given this framework, policy can be defined as a "plan of action" that guides decisions, which in turn lead to achievable rational outcome(s). Governments, private sector companies, corporations, and academic institutions have policies.

Furthermore, policy can mean the decision- making process and can include the identification of programs and development of budgets and fiscal priorities and the determination of the impact these choices may have on a targeted community. According to Patton and Sawicki (1993, pp. 2-7), systematic procedures or policy analysis methods can be used to tackle current policy problems. Consequently, the methods used could involve quick analysis or planning or a more systematic searched kind of analysis or policy analysis. Furthermore, several skill sets are associated with planning and policy analysis. In previous studies, some investigators (Patton and Sawicki, 1993, pp. 8-23) have detailed the learning methods associated with policy analysis and planning, citing learning to recognize specific basic methods and their quick application and competency of using the methods in design and analysis, in addition to the communication of results as key steps. The authors state the key practical principles for being policy analysts are (1) to learn to focus quickly on central decision criterion of a problem; (2) to strongly consider about the type of policy actions that can be taken; (3) to avoid using tools because a particular method of analysis is favored; (4) to learn to deal with uncertainty; (5) to quantify variables numerically and emphatically; (6) to make an analysis simple and visible; (7) to check the facts; (8) to learn to advocate the position of others; (9) to present the client with analysis and not decisions; (10) to push the boundaries of analysis beyond the "policy envelope"; and finally, (11) to make absolute decisions, but rather to make rational and complete analysis.

According to Thomas Birkland (*An Introduction to the Policy Process, 2001),* there is a lack of consensus on the definition of policy. Furthermore, other investigators like William Jenkins, in *Policy Analysis*: *A Political and Organizational Perspective* (1978), states, "a policy is a set of interrelated decisions taken by a political actor or group of actors concerning the selection of goals and the means of achieving them within a specified situation where those decisions should, in principle, be within the power of those actors to achieve." This quote implies that policy making may be a process, and not simply a choice.

In addition, other authors define policy in terms of actions of government and the intentions that determine those actions and the outcome of the struggle in government over who gets what or who makes the political decisions for implementing programs to achieve societal goals. According to B.G. Peters, public policy is the sum of government activities, whether acting directly or through agents, as it has an influence on the life of citizens. Finally, policies can be defined as miscellaneous and distributive policies when they are stated in terms of executive government agencies or are constitutive and regulative in terms of legislative agencies. Miscellaneous policies may also be used to refer to official legislation, guidelines, are broad ideas in political manifestos and pamphlets. On a cautionary note, implementing policy may have unexpected results in consequence of gaps in existing policy, stemming from a policy.

A. POLICY ANALYSIS PROCESS

There are six basic steps involved in policy analysis:

- Define or identify the problem
- Establish evaluation criteria
- Identify alternative policies
- Evaluate alternative policies
- Characterize and communicate alternative policies
- Monitor and implement the policy

Regarding content, policies should be developed through official written documents with standard formats in terms of its purpose statement, applicability and scope, effective date, responsibilities to include oversight and/or governance structures, regulations, and requirements, and relevant history and justifications. Policies should include clear definitions to complex issues. When administered effectively, policy goals can vary widely according to the institution and scope for which they are designed. Generally, policies are administered to limit unintended effects and counter intuitive outcomes and consequences within the organization or communities and environment. Collectively, this is known as complex adaptive systems. Good policy should promote positive feedback. Conversely, due to the nature of these complex adaptive systems, it may not be possible to perform assessments on most feasible impacts of a given policy. Nonetheless, political scientists use policy cycles or the "stagiest approach" as a tool for analyzing the impact of policy items. The process involves agenda setting, policy formation, decision-making, policy implementation, policy analysis, and evaluation. Finally, good policies should contain the goals of the institution

B. APPROACHING SOCIAL PROBLEMS

Positivists or modernists approach social problems by assuming that problems are not entirely realistic, but that they can be measured and observed (objects) and that solutions are expert driven. Conversely, relativism holds the assumption that problems are social constructs (symbols) that should be understood in respect to specific social contexts. Furthermore, solutions to social problems that may or may not be ambiguous can emerge through thesis, anti thesis, and synthesis (dialectic process).

1.5. RISKS ASSESSMENTS

A. ASSESSING THE IMPACT OF INFECTIOUS DISEASE OR ATTACK RATES (RELATIVE RISK)

QUALITATIVE METHOD

Risk (Relative Risk) assessments on infectious disease intervention programs should be performed to determine a disease impact and used to reduce the prevalence of infectious disease. When probabilities are unknown it is best to assume there is a half and half chance for risk to pay off. In the absence of magnitude or the ability to quantify outcomes, a simple assessment is mere quantitative comparison of the pro and cons of an intervention.

QUANTITATIVE METHOD

In the context of infectious disease intervention programs, numerous assumptions are made when quantifying risks associated with infectious disease outbreaks. Some investigators rely of historical outbreak metrics for use in benchmarking, or the use linear or multiple regression analysis. Relying on historical events is useful when investigators can assume with certainty that the infecting microbe in both cases is one and the same. Note that linearity and exponential multiplications are two mutually exclusive events; this occurs when impacts of herd immunity can be ruled out. Consequently, in this state, microbial transmission will be independent of demographic variables and cohorts like age, race, religion, gender, occupation, etc, but more dependent on socio-economic and biological variables like behavior, environment, and the biochemistry of the pathogen. Regardless of the assumption, when quantifying risks for the purposes of making assessments on impact of microbes attack rate the uniform outcome of any intervention should be the decrease in number of new and old cases or prevalence (P) and incidence (I). Outcomes of this nature can be achieved numerically using ratios as indices.

In summary:

A= Microbial Attack Rate = [(I real-time / I start of outbreak) ^ (1/d)]-1
P = Prevalence (ID)
ß: Transmission coefficient= 1
ω= Outbreak coefficient = [1/ß*(Y2/ (Y1*Y3)]
Y1 = number of ways SARS virus is spread = 1
Y2 = Infective dose of SARS virus = 1 PFU
Y3= Location Quotient (economic development index)
[% employed in manufacturing any location / % employed in manufacturing in the US]
X = Number of susceptible individuals
Z= Density of infectious persons N / Km^2
Iß = bXZ (when b=1)
D= length of time (in years) of primary case
d= length of time (other than tears) of primary case
R0 = bXD
N = size of case

In the equation above, the term "Relative Risk" (RR) is used instead of risk to assess the impact of an outbreak (I), defined as ßY2/Y1, on disease incidence in a general population. Lower risk means a lower probability for infectious disease outbreak to develop into an epidemic. Mathematically, (P) is the prevalence of a disease or infectious agent in the general population, and expressed as a percentage (e.g., 0.85 = 85%). (I) is the incidence of a disease or infectious agent in a specific population (outbreak community) of interest, or the percentage of people exposed to the agent. This (possibly hypothetical) outbreak shall be called the "present case" (1– I) or (I') is the percentage of people NOT exposed to the Infectious agent in the "present case." (I) is the incidence of a disease or Infectious agent in the general population (a state or country) being used as a basis of comparison or the percentage of people in that population. Often, historical cases of outbreaks are used for such comparisons. This outbreak, which is probably not hypothetical, shall be called the "control case." (1– I) or (I') is the percentage of people NOT exposed to the agent in the "control case."

Table 1: Summary of Relationships in Relative Risk (RR)

	Present Case	Control Case	Total
Exposed (F x)	$I_\omega P$	$I_\beta(1-P)$	$I_\omega P + I_\beta(1-P)$
Not Exposed (F 'x)	$(1-I_\omega) P$	$(1-I_\omega)(1-P)$	$(1-I_\omega) P + (1-I_\omega)(1-P)$

RR = (F X) / (F 'X)….. (8)
Where, F represents disease frequency.

1.6. NEEDS ASSESSMENTS

A. INTRODUCTION

One of the greatest threats to assessing socio-economic needs and biotechnology platforms are social problems. Accordingly, one way to identify needs is through studying the existing policy process and social problems. Social problems can be found hidden in stories, symbols, labels, medals, typology, ethics, and epistemology. When searching for social problems, the analyst has to weigh between what is just and what is fair and between Utilitarianism and Equity. Once identified, a goal can be explained in terms of its final cause and purpose as an explanation of the natural phenomena (Teleological) or in respect to moral obligations (Deontological).

According to John Rawls, needs should be in a league with the society (social contract theory). Other thinkers like Thomas Hobbes in *The Leviathan* talks of the "state of nature" concepts. His concept describes the state of nature as a world without governance institutions where everyone fights each other to protect liberty and safety. Furthermore, according to Hobbes, the *sine qua non* function of the government is to maintain safety and peace. John Locke takes a more positive view of the contract theory and argues that humans have "natural rights" and government must be limited so they do not violate the "natural rights." One of the fundamental problems in public administration and international relations is the predominant concern of equity. Thinkers like Karl Marx refer to this significant reservation as the "social product." In his writings on dialectical materialism, he suggests that its solution be one of collective bargaining. Interestingly, equity was not an external matter for early scholars in the field.

Woodrow Wilson, regarded as the father of modern public administration, in his genius, created a science with evolving tendencies when he recommended that governments be institutionalized and be given the ability to decentralize. Perhaps without knowing it, he laid the foundation for the dispersment of power and the adaptation of policy implementation. According to Bentham and J.S. Mill the solution to this equity problem may lie in the use of welfare economics, individual freedom, and the utility of maximization of the sum of the individual efforts in the society for the greatest good, for the greatest number (teleological theory).

As we see today, one of the consequences of rational theories has been technology implementation, privatization, and outsourcing by governments in developed democracies that use these tools as the center stage when it comes to addressing the "equity" question. Accordingly, the scientific inquiry model (Blanco, 1994, pp.24) favors the use of technology, where needs are unknown, to address commonly agreed on goals. In other words, the use of technology, when in comparison with human effort, can minimize risk and reduce cost, thus justifying its need. There are plenty of examples of this model being used by the United States government in the global war on terror and in its goal to expand humanitarian programs in developing economies. On a cautionary note, there are many cases where known technologies cannot match with agreed goals creating what is known in politics as a pluralistic paradigm, and even worse, leading to "wicked problems." This is usually the case when unknowns and goals cannot be agreed on. Examples can be found in today's Iraq and Palestine and in the Darfur area of Sudan. Wicked problems are a threat to national security and the welfare and equity of mankind. In subsequent chapters, this book will address and provide management solutions for social problems. For now, the main goal of the needs assessment is to achieve *Pareto superior* conditions. This is a high bar to set, however, in most cases; as a result, an outcome tends to be Pareto optimum. According to Paul Davidoff, the *pro bono* planner (analyst) should be an advocate of equity and justice, and that the key to realizing this goal is empowerment.

According to Peyton Young, analysts should look for equitable solutions to achieve cooperation, which can create benefits (core) that need to be distributed according to equitable rules. In other words, you only have to pay for what you use. On the subject of games, according to aspects of "game theory," the planner's goal is for productive and cost-effective completion between players or stakeholders. Maximum benefit and need can only be achieved when the system or program functions in this way. As simple as it sounds, fundamentally, reaching this state can be very challenging.

B. PERFORMING NEEDS ASSESSMENTS

The first step to performing needs assessment is for the performer to ask, what needs to be evaluated? The next step is to develop an impact model that depicts administrative standards and objectives that monitor service utilization and coverage as well as organization functions. Traditionally, health promotion interventions target to modify changes in behavior or the environment. Consequently, the next step in performing a needs assessment is to define the target population in terms of urban and rural.

Metaphorically, *urban* is used to describe progress and affluence. The term *urban development* symbolizes an urban "make over" and is frequently used to label projects needed to develop inner cities or slums. Evidently, according to recent studies, the systematic approach (Rossi et al, 2004; Bingham and Felbinger, 2002) to quantifying and evaluating impact of urban development measures on infectious disease intervention outcomes for health care policy, cost-effective analysis, and performance of quasi-judicial reviews has been problematic. Currently, most policies surrounding urban development and its relationships to infectious disease are confronted by "wicked problems" and analysis is performed using branched evaluation techniques (Blanco, 1994; Lindblom, 1958). One limitation of this inadequacy is that these executive branch agencies and institutions may not be able to effectively justify the need for urban development as a line item in respective budgets for accountability purposes to congress, quasi-judiciary branches of government, or article III courts for the purpose of judicial reviews or appropriations.

Furthermore, numerous investigators of epidemiologic transition have measured and quantified the impact of economic development and industrialization on infectious disease using gross domestic products (GDP) of defined locations and corresponding infectious disease prevalence to measure the size of the problem and impact (Serow et al, 1998; Hackenberg, 1988; Orman, 1977). In addition, recent studies show that a complex range of socio-economic and biological factors are associated with epidemiologic transition (Serow et al, 1998; Hackenberg, 1988; Omran, 1977).

At present, certain interests like the executive branch agencies tasked with rural urban development, and healthcare and security along the US-Mexico border are unable to effectively evaluate impact of urban development projects on infectious disease health care interventions along the US Mexico border. These agencies include the Departments of Labor, Health and Human Services, Homeland Security, and Defense as well as non-governmental agencies like the Pan American Health Organization. Public Health Advocacy groups and academics in the field are yet to determine whether the cost of industrialization is less than the benefits it presents to infectious disease eradication in comparison to existing intervention programs like education, diseases surveillance, testing, and treatment. In conclusion, investigators may have to think out of the box to investigate trends against the status quo.

1.7. SELECTING AND MANAGING A WORKFORCE

A. INTRODUCTION

Organizing is the process of grouping responsibilities and activities into working units for the purpose of achieving productive, common, and detail goals; clear authority and responsible relationships; goal directed reconciliation of power and authority; clear organizational relationships for the purpose of conflict resolution; reconciliation between individual and organizational needs; prevalence of command unity; and authority delegation.

Steps of organizing should include goal reconciliation and statement, review of organizational environment; determine structures needed to reach goals, determination of the degree of centralization, determination of authority relationships, organizational charts, and outlining of job descriptions.

Once an organization has been instituted, then its hierarchy or chain of command can be defined. Traditionally, there should be top management, division and department heads, unit supervisors, and line or rank and file workers. Some factors that shape the span of the management include type of work, degree of training of worker, organizational stability, geographical location, work flow, qualifications, staff availability, and organizational core values. Most non-hospital health organizations are made up of line and staff employees. For the most part, staff refers to groups of employees who perform the work of the department or unit and help the line unit in reaching organizational objectives. On the other hand, line refers to those who have direct responsibilities for accomplishing the objectives of the organizations. They usually posses high levels of authority within the institution.

Furthermore, in most non-hospital healthcare organizations, there are dual pyramid organization arrangements because of the traditional relationship between scientific researchers, medical staff, social workers, legal departments, advocacy units, and administrative staff. This results in two lines of authority. Ultimate authority and responsibility for management is vested in the governing board. One line of authority is headed by a chief executive officer; the other line of authority is headed by the chief medical officer. In some instances a "central officer" is appointed to consolidate power.

B. MATRIX ORGANIZATIONS

Matrix Organizations are institutions involving multi-national cooperation and are defined as organizations that involves both functional and product departmentalization. This arrangement involves a chief heading the technical aspects to provide flexible and adaptable organizational structures for specific projects like engineering and research. In addition, there are administrative officers for the managerial aspects and project coordinators that function as the final authority. In addition, workers can be borrowed from functional units and assigned to project units. One major characteristic of these organizations is that the participants tend to be highly trained.

C. DEPARTMENTALIZATION

Departments traditionally serve as adjuncts to specialization. Departmentalization facilitates the coordination process. Patterns associated with departmentalization can be characterized by function, product, territory or geographical boundaries, customer, time or time of day performed, process or technology/specialization, and number or work volume.

D. ORGANIZATIONAL CHARTS

By definition, an organizational chart is a management tool used for depicting organizational relationships in terms of major departmental function, relations or functions of departments, lines of authority or communication, and positions within departments or units. Reasons for using charts include the following: to review and identify inconsistencies and complexities in the organizational structure, to orient employees, and to perform managerial audits. Charts are limited in that: they only show formal lines of authority, informal lines of communication are omitted. Organizational charts need to be updated frequently. Most organizational charts become obsolete after about two years, and proper training is required for their interpretation. Furthermore, they cannot be properly interpreted without support information from manuals or related job experiences.

E. THEORIES FOR ORGANIZING THE WORKFORCE

Interestingly, one method for characterizing organization is the use of metaphors like machines, organisms, brains, cultures, political systems, and psychic prisons. According to Morgan (1943, pp. 11-15), when referencing the metaphor of *mechanization* and its characteristics to organizations, the working establishments of the organizations should typify the mechanistic organization. Furthermore, the author notes that organizations should adopt operational scenarios that lack fragmentation on one hand, but that are flexible enough to decentralize and transform itself so the mission goals or the production process can play itself out in the presence of *wicked problems*, and the routinization of movement, which are both characteristic of the origins of mechanization. In reference to the routinization of movement, these attributes appear to reflect on Fredrick the Great's approaches to mechanization (Morgan, 1943, pp. 15-17).

The military, unlike most nonprofit organizations, take seriously this approach of transforming people into "fighting machines" to effectively eradicate idiosyncratic behavior. This is not necessarily a bad thing when the mission is dependent on total team activity. However, bureaucratization would be a more realistic approach in matrix organization. (Morgan, 1943, pp. 17-24). Furthermore, unlike non profits and the government, military organizations display little or no redundancy between departments and do not encourage their members to think "outside the box." Again this is necessarily not a bad thing given the fact that the mission of the military, as opposed to industry, gives greater priority to defense and teamwork, while innovation tends to be "outsourced" to the private sector. Regardless of the nature of an organization, obedience should be the single means to pass through the hierarchy and one route to the top for any worker. Workers should have a single immediate supervisor because fragmenting actions means that responsibility lies within no single party. The downside would be a workforce that results to *Taylorism*. Here, there is a clear separation of planning and work design in the sense that an organization's policy can be established to exploit the workers. This should be avoided. A good management system should not foster apathy and lack of stake in the enterprise for the workers. In other words, workers should feel ownership in the venture.

Taylorism can manifest in the form of straightforward tasking and precision and the attention to details for planning of operations. However, this can be problematic in the sense that there are limitations and specializations when it comes to dealing with a broadened sense of scenarios (Morgan, 1943, pp. 23). In some instances, especially in cases where the goal is to grow or transform with the environment, organizations should function like microbial organism. Here, the operation should take into account its environment and the social needs of the workplace (Morgan, 1943, pp.33-34). This can be manifested as an indiscriminate need to blend in. For this form of organization to work, there is no room for lack of socialization. Furthermore, the organizations should be open to the environment and not hostile to it (Morgan, 1943, pp. 40-42).

A major downside or obstacle in transformation is the presence of other conflicting systems or *predator* within the environment. Here, some components of the organization, say an institution, can refuse to transform with the collective, resulting in an internal attempt to destabilize the operations. In the same token, development of sub-systems within the organization that do not match those of the parent organization can cause differentiation and integration problems which can, in some cases, work against other systems, resulting in internal conflict.

According to Morgan (1943, pp. 45 -51), organizations should be open systems that need careful management; there is no one best way of organizing. Attention to fitness and alignment is paramount. Furthermore, multiple management approaches may be needed, and the environment should determine the species of organization needed (transformation). In the opinion of most investigators and performers, when used well, Contingency *Theory* is perhaps the most effective way to organize. Here, mangers can use personnel skill in the art of coordination and conflict resolution to deal with varying sub units which require different management and organizational approaches in dealing with mechanistic, professional bureaucracy, and matrix organizations. The manager can combine bureaucratized structure with a project team structure, and the project team focus. In the process, the manager can deal with the problems of a strong bureaucracy, an insufficiently superimposed internal team, and the consequence of becoming representatives of another unit rather than a member of the project team. Furthermore, a major advantage of the contingency theory is its ability to neutralize an organizational trend known as *Natural Selection.* Here, collaborative behavior and the Baldwin effect lead to the natural emergence of conflict (Morgan, 1943, pp. 60-64). In essence, this is a form of entropy, a state where systems tend to naturally disorganize (Morgan, 1943, pp. 77-103).

Finally, organizations can function as humans when certain culture or traditions affect operations negatively. According to Bilton and Sim, the aggregation of humans can lead to the development of rules to control individual behavior and look at sub classes within groups for unwritten rules on how to act. In effect, organizations, like humans, participate in group thinking within culture classes resulting in outcomes that can lead to institutional growth or evolution. In addition, humans go about and organize with bounded rationality and a desire for negative feedback. So do organizations. In almost all cases, organizations can acquire disabilities in the sense that there are misinterpretations and misperceptions of outcomes by managers. Outcomes from these can have negative effects on organizations in the same way they do on humans (Morgan, 1943, pp. 84-103). According to Morgan (1943, pp. 155-207), organizations can function as systems of government, and can be characterized by personalization of power as with the US political system, where there is a divorce of personal power and official power since mixing of personal and official power is seen as illicit. Conflict is inevitable when people are forced to compete for scarce resources. Central to this conflict is power, and its ability to get others to act in conformance with one's desires. Usually, the resistance to power results in conflict. According to Morgan (1943, pp.155-207, and pp. 216-236), loss of imaginative capacity can lead to arrogance of power and can cause organizations to appear shortsighted to their own weaknesses.

F. HUMAN RESOURCES MANAGEMENT

Standards and regulation that govern management in the United States workforce are among the best and most desirable standards in the world. These standards are regulated variously by US federal, state, and local government laws. When a US employer situates her workforce outside the US, federal laws tend to apply if corporations are registered in the US. There can be little dispute that US federal workforce laws and standards have made the work environment in the US much desired by the rest of the world. A rule of thumb for human resource managers whenever employment involves a mix of national and international employees is to extend US standards for human resource management to both US and non US employees, even when outsourcing is the case or when employment is based overseas.

G. SOME NOTABLE US REGULATIONS AND STANDARDS

This section offers a synopsis and a few limitations of US labor regulations and standards. According to Kearny and Feldman (2004); and Klinger and Nalbandian (2003. pp.348) generally, *Title VII* of the 1978 *Civil Service Reform Act*, regulated by the Federal Labor Relations. Authority is applicable to all states. Title VII includes the *Social Security Act* of 1935; *Fair Labor Standards Act*, 1938; *Civil Rights Act* of 1964; *Urban Mass Transport Act* 1964; *Age Discrimination in Employment Act* 1967; *Occupational Safety and Health Act* 1972; *Employee Retirement Income Security Act* 1974; *Americans with Disabilities Act* 1990; *Civil Rights Act* 1991; and *Family and Medical Leave Act* 1993.

Collectively, these federal laws and other laws from state statutes, attorney general opinions, gubernatorial executive orders, court decisions, and local ordinances form the basis for the current US labor guidelines. According to Klinger and Nalbandian (2003, pp.349-350), some obligations of these federal laws include prohibition of common practices of black listing of union members; elimination of *sweetheart contracts*, the establishment of the *National Labor Relations Board* (NLRB) to certify unions as appropriate negotiating partners, and establish good faith bargaining practices and adjudication of disagreements that hinder negotiations. Human resource managers should also implement the *Taft-Hartley Act*, which was introduced in 1947 to prevent unions from participating in unfair labor practices. These laws are expected to reduce and expose labor malpractices, improve labor relations through better administrative practices, identify appropriate personnel policies needed in the collective bargaining process, develop protocols for resolving issues, and specify treatments for distinct bargaining units.

According to Klinger and Nalbandian (2003, pp.350), with the exception of some provisions of the *Taft-Hartley Act* and the Postal Service Reorganization Act of 1970 neither the *Wagner Act*, the Taft-Hartley Act, nor the NLRB is involved in public sector collective bargaining. Furthermore, according to Kearny and Feldman (2004), regulation of public employee labor relations is the responsibility of the respective state government jurisdiction. The perspective that the public workplace is subject to public scrutiny and public expectations appears to hold true under the US labor statutes due to the collective bargaining limitation imposed on public sector employees. Consequentially, some labor laws compromise the validity of the first amendment and due process rights under the US constitution which guarantees the right to freedom of speech and expression for all.

In conclusion, the key difference between public employment relationship from that of the private sector are that no national laws sets bargaining and other rights for state and local employees and their unions (Farber H.S., 2005; Kearny and Feldman. 2004). According to Hays and Kearny (2003, pp. 197-198), in today's economy, local government human resource managers can expect to encounter several challenges when privatizing or outsourcing functions are carried out. Some of the more apparent challenges include limiting the displacement of public workers; ensuring job security, wages, and benefits to displaced workers; and promoting in-balances to public and private competition, since in numerous states, public employees are given the chance to compete against private vendors.

Furthermore, in free market competition there should be no preference on the part of government. On this point, outsourcing creates the appearance that there is preference. The process of outsourcing can lead to the need to increase time to contract management. Subsequently, problems associated with understaffing could be overlooked until they become too difficult to solve. In the process, governments can become limited in options by the vendor when time comes to renew contracts to loss in competition. In addition, cost savings and increased customer satisfaction can be lost (Hays and Kearny, 2003, pp. 206). Trends like this can only be corrected when government implements strong monitoring and evaluation protocols (Hays and Kearny, (2003). pp. 206.

In summary, some economic, human, and political considerations will be critical in the decision-making process of human resource managers. Firstly, the manager faces the issues of interpreting laws, personnel regulations, and union contracts. Secondly, since the overall role of the Human Resource manager is the comprehensive assessment and evaluation of outsourcing labor there can be a problem of limitations associated with monitoring and measuring performance of human resource functions like displaced employee assistance programs and increases in petitions and complaints from professional employer organizations due to wage and benefits losses of their members.

1.8. PROGRAM INPUTS, OUTPUTS AND OUTCOMES

A. INTRODUCTION

A Program input can be defined in terms of as what is needed to implement the program. Some examples include human resources, the operational budget, office space, or computers. Conversely, the output signifies activities or services delivered to accomplish the program goal(s); these can include number of workshop, percentage of clients attended and percentage of referrals.

B. SELECTING ACTIVITIES (INPUTS) AND SERVICES (OUTPUTS*)*

GANTT CHART

A Gantt chart can be used to compare and weigh desired activities or tasks against measured risks and dependencies. Consequently, the performer can use this arrangement to determine the best pattern or sequence for flow of events or activities.

PERT DIAGRAM

A Pert diagram can be used to compare internal dependencies between activities or services. Arrows are used to show dependencies. The longest path is the most critical path. When this path is delayed or interrupted, the whole "target" or "treatment" is consequently delayed.

C. OUTCOMES

A program's outcome is the state of the target population or the social condition that the program is expected to have changed. Outcome levels define program changes and effect (Rossi et al, 2004, pp. 203-206). The first step in developing measures of program outcomes is to identify what outcomes are relevant for measurement using both stakeholder perspectives and the program impact theory and data from prior research (Rossi et al 2004, pp. 208-212; Bingham and Felbinger, 2002, pp. 20-27). There are distinct measurement procedures and properties like reliability validity, sensitivity, and choice of outcome measures (Bingham and Felbinger, 2002, pp. 32-43). The adaptation or minimization of these properties reveals the presence of unintended outcomes (Rossi et al 2004, pp. 213).

Some problems may arise in selecting the best inputs and outputs. There can be a conflict between individual and collective rationality during this process as well as other unit criteria. To overcome these obstacles the performer can use paired comparisons, *satisficing,* lexicographic ordering, non-dominated-alternatives methods, equivalent alternatives methods, standard-alternative methods (Patton and Sawicki, 1993, pp. 340-349), and matrix scored display or other matrix systems system (Patton and Sawicki, 1993, pp. 352). Program outcomes can be identified, measured, monitored, and interpreted using statistics, all for the purpose of making impact assessments and evaluations (Rossi et al, 2004, pp. 204).

An outcome can also be defined as the state of a target population or social conditions that a program is expected to have to change. An outcome level is the status of an outcome in a time. The ultimate goal of program inputs and outputs is not to function well but to bring about change or desirable outcomes. The program outcome is the state of the target population or the social condition that the program is expected to have changed. Subsequently these outcome levels will define outcome changes and program effect (Rossi et al, 2004, pp. 203-206). For more practical purposes, a programs outcome can be defined in terms of or in comparison to a control population. During the pre-test phase, both treatments and control may have been different properties. Once inputs and outputs are implemented (treatment), in the post-test phase (at the end of intervention), the outcome is convergent when the treatment group acquires similar properties with the control group over time.

Conversely, under some circumstances, both treatment and control can be identical at the pre-test phase. However, over-time a divergent outcome can result in which case the treatment properties would differ greatly. In more complex scenarios, inputs and outputs, during pre-test phase for a treatment, can be less in comparison to the control. Additionally, the outcome in post-test can surpass those of control. Under these ideal conditions, the program may be said to be cost-effective. Regardless of the outcome, during assessments and evaluation, changes to look for should include changes in cause and effect, rate of change of cause and effect (Mathematical slope), cross patterns or changes, and to outcomes when control and treatment intercept.

D. FACTORS INFLUENCING OUTCOMES

Some of the factors that determine outcome include stakeholders, whose opinions, can be obtained from client satisfaction surveys, focus groups, participant observation, etc.; program impact studies (evaluations of prior or earlier program outcomes) or prior research; and from unanticipated outcomes or positive and negative externalities. The ultimate goal of any program is to bring about change. Assessing the degree to which a program produces these outcomes is a product of programs. In conclusion, unbiased estimates of program validity or lack of validity in the case of selection, secular trends, interfering events, and maturation can best be determined with nonrandomized designs and the use of quasi-experimental impact assessments using procedure like the construction of control groups. This can be achieved by matching, which involves choosing variables to match, and by equating groups by using statistical controls like multivariate statistical techniques and the modeling of determinants of outcome and selection; regression discontinuity designs; reflex controls simple pre-post studies; and time series designs (Rossi et al 2004, pp. 268-297).

1.9. PERFORMANCE BUDGETING

A. INTRODUCTION

According to Bingham and Felbinger, performance measurements and benchmarking can be used to bring about effective management and to change the focus from management to results. The authors define performance measures as the results act (Bingham and Felbinger, 2002, pp. 45) or the comparisons of ideals (Patton and Sawicki, 1993, pp. 224). The authors distinguish performance measures from performance evaluation stating that evaluations tend to be performed by people from outside the agency (Bingham and Felbinger, 2002, pp. 46). Furthermore, other investigators have proposed the use of crosscutting as a quick "evaluation fix" as well as the identification of alternatives as a means of improvement (Patton and Sawicki, 1993, pp. 74; 227).

Collectively, performance based management describes the process utilizing performance measures, goals, and information to achieve quality. Performance measures can be used in budgeting or to measure intervention outcomes. Performance measures can also be used to assist organizations to determine whether they are meeting program and agency objectives and purposes (Behn, 2005). Some scholars have argued that good performance systems do not exist (Behn, 2005) and that performance measures are imperfect and require a great deal of work to produce (Hatry, 2004). Nonetheless, performance targeting can be useful to increase workplace motivation (Behn, 2005). Furthermore, outcome measurements can be used to improve agency accountability (Hatry, 2004). Effective performance budgets should include monthly or weekly targets and emphasize agency activities, objectives, and accomplishments rather than the purchase of resources (Behn, 2005; Mikesell, 2003); they should measure beneficial results and outcomes— a critical first step in strategic planning (Hatry 2004; Mikesell 2003). Traditional budget processes are often driven by cost estimates and have been structured to facilitate and control spending at the expense of resource allocation (Mikesell, 2003, pp.186).

Furthermore, performance measures outline the cost and effectiveness of accomplishments. On the down side, performance measures can expose a public agency to criticism and therefore create opposition to their implementation within organizations. At present, performance measures are being used in public health management in a variety of ways. For instance, in infectious disease eradication programs like tuberculosis (TB), intervention projects can improve quality of care. Secondly, through the use of performance measures, local public health care systems are targeting the identification of ineffective TB interventions that need remedy and best practices for education and treatment interventions (Dick et al, 2004). Finally, with respect to TB intervention programs in the United States, different local, and state government health departments have adopted the use of different performance measures in their *logic*, behavioral, and environmental matrices with the aim of reducing TB disease prevalence (Dye, et al, 2005).

B. PERFORMANCE MEASURES FOR PROGRAM OUTCOMES

Performance measures can be used to measure program outcomes using observable characteristics. An outcome can be something very tangible that is easy to measure when the concept is one-dimensional. Alternatively, multi-dimensional outcomes can be harder to measure. In such cases, the measurements of multi-dimensional outcomes can be achieved using scales (normalization, standardization) or an index, which work better with interval and ratio variables. Scales, on the other hand, assume that the weight across variables is the same. A good index should meet standards of reliability, validity, and sensitivity. Reliability means that the measure produces the expected result repeatedly. Validity is the measure of what is considered the intended outcome. Sensitivity is the measure in the change or cause in variation of an outcome. Statistics can be used to determine whether or not there is a difference in measurements. In most cases, stakeholder or sponsors prefer tangible and meaningful measurements like profit and loss, time, cause and effects, or policy scenarios as defined by various game theories.

1.10. BENCHMARKS AND PROGRAM EVALUATION

A. INTRODUCTION

Historically, benchmarking evolved as a private sector management tool and was later adopted by the public sector in compliance to the *Government Performance Results Act,* 1993, as a direct result of the new public administration movement which demanded results oriented and performance-based management. The hallmark of this movement was for the use of quantifiable measures in management and budgeting; citizens become customers in a service or customer satisfaction oriented cost-effective environment.

Benchmarking can be defined as a point of reference from which measurement may be made. During this process, an entity serves as a standard is used to measure or judge other entities. Traditionally, a standardized problem or test can serve as a basis for evaluation or comparison. This standard, or performance level, is established or aspired to by the benchmarking agency (Keehley et al.). Furthermore, benchmarking is an evaluation process that involves comparisons between treatments (outcomes) on a target with outcomes from a control group. The control group could be historical data: previously collected data in longitudinal or cohort studies. Once collected, statistics can be used to determine whether or not there is a difference between the treatment and control. Some types of comparisons include the comparison of components in the form of proportions, percentages using pie charts, or comparison of items in terms of size. Frequency distribution can be compared in terms of variations, concentration, or relative frequency using histograms.

In addition, benchmarking can be based on correlations in terms of how treatment and control is related directly or indirectly; correlations can be positive or negative using linear or multivariable regression analysis. Finally, benchmarks can be based on time series and trends as they occur at different time points using time series plotting. Benchmarking is a tool for quality management because it is an efficient way to perform input/output analysis as well as cost-benefit analysis; it is an effective outcome measurement tool for cost-effectiveness analysis. Benchmarking can be used for accountability during financial or fiscal (budget) policy analysis for internal legal (statutory) reviews, and for transparent decision making. Organizations can enhance customer satisfaction by continually meeting customer and applicable regulatory requirements to improve their performance and meet customers' quality requirements.

B. IMPLEMENTING BENCHMARKS

According to other investigators, benchmarking is the process of comparing internal performance measures and results against those in the industry or sector (Bingham and Felbinger, 2002, pp. 50; Keehley et al, 1997). There are seven key steps in benchmarking: (1). Determine which functions to benchmark; (2). Identify key performance variables to measure; (3). Identify the best in class companies; measure performance; (4). Specify programs and actins to surpass; finally, (5). Implement and monitor results, and compare (Bingham and Felbinger, 2002, pp. 52). Some investigators recommend the use of benchmarking for best practices by governments and private sector (Keehley, et al 1997).

Performance management can be achieved through nine key steps. (1). Define omission and desired outcomes (Bingham and Felbinger, 2002, pp. 48). (2). Determine the purpose and scope of project; (3). Develop an internal process for analysis; (4). Identify stakeholders; (5). Choose appropriate performance measures; (6). Collect internal data for performance measurement; (7). Collect similar data from other or similar industry partners; (8). Conduct a gap analysis to determine variations; (9). Try and close gaps before monitoring the results and recalibrating findings.

C. PROGRAM AND IMPACT THEORIES

Program theory and impact theory promote the use of service and activities to compare input and output of a program with long and short term expected and or actual outcomes relative to the target population and service arena. Accordingly, a good evaluation question should be shaped by input and output function. According to Rossi et al, (2004, pp. 69), a key criterion for evaluation questions is that they are answerable. However, according to the *theory of failure,* inadequacy in this area can lead to implementation of other failures (Rossi et al, 2004, pp. 71-77). In other words, programs may be well implemented but fail when the program concepts that correspond to the service are faulty. To avoid this, specific questions should represent the concerns of the evaluation sponsor and major stakeholders.

D. HISTORY OF PROGRAM EVALUATION

The great depression in the United States brought about a major paradigm shift with respect to the philosophy of government. For one thing, it leveled the *laissez-faire* philosophy that the ideal government is the one with the least involvement in internal affairs. According to Rossi et al, 2005, *program evaluation* is a relatively recent invention and can be used in evaluation research as a social science activity. Evaluation research boomed after the Second World War as a result of his introduction of several key social programs by government, specifically, because of the *new deal* initiatives that increased social policy and public administrative practices. Consequently, the era saw the emergence and development of policy and public administrative specialists whose job was the evaluation of private and nonprofit sectors Furthermore, these technocrats adopted social research methods to increase management effectiveness. (Rossi et al, 2004. pp. 1-27).

Finally, a major goal of a good evaluation program is its adaptability or transformability (Rossi et al, 2004, pp. 32-37). Furthermore, as a result of "trickle down economics," the downsizing of government and reemergence of *neo-liberalism* during the Regan and Thatcher era caused the government in the US to decentralize power to state and local governments and to outsource programs to the private sector.

E. TYPES OF EVALUATION

Impact Evaluation: Impact evaluation employs use of scientific methods to estimate successful implementations and associated outcomes for policies and programs for decision making purposes by focusing on summative evaluations and the end results. Here, the performer is interested in quantifying what is happening to participants and in measuring effectiveness.

Policy Evaluation: Policy evaluation is often used when big questions arise and involves the use of scientific methods to estimate successful implementations and associated outcomes for policies and programs for decision making purposes by assessing the impact of the problem and determining what changes are evident in the problem.

Meta Evaluation: A Meta evaluation involves the use of scientific methods to estimate successful implementations and associated outcomes by the use of literature reviews o synthesize evaluation of research findings.

Process Evaluations: A Process evaluation involves the use of scientific methods to estimate successful implementations and associated outcomes by testing for research validity in design.

Program Evaluation: Program evaluations can be defined as the use of scientific methods to estimate successful implementations and associated outcomes for policies and programs for decision making purposes; it involves the inspection of the basic goals and objectives of a program

F. APPROACHES TO PROGRAM EVALUATION

Several approaches can be used in program evaluation to verify, define, and detail problems of interventions. These approaches include a pragmatic approach which describes how policy analysis is conducted when there is disagreement on how an issue or problem is handled or a social-criterion approach where the analyst seeks out expressions of discontent and tries to define social problems that should be solved (Patton and Sawicki, 1993, pp. 148-151; Rossi et al, 2004, pp. 118-121), a third possibility is the scientific approach which relies on rational methodology.

Interestingly, the pragmatic approach to program evaluation uses social research methods, i.e. systematic observational and analysis to distinguish worthwhile programs from irrelevant ones. According to Rossi et al, during the process, the evaluator should ask the following:

- Is the intervention reaching the target goal?
- Is the intervention implemented well?
- Is the intervention effective?
- Is the intervention well implemented?
- Is the program cost-effective and, or cost-beneficial?
- What practical interventions can be used to improve the problem?
- What are some of the justifications of the social intervention?
- What is the nature and parameters of the problem?

According to Rossi et al, (2004, pp. 374-379), *Taylorism* evolved as the solution and need for scientific management. Consequently, in the social and political context, evaluation of activities needs to be performed to conduct good evaluations. Furthermore, evaluators need to assess the social ecology of the arena in which they work, pointing out that there are multiple stakeholders that have interest in the work and outcome of evaluations. These stakeholders range from research centers to federal and state governments, as well as private agencies, universities, and foundations. In addition, having multiple stakeholders can lead to complexities and conflicts. Therefore, evaluators should create political and evaluation time tables to support the dissemination of results and evaluation of the political process Rossi et al, (2004, pp. 390-395).

There is wide variety and diversity in the scope of evaluations; this attribute can bring about various consequences. Accordingly, evaluators and stakeholders need to be educated and oriented on the origins of these diversities and cultural differences to minimize quantitative and qualitative differences that may exist in inside or outside evaluations (Rossi et al, 2004, pp. 402-405). A good way to achieve these initiatives would be the use of evaluation standards and guidelines. In similar reports, investigations on how to think about social problems and the role of pragmatism note that new ideas and methods do not appear to be the intellectual task of the twentieth century (Blanco, 1994, pp. 1). These investigators have proposed a rational model of planning as a hallmark of modernity (Blanco, 1994; Lindblom, 1958). This form of analysis characterizes organizational settings and performance impacts output's and outcomes. The limitation here is that it cannot address issues of cause and effect.

Interestingly, the scientific approach offers a more methodological basis for program evaluation. Here, the assumption is one of unbounded rationality. Furthermore, both experimental and quasi-experimental approaches can be adopted. During the process, scientific methods are applied, and a high value is placed on precision. The key challenge here is to assess the threats to internal and external validity. Conversely, the pragmatist approach tries to evaluate within the context in which the evaluator works. It is about giving good advice and information to policy makers. The concept here is that it would be more desirable to be less correct than wrong. This notation is based on the assumption that the investigator does not know everything (bounded rationality).

Finally, in reference to the scientific approach, the goal of a good evaluation program is in its adaptability or transformation (Rossi et al, 2004, pp. 32-37). The first goal of the rational model which adopts an incremental approach is to find the best objective alternative. Furthermore, internal process analysis is used to identify relevant factors or components associated with inputs and outputs and to determine how they are related. This is often achieved through modeling to establish sensitivities and influences. In addition, benchmarking can be used in policy evaluation when an organizations performance is in focus. The goal of the incremental approach is to find a good enough alternative. Secondly, the key assumption in the incremental approach is bounded rationality. Conversely, the key assumption of the rational approach is unbounded rationality. Thirdly, in the rational approach, policy and politics are independent with respect to their relationship. Conversely, with the incremental approach, policy and politics are intertwined. Fourthly, in the incremental approach, the analyst's role is to broker acceptable consensual solutions. Conversely, in the rational approach, the analyst's role is as the scientist applying technical knowledge. Finally, in the rational approach, change is by the root. Conversely, in the incremental model, change is by the branch.

Regardless of approach, to formulate and develop evaluation, some questions need to be asked such as which questions the evaluation should ask and what makes a good evaluation. A good evaluation question should be shaped by the functions it must perform (Rossi et al, 2004, pp. 69).

Furthermore, according to Rossi et al, (2004, pp.71-77), reason and appropriateness should form the major dimensions of the program performance. A key criterion for evaluation questions is that they be answerable. However, inadequacy in this area can lead to implementation failures. Furthermore, evaluators need to develop a problem statement and decide how to think a problem through. They also need to delineate boundaries of the problem, develop a fact base, list goals and objectives, identify the policy envelope, display potential costs and benefits, and review the problem statements and how to explain the role of evaluators in diagnosing social conditions and service needs (Patton and Sawicki, 1993, pp. 152-155; Rossi et al, 2004, pp. 103-111).

In addition, experts can be used for quick-decision analysis of processes and target populations and the nature of service needs. They can also analyze the need to create valid operational decisions for political analysis and explain the differences between issues papers and first cut analysis using social indicators to identify trends (Patton and Sawicki, 1993, pp. 156-182; Rossi et al, 2004, pp. 112-132). Evaluators needs to establish goals and detail the processes for establishing evaluation criteria and for expressing and assessing program theory (Rossi et al, 2004, pp. 133-139) using distinct objectives, criteria, and measures.

G. CONCLUSION

Several important economic concepts come into play when implementing program theory and the role of impact theory. These include the free market model and role of cost, benefits, standing externalities, elasticity, marginal analysis, and equity (Patton and Sawicki 1993, pp. 188-208; Rossi et al, 2004, pp. 133-142). According to Bingham and Felbinger, (2002, pp. 1-3), process evaluation uses scientific methods for gathering empirical data to test hypotheses. Evaluators should look for broad based goals and for clearly stated measurable objectives by which the goals can be reached. In addition, evaluations should involve fundamental goals and objectives of the program and a process that involves assessing program activities Bingham and Felbinger, (2002, pp. 4-5). According to Bingham and Felbinger, (2002, pp. 5-7), impact evaluations refer to impact, outcome, or summative evaluations that are interested in quantifying what is happening and are of two types: one that revolves around assessing an output and another that measures effectiveness. Both focus on measuring outcomes. Meta evaluations, which are basically literature reviews, can be used to achieve these goals (Bingham and Felbinger, 2002, pp. 8). Once data is collected, it should be utilized after internal and external factors are validated, corrected for the occurrence of either type one or type two errors, and weighed in for ethical considerations (Bingham and Felbinger, 2002, pp. 10-12).

Without question, there are problems associated with outcome evaluations; these include identifying goals and objectives, constructing impact models, measuring impact, and collecting data. Other problems include internal (history, maturation, testing, instrumentation, regression artifact, selection bias, and experimental mortality) and external (representative of sample, and reactive arrangements) threats. To identify these problems, the performer can use basic methods of outcome evaluation like reflexive designs, one-group pretest and post-test designs, simple time series designs, quasi-experimental designs, pretest-posttest comparison group designs, experimental designs, and pretest and posttest control group designs (Bingham and Felbinger, 2002, pp. 15-20).

Interestingly, the Nachmias and Felbinger approach is both pragmatic and incremental in the sense that they recommend that program evaluation process should be divided into seven pragmatic stages: agenda setting, policy deliberation, policy formulation, policy adaptation, appropriation process, policy implementation, and policy program evaluation. Furthermore, in the rational phase of the approach recommended, Meta evaluations can be used to select the agenda. Afterwards, policy evaluations are conducted rationally or pragmatically before policy deliberations are made. Finally, between the fifth and sixth stages, impact evaluations are performed after appropriations and before policy implementation, followed by a process evaluation after implementation.

1.11. COST BENEFIT & COST EFFECTIVE ANALYSIS

A. INTRODUCTION

KALDOR-HICKS EFFICIENCY: Kaldor-Hicks efficiency theory stresses *Pareto efficiency* where an outcome is more efficient if at least one person is made better off and nobody is made worse off. Under Kaldor-Hicks efficiency, an outcome is more efficient when individuals impacted by an intervention are better off and could theoretically compensate those that are worse off as a result of an intervention.

OPPORTUNITY COST: Opportunity cost, or the shadow price, is the net revenue forgone by rejecting an alternative use of resources such as time, money, or facilities.

COST BENEFIT ANALYSIS: Cost benefit analysis is derived from Kaldor-Hicks efficiency theories. The following are basic assumptions to Cost-Benefit analysis: (1), each costs-and-benefit unit must be converted to a common measure; preferably the dollar ($) since this sign is the standard international currency against which most currency values are measured; (2), cost and benefits being analyzed should be quantified and miniaturized; (3), the performer should seek to determine the value of service, product, or activity benefits relative to costs. Cost benefit analysis can be used ex-ante and ex-post. Regrettably, one limitation of cost benefit analysis is that it is not designed to solve problems.

COST BENEFIT RATIO: If the sum of cost outweighs the cost of benefits the decision rule is NOT to go on. In a favorable cost benefit analysis, benefits should always outweigh cost. The ratio should always be less than one.

$$\frac{\sum \text{benefits}}{\sum \text{costs}} > 1$$

NET PRESENT VALUE: Net present value estimates the future cost of goods or services. As a socio-economic tool, cost benefit analysis can be used to aid social decisions making, and ably assist and justify the need for program interventions. Here, evaluations are in terms of the public's willingness to pay (benefits) or willingness to pay to avoid them (costs). Inputs are typically measured in terms of opportunity costs. During cost-benefit analysis, monetary values may also be assigned to less tangible effects such as the various risks which could contribute to partial or total project failure; loss of reputation, market penetration, long-term enterprise strategy alignments; etc. This is especially true when governments use the technique to decide whether to introduce business regulation, build a new road, or offer a new drug on the state healthcare. In the case of the later, a value must be put on human life or the environment; often, this causes great controversy. According to the cost-benefit principle, cost benefit calculations should involve the use of time value of money formulas. This is usually done by converting the future expected streams of costs and benefits to a present value amount.

$$NPV = \mathrm{B}_0 - \mathrm{C}_0 + \frac{C - B_{t+1}}{(1+R)^1} + \frac{C - B_{t+2}}{(1+R)^2} + \ldots + + \frac{C - B_{t+n}}{(1+R)^n}$$

C= costs
B= Benefits
R= interest rate
n= year

On the subject of infectious disease interventions, one application of cost-benefit analysis in program planning is to determine if the rate of return of the interventions are feasible. The accuracy of the outcome of a cost-benefit analysis is dependent on how accurately costs and benefits have been estimated. A major consequence of an inaccurate cost-benefit analyses may be an increase in risk in planning because inaccuracies of the size documented are likely to lead to inefficient decisions as defined by Pareto and Kaldor-Hicks efficiency (Flyvbjerg, Bruzelius, and Rothengatter, 2003). Another limitation of cost-benefit analysis is in the determination of which costs merit inclusion in an analysis (the significant cost drivers). This controversial decision often leads to conflict among stakeholders.

COST-EFFECTIVE ANALYSIS: Cost effective analysis is a form of economic analysis that compares the relative expenditure (costs) and outcomes (effects) of two or more courses of action. The following are basic assumption made in cost-effectiveness analysis: firstly, it assumes that the program is making a difference in the outcome; secondly, it investigates how many inputs and outputs may be efficiently achieved and which costs are attached to them for reaching different levels of the desire outcomes (Bingham & Felinberg, 2002, pp.197). Furthermore, it deals with whether or not the technology being used to make a difference costs the least; it is used as an ex-post evaluation tool.

In the pharmaceutical industry, cost-effectiveness of a therapeutic intervention is the ratio of the total cost of the intervention relative to the measure of its effect. Cost refers to the resource expended for the intervention, usually measured in monetary terms. For example, the cost of introducing antibiotics and vaccines in developing counties can outweigh the measured effects. According to current data and the epidemiological transition theory, infectious diseases in developed countries are on the decline. Consequently, manufacturing practices that profit from economies of scales can be more cost effective for the production and sales of normally expensive, high-quality antibiotics and vaccines in poor countries. In monetary terms, at \$ 1.00 or less, new vaccines for malaria or AIDs in a market of six billions (developed and emerging tropical economies) would be more cost effective to manufacture than say the manufacturing of a drug for sale at \$ 3,000 in a 300 million market like the US to drive sales cost down. Cost-effective technologies can be used in the research and development processes to replace more expensive technologies. For example, in this case, computational genomic and proteomics can replace cloning. Cost-effectiveness is usually expressed as an incremental cost-effectiveness ratio or the ratio of change in costs to the change in effects. This incremental approach makes the method ideal for use in performing rational program evaluations.

B. GAME THEORY: USE IN COST-EFFECTIVE MANAGEMENT

From a manager's stance, game theories promote pareto optimality by ensuring individual players or workers avoid conflict when they compete for scarce resources. Perhaps, one way of achieving this is by the use of *Hicks criterion;* that is: most of the less fortunate workers or communities are prepared to make offers or concessions to the more fortunate workers or communities in order to prevent negative changes in the bottom line of more affluent communities. Alternatively, the more fortunate can be encouraged, through incentives and coercion, to forgo positive changes that would decrease welfare of the less fortunate. When gaming, managers need to take into account the opportunity costs of stakeholders, the absolute level of income, and income distribution. In addition, managers should consider the net positive values of private property and private income relative to the environment. *Satisficing* as a trade-off should be considered in negotiations with stakeholders.

C. EFFICACY EVALUATIONS

Efficiency analysis (cost benefit or cost effective) may be dependent on untested assumptions or require partially available data. On the subject of efficacy, an analysis can be conducted prospectively or *ex ante* efficiency during the planning and design phase of an imitative or retrospectively (Patton and Sawicki, 1993, pp. 257-259). An *ex ante* efficiency analysis is important for programs that are difficult to abandon due to extensive commitment needs in funding and time. *Ex post* efficiency analysis, on the other hand, is useful after a program has been in place for a time and has been demonstrated to be efficient by an impact evaluation. This application rests on dubious assumptions, and should be limited to utility; the program has to have independent or separable funding (cost can be separated from those of other activities); the program should be ahead of its developmental stage and should have certain effects. Furthermore, the programs impact and magnitude should be known or easily estimated; benefits should easily translate into monetary terms and decision makers should consider alternative programs (Rossi et al, 2004, pp. 336, 361-362).

Cost benefit analysis requires estimates of both tangible and intangible aspects of a program and both direct and indirect cost estimates (Bingham and Felbinger, 2002, pp. 182). Conversely, efficacy analysis, at least *ex post* analysis, is an extension rather than an alternative to impact evaluation. In other words, it would be impossible to develop *ex post* analysis for programs whose impact is unknown or inestimatable (Rossi et al, 2004, pp. 338; Bingham and Felbinger, 2002, pp. 182). The first step in conducting cost benefit analysis is assembling data through agency fiscal records, target cost estimates, and through cooperating agencies. The second step would be to measure costs and benefits. This can be achieved monetarily using money measurements, using market valuation, econometric estimation, posing hypothetical questions, and observation of political choices (Rossi et al, 2004, pp. 338). Cost and benefits can also be measured using shadow prices (Heikkila, 2000) or accounting prices which are defined as derived values for goods and services that are supposed to reflect their true benefits and costs to society. Other methods include use of opportunity costs, secondary effects or externalities, distributional considerations, and discounting or the use of time-point patterns in estimating cost and benefits (Rossi et al, 2004 pp. 3359-361). The third step in the analysis of cost and benefit is to compare both attributes.

Finally, cost effective analysis, unlike the cost benefit analysis, allows evaluators to compare the economic efficacy of program alternatives when the intervention are not aimed at common goals. Cost effective analysis can be viewed as an extension of cost benefit analysis to projects with achievable goals. It is based on the same principle and uses the same techniques as the cost benefit analysis. However, in contrast to cost benefit analysis, it does not require that benefits and costs be reduced to a common denominator. Rather, a program's effectiveness is related to both non-monetary or monetary (dollar) value of costs (Bingham and Felbinger, 2002, pp. 179). In cost-benefit analysis, outcome is measured strictly in dollars. In cost effective analysis, programs with similar goals are evaluated and their costs compared.

Efficiency is determined by comparing costs for units of outcome (Rossi et al, 2004, pp. 62-363; Bingham and Felbinger, 2002, pp. 197). In summary cost benefits look at outcome in terms of benefits; and cost efficacy in terms of efficiency.

REFERENCES

1. **Bingham, R.D, and C.L. Felbinger.** *2002. Evaluation in practice: a methodological approach.* (2nd ed.) New York, USA. Chatham House Publishers.
2. **Birkland, T.A.** 2005. *An introduction to the policy process: Theories, concepts, and models of public policy making.* (2nd ed.) New York USA: ME Sharpe
3. **Blanco, H.** 1994. *How to think about social problems: American pragmatism and the idea of planning.* London, UK: Greenwood press.
4. **Blaug, M.** 1985. *Economic theory in retrospect.* Cambridge, UK: Cambridge University Press.
5. **Dye, T.R.** 1976. *Policy analysis.* Tuscaloosa, AL: University of Alabama Press.
6. **Farber, H.S**. 2005. Union membership in the United States: The divergence between the public and private sectors. Retrieved July 26, 2006. *http://www.irs.princeton.edu/pubs/pdfs/503.pdf.*
7. **Flyvbjerg, B., K. Mette, H. Skamris, and S.K. Buhl**. 2005. How accurate are demand forecasts in public works projects? The case of transportation. *Journal of the American Planning Association 71.2:131-146.*
8. **Flyvbjerg, B., N. Bruzelius, and W. Rothengatter.** 2003. *Mega projects and risk: An anatomy of ambition.* Cambridge, UK: Cambridge University Press.
9. **Flyvbjerg, B., K. Mette, H. Skamris, and S.K. Buhl**. 2002. Underestimating costs in public works projects: error or lie? *Journal of the American Planning Association.* **68.**3:279-295.
10. **Morgan, G**. 1943. *Images of Organization.* (2nd ed.) Thousand Oaks, CA, USA. Sage Publications.
11. **Hays, S., W. Richard, and C. Kearny.** Eds. 2003. *Public personnel administration. problems and perspectives.* (4th ed.) Upper Saddle River, NJ: Prentice-Hall.
12. **Heikkila, E.J.** 2000. *The economics of planning.* Rutgers, New Jersey, USA: Rutgers.
13. **Kearny, R.C, and B.M. Feldman**. 2004. *Labor management relations and collective bargaining* (2nd Ed.). *In IMCA, Freyss (ed.), Human resource management in local government. (pp. 94).* Washington DC: International City County Management Association.
14. **Keehley, P., S.M. Medlin, and S. McBride.** 1997. *Benchmarking for best practices in the public sector; Achieving performance breakthroughs in Federal, State, and Local Agencies.* San Francisco. CA. USA. Jossey-Bass Public Administration.
15. **Klein, L.A.** 1953. *A Textbook of Econometrics*. (2nd ed), Englewood Cliffs, NJ, USA: Prentice-Hall, Inc.,
16. **Klinger, D. E, and J. Nalbandian**. 2003. *Public personnel management: Context and strategies* (5th ed.). Upper Saddle River, NJ: Prentice-Hall.
17. **Kono, T.** 1994 Changing a company's strategy and culture. *Long Range Planning.* **27**.5:85-97.
18. **Kotler, P.** 1986. Mega marketing. *Harvard Business Review.*
19. **Levitt, T.** 1960. Marketing myopia. *Harvard Business Review.*
20. **Lindblom, C.E.** 1958. The science of muddling through. *Administration Review. 19:79-88.*
21. **Lorenzen, M.** 2006. Strategic planning for academic library instructional *programming. Illinois Libraries.* **86.**2:22-29.
22. **Lusch, R.F., and V. N. Lusch,** 1987. *Principles of marketing,* Richmond, VA, USA. Kent Publishing.
23. **Mikesell, J.** 2003. *Fiscal administration: Analysis and applications for the public sector.* (6th ed). New York, New York, USA: Wadsworth Publishing.
24. **Omran, A.R.** 1977. Epidemiologic transition in the United States: The health factor in population change. *Population Bulletin. 32.2:1-42.*
25. **Patton, C.V, and D.S. Sawicki**. 1993. *Basic methods of policy analysis and planning.* (2nd ed) Upper Saddle River, NJ, USA: Prentice Hall, USA.
26. **Peters, B.G, and J. Pierre.** 2003. *Handbook of public administration.* Thousand Oaks, CA. Sage publications. pp. 11-38: 116
27. **Peters BG.** 1987. Policy design and the development of policy indicators. *Science Communication.* **9.**2:278-296.
28. **Price-Smith, A.T.** 2002. *The Health of Nations: Infectious disease, environmental change, and their effects on national security and development.* Cambridge, MA, USA: MIT Press. pp. 324-683.
29. **Rawls, J.** 1999. *A theory of justice.* Oxford UK: Oxford university press.

30. **Rogers, R.G, and R. Hackenberg.** 1987. Extending epidemiologic transition theory: a new stage. *Soc Biol. 34:3-4:234-43*
31. **Rossi, H. P., M.W. Lipsey, and H.E. Freeman**. 2004. *Evaluation: A systematic approach. (*7th ed.) Thousand Oaks CA, USA: Sage Publications.
32. **Serow W.J., Cowart, and M.E. Camezon.** 1998. Epidemiologic Transition Theory and Aging: Hispanic Populations of North America and the Caribbean. *J. Health and Human Services Administration.* **20**.3: 333-47.
33. **Tevfik, F.N**. 1996. *Cost benefit analysis: Theory and application.* Thousand Oaks CA, USA: Sage Thousand Oaks, Ca.
34. **United Nations Industrial Development Organization UNIDO**. 1980. Industry in developing countries: some recent trends. *Dev Dig. 18.1:1-16.*
35. **William, I.J.** 1978. *Policy Analysis: A political and organizational perspective.* New York, New York, USA: St. Martin press.
36. **Wilson, Woodrow.** 1887 The study of administration. *Political Science Quarterly.*
37. **Zavala De Cosio, M.E.** 1992. The Demographic Transition in Latin America and Europe. *Notas Poblacion. 20.11-32.*

BiologicalAgents INDEX (Third Edition): Quality Management of Infectious Disease Intervention Programs
Author: Nze Robert Olisa
©2008 American Journal of Biological Defense, Washington, DC 20013

Chapter 2

CONCEPTS IN MICROBIOLOGY

1.1. BACTERIA: A HISTORICAL PERSPECTIVE

The study of microbiology, as we know, started in the 19th century when Leeuwenhoek discovered microorganisms using a simple magnifying glass he invented. In 1674, he reported his findings to the Royal Society of London, describing microbes as "beasties" and "animanicles" of different shapes and sizes. Other discoveries were made by Carlos Linnaeus 1707-1778 in the Golden age which lasted 50 years. During this time, scientists were asking questions like: Is spontaneous generation of microbial life possible? What causes fermentation? What causes disease? How can we prevent infection and disease?

Early theories of spontaneous generation were promulgated by Aristotle and demonstrated by the Italian scientist Francesco Redi (1626-1697); the British investigator John T. Needham's experiment (1713 – 1781) and the Italian Lazzaro Spallanzani's (1729-1799) experiment. For the most part early scientist spent a great deal of time contradicting each other. However, the definitive proof of spontaneous generation came from experimentations by the Frenchman Louis Pasteur's Experiment (1822-1895). He was able to establish his hypothesis using rational scientific experimentation methods like fermentation. These experiments marked the beginning of biotechnology or industrial microbiology. In later years, Eduard Buchner (1869-1917) who is widely regarded as the father of modern biochemistry showed that fermentation can occur without microbes, and that fermentation can occur from enzymatic reactions and that enzymes are cell-produced proteins.

The German, Robert Koch (1843-1910), in part due to Pasteur's discoveries, established the theory that a bacterium was responsible for disease. This later became known as the "germ theory of disease." Koch discovered anthrax and *Mycobacterium tuberculosis.* Koch's Postulate shows that for a microbe to be attributed as the cause of infectious disease, a causative agent must be found in every case of the disease; the agent must be isolated and grown outside host. When agent is introduced to a healthy host, this host must contract the disease; and microbe must be re-isolated from diseased host. Koch and the Danish scientist Christian Gram (1853-1938) were also responsible for reported staining techniques.

1.2. BIOCHEMISTRY OF BACTERIA

A. MATERIAL TRANSPORT

Microbes are known as prokaryotic cells. Prokaryotes lack membrane surrounding genetic material; i.e. they do not have a nucleus. Other organisms like eukaryotes have membrane surrounding nuclei and organelles. The cell walls of some prokaryotes like *Streptococcus pneumoniae* are made up of *Glycocalyx* or *Capsule*. Literally, this means sugar cup. When soluble in water, they are known as a slime layer. Glycocalyx structure plays an important role in the evasion of human host immunity, thus the subsequent survival of the bacteria.

Other prokaryotic cells have *flagella.* These are long extended structures used in locomotion. Flagella come in different arrangements: some are *peritrichous* when the entire surface of cell is covered by flagella and are said to be *polar* when the flagella are found at the ends. Flagella could be spiral and polar like *endoflagella* in *spirochetes,* in which case, rotation of endoflagella cause *axial filaments* to rotate and move at 360 degrees and whip side to side; motion can be clockwise or counter clockwise. Bacteria move in runs and tumbles and can align and rotate as a unit. The presence of external stimulus can affect runs and tumbles. These stimuli can be *phototaxis* or *chemotaxis*. Variations of flagella are known as *fimbriae, pilli,* and *flagella. Gram negative bacteria* use fimbriae; these are sticky and protein rich and are shorter than flagella and play an imp role in biofilms. Pilli are tubules composed of proteins that are used in attach, and pull way during conjugation.

Generally most bacteria have cell walls composed of *peptidoglycan.* Peptidoglycan is composed of two alternating sugars: *N-acetylglucosamine (NAG*) and *N-acetylmuramic acid (NAM).* Millions of NAG and NAM are linked covalently; that is, they are attached by cross bridges of 4 amino acids or tetrapeptide. Gram positive cell walls are rich in peptidoglycan that contain poly alcohols called *teichoic acid* that can be linked to lipids to form lipoteichoic acid. Teichoic acids are negatively charged and retain the gram stain very well. Additionally *mycobacteria* have *mycolytic acid*—a waxy lipid which makes staining with regular stains difficult. Mycobacterial cells are stained with *acid fast stains*. There are some important implications of this. Unlike gram positive bacteria, *gram-negative bacteria* have very thin layers of peptidoglycan, a *bilipid membrane* which is composed of inner *phospholipids* and proteins, and an outer layer of *lipopolysaccharide* (LPS). Integral proteins called channels exist and transport material in and out of cells. LPS is a union of lipid and sugar; the lipid is known as *lipid A*— an *endotoxin* that causes fever, *vasodilatation* and *inflammation.*

Interestingly, some bacteria like *Mycoplasma pneumoniae* lack cell walls. Other types of *archaeal cells*, unlike bacterial cell, walls lack peptidoglycan and have thick cell walls and gram stain purple. Others that are gram negative have a layer of protein covering the wall. Further, with respect to permeability of *cytoplasmic membrane*, it is worthy to note that most are selectively permeable. That is to say, they enable cells to concentrate chemicals. By so doing, they create a concentration gradient and/or corresponding electrical gradient. In comparison, eukaryotic cells lack glycocalyx. Furthermore, they have polysaccharides and NOT peptidoglycan in their cell walls. The plant (eukaryotic) cell walls have cellulose and chitin; other eukaryotic cell walls have cytoplasmic membranes in addition. Eukaryotic membranes contain steroid lipids like cholesterol. Furthermore, eukaryotic cells have membranous organelles that include the following:

- Nucleus composed of phospholipids bilayer
- DNA "center of control"
- ER or transport system for proteins that are synthesized
- Golgi body or the shipping department
- Lysosomes
- Vacuoles, vesicles that resemble membranous sacks
- Mitochondria that are composed of phospholipids bilayer, and contain DNA which are the power house and site for ATP production

Chloroplasts can be found in plants in light harvesting cells and are composed of a bilipid membrane and DNA which can synthesize polypeptides. In addition they contain non membranous organelles that include the following:

- Ribosome's like the 70S in prokaryotes, 80S in eukaryotes cytoplasm, 70S in eukaryote mitochondria
- Cytoskeleton
- Centrioles and centrosomes
- Mitochondria and chloroplasts that are semicontinious i.e., they divide independently of the cell but remain dependent of the cell for its proteins

One theory suggests that eukaryotic cells are formed from the union of small aerobic prokaryotes with larger anaerobic prokaryotes; smaller prokaryotes are not destroyed but become internal parasites surrounded by vesicular membrane of the host.

B. PASSIVE TRANSPORT

During the passive process of transportation, and electrochemical gradient provides a source of energy, and the cell does not expend ATP. An example is *diffusion* where there is movement of molecules from areas of higher concentration to area of lower concentration. During *facilitated diffusion*, phospholipids bilayer blocks movement of charged molecules across membrane except there is a pathway for diffusion, for example, through channel protein. Another method for passive transport is *osmosis*. Here, diffusion of water occurs across a *selective membrane*. While simple and facilitated diffusion are defined in terms of *solutes*, osmosis is a special term for the diffusion of water, *a solvent*, across a *selectively permeable membrane*. When solutions on either side of the membrane have the same concentration of solutes, the situation is termed as *isotonic*. When concentration is unequal, the solution with the higher concentration of solute is *hypertonic* to the other. Conversely, the solution with the lower concentration is *hypotonic*.

C. ACTIVE TRANSPORT

Generally speaking, cells expend energy to move material across cytoplasm. Like facilitated diffusion, active transport utilizes *permease proteins*, but in the case these permease expend ATP. Such proteins are referred to as gated channels or ports because they are controlled. Movement is termed *Uniport* when one substance is transported at a time; *Antiport* when there is simultaneous transport of two chemicals— in opposite directions, i.e. one into cell and the other out of cell; and *Symport* when chemicals move together in one direction. The basic composition of prokaryotic cytoplasm includes *cytosol*, a liquid portion of cytoplasm; *inclusions*, which function to reserve deposits of lipids, starch, sugars, polymers; endospores, which are not reproductive structures but vegetative cells; ribosome's, which are sites of protein synthesis; and cytoskeleton, which are and internal network of fibers.

D. EXOCYTOSIS AND ENDOCYTOSIS

Like prokaryotic cells eukaryotic cells control movement of materials actively and passively but they do not perform group translocation. The types of active transport in eukaryotic cells include the following: endocytosis, which is a process of export into cell and involves the use of an organelle used in motion called pseudopodia; phagocytosis; pinocytosis which is a process for incorporation of fluids into cells; and exocytosis or the export out of the cell.

E. MICROBIAL METABOLISM

Several fields of study like bacteriology, virology, molecular biology, and epidemiology make up microbiology. To better understand the relationship that exists between these fields of study it is important to understand key definitions. First, genetics is the study of the genes activity as a function of a specific protein. Second, molecular biology combines biochemistry and cell biology to explain cell function at the molecular level. Third, recombinant DNA technology or genetic engineering is based on the manipulation of genes. Finally, gene therapy uses genes to cure disease. Furthermore, organic compounds should be viewed as carbon containing compounds. In addition, organic macromolecules make up functional groups and these are the sum of all of the chemical activities cells undergo throughout their lives. There are two main subdivisions of chemical reactions in microorganisms.

CATABOLISM: Is the breakdown of biological molecules. Healthy cells need nutrients that contain energy stored in the carbon-to-carbon bonds of organic compounds. Furthermore, inorganic substances act as major components in all metabolic activities.

The goal of the catabolic reactions is the release of energy in nutrients for use by the cells.

ANABOLISM: This is a form of biosynthesis and involves the building of new, novel organic compounds. The process utilizes substances broken down by catabolic reactions. Anabolic pathways are necessary to synthesize metabolic and genetic materials as well as those necessary for growth and reproduction. Catabolism and anabolism occur from a series of enzyme-mediated steps called metabolic pathways. Both processes are linked by amphibolic pathways. The base line molecule used to store and deliver energy for all cell functions is *adenosine triphosphate (ATP.* This is a form of RNA nucleotide composed of the nitrogenous base adenine; five-carbon sugar ribose, and three phosphate groups which the last two are linked by high-energy covalent bonds.

Metabolic processes utilize chemical reactions known as Reduction-oxidation (redox) reactions which are coupled. During this time the transfer of electrons, hydrogen or oxygen takes place simultaneously. *Oxidation* can be defined as the loss of electrons, hydrogen, or both, or the gain of oxygen. *Reduction* is the gain of electrons, hydrogen, or both, or the loss of oxygen. Oxidoreductases are enzymes that facilitate these reactions that occur during metabolism. During this process, which can involve energy-release and storage, hydrogen atoms are removed from organic molecules through a process called *dehydrogenation.*

Dehydrogenation produces electron-transport molecules. Electrons damage molecular structure of the cells so they are retained by receptor substances that are easily reduced and oxidized. Some examples include vitamins which are major components of enzymes called *coenzymes* like *nicotinamide adenine dinucleotide* (NAD+), *nicotinamide adenine dinucleotide phosphate* (NADP+) and *flavine adenine dinucleotide* (FAD+). Other examples which include *flavoproteins* and *cytochromes* are embedded in the cell membrane of bacteria or inner membrane of eukaryotic organelles such as mitochondria and chloroplasts. The build-up and transfer of electrons is needed for the synthesis of new energy-storage molecules such as ATP. Electron accumulation builds reducing power, while electron transfer releases energy in small manageable amounts. ATP is a molecule that can be recycled by cells. Recycling molecules enables the cell to conserve energy that might otherwise be expending in the building of new substances.

The process of generating or regenerating a molecule of ATP is called *Phosphorylation.* ATP can be generated by cells in three different ways: (1). *Substrate-level Phosphorylation* which involves the *anaerobic* transfer of high energy phosphate groups from organic compounds to ATP or other molecules. This process takes place during anaerobic metabolic pathways such as glycolysis and the *Krebs cycle* reactions. (2). *Oxidative Phosphorylation* occurs via a series of *redox reactions* that occur during respiration involving inorganic terminal electron and hydrogen acceptors such as *oxygen* (O_2), *nitrate* (NO_3^-), *nitrite* (NO_2^-) *and sulphate* (SO_2^-).

Most chemical reactions do not occur spontaneously in nature since the amount of free energy called activation energy necessary for this is too great. Enzymes can be defined as biological catalysts and play an important role in metabolic pathways since they lower the activation energy necessary for chemical reactions to occur. Enzymes are named from the type of substrate they act upon, followed by the suffix *-ase*. The primary structure of any enzyme is composed of protein. Some enzymes, called simple enzymes, are completely protein. Others, called conjugated enzymes, are composed of a protein portion called the apoenzyme and one or more non protein portion. There are two main categories of such substances: (1). *Cofactors* which are inorganic metal ions such as iron, magnesium, or zinc. (2). *Coenzymes* which are organic compounds composed of vitamins or vitamin derivatives. Examples include NAD^+, $NADP^+$ and FAD^+ · These serve in the transfer of electrons and hydrogen released by catabolic pathways. Both cofactors and coenzymes help to complete the structure of a conjugated enzyme, forming a holoenzyme. Some RNA molecules have enzymatic function and are called ribozymes which function to remove fragments of nonfunctional messenger RNA (mRNA) called *introns* and splice the functional portions called *exons*. Furthermore, enzymes function by temporarily binding to substrates and lowering the activation energy needed to facilitate or initiate reaction to take place. The catalytic (active) site is the portion of the enzyme where substrate binding occurs. Each enzyme is specific for one or more substrate types. Two different theories about how enzyme-substrate binding exist. (1). In the *Key and Lock (In the induced-fit) model*, the active site of an enzyme has a shape specific to the substrate. (2). In the *Conformal (space-filling) model*, the holoenzyme conforms its shape so it can bind the substrate(s). Factors that affect enzyme activity include the following: pH, temperature, and substrate concentration. High temperatures and high or low pH can cause enzymes to denature or lose their shape. Consequently, they will no longer bind to a substrate.

Enzyme molecules will bind to substrate and experience increases in activity until saturation is reached. Heavy metal compounds such as mercury and silver nitrate can also block enzyme activity by binding to sulfhydryl groups that hold the structure of the protein portion of the enzyme together. Enzyme activity can also be blocked by *competitive inhibition*. This occurs when a substance having a similar chemical composition to the usual substrate competes for the enzyme's catalytic site. One example is the activity of the antimicrobial compound *sulfonamide* that competes with the binding site for the substance *para-aminobenzoic acid (PABA)*. Some bacteria use PABA in the synthesis of folic acid compounds a major precursor of nucleic acids. Enzyme activity can be regulated in several ways: (1). On a genetic level, enzymes are controlled by special DNA pathways called operons that can be activated or shut down due to the presence or absence of the substrate. (2). In *allosteric inhibition* an enzyme having a secondary active site called an allosteric site closes the active site, and in the process they prevent the formation of the *enzyme-substrate complex*. (3). In *allosteric activation* the substrate binds to the allosteric site allowing the active site to open. Allosteric enzymes can be used to regulate enzymatic pathways. (4). In *a negative-feedback* pathway, the end product of a pathway binds to the allosteric site of the first enzyme closing its active site and blocking the rest of the reactions.

CARBOHYDRATE CATABOLISM (GLYCOLYSIS)

In *carbohydrate catabolism* or *Glycolysis*, organisms oxidize carbohydrates such as glucose to release stored energy used in the production of ATP or to utilize the breakdown of other molecules such as lipids to similar products of sugar catabolism.

During this process oxidation occurs either by respiration, which involves the complete breakdown of sugar to the low energy products carbon dioxide and water, or by fermentation, which is the partial breakdown of the sugar to substances like acids, or alcohols that retain carbon-to-carbon bonds. Most cells begin the process of sugar catabolism via the *Ebden-Meyerhof pathway*, commonly called glycolysis. This pathway occurs in the cytoplasm of the cell and is anaerobic. The end product of glycolysis is a two, three-carbon molecules of *pyruvic acid.* These can either be completely oxidized during later steps in the respiratory process or serve as the final acceptors of hydrogen and electrons during the anaerobic processes of fermentation. Though 4 ATP are generated as a gross gain during this process 2 ATP are used during the initial stages. Consequently, the real net gain to the cell is only 2 ATP. Alternative to glycolysis glucose is the initial molecule for two alternative pathways to glycolysis.

First, in the *pentose-phosphate pathway*, five-carbon products of the *substrate-level phosphorylation* of glucose are used in the biosynthesis of nucleotides, amino acids, and glucose during photosynthesis. A single ATP is generated by this pathway rather than the two generated by glycolysis. Second, the *Entner-Doudoroff pathway* utilized by bacteria such as *Pseudomonas aeruginosa* and *Enterococcus faecalis* also generates only 1 ATP and use different enzymes and different precursor molecules than those of glycolysis or the pentose-phosphate pathways to generate NADPH. After glycolysis or one of the alternative pathways, pyruvic acid can be further oxidized by a transitional step involving a process called *decarboxylation.* In this step, an enzyme containing coenzyme A removes a carbon dioxide molecule producing a new two-carbon intermediate called *acetaldehyde.* Coenzyme A binds to this molecule forming the new intermediate acetyl coenzyme A or *acetyl-CoA.* Though no ATP is generated, a molecule of NAD is reduced. The hydrogen and electrons stored by reduced NAD will either be used in the final stages of respiration to generate new ATP or will be given to an intermediate organic compound during fermentation. In the complete oxidation of glucose during respiration, *acetyl-CoA* releases acetaldehyde either into the cytoplasm of the bacterial cell, or the mitochondrial matrix of the eukaryotic cell. Regardless, the two-carbon acetaldehyde is enzymatically joined to a four-carbon compound called *oxaloacetic acid.* This produces a new six-carbon compound called *citric acid.* Citric acid is decarboxylated twice and the four-carbon intermediate is ultimately converted back into oxaloacetic acid. During this cyclic pathway, two molecules of CO_2 are released as waste, three NAD molecules are reduced to NADH+ one FAD is reduced to $FADH_2$ and one ATP molecule is generated by substrate-level phosphorylation. Since two molecules of pyruvic acid are produced for each original glucose molecule, the Krebs's Cycle reactions occur twice. After glycolysis, decarboxylation and the Krebs's Cycle reactions have occurred all of the carbons and oxygen's in the original glucose molecule are released as CO_2. Hydrogen and their electrons will be used to reduce NAD, and FAD. Both molecules will be delivered to the coupled reactions of electron transport and chemiosmosis.

During electron transport the reduced coenzymes NAD and FAD release their high-energy electrons and hydrogen to specialized molecules called flavoproteins which are metal-containing ions and cytochromes found in the plasma membrane of prokaryotes or the inner membrane (cristae) of the eukaryote mitochondrion. Electrons reduce and oxidize these molecules as they pass from one to the next releasing small amounts of energy. Ultimately the lower-energy electrons are attracted to singlet oxygen brought into the cell or mitochondrial matrix by diffusion. Oxygen serves as the final electron acceptor in the process of complete aerobic respiration. Hydrogen from reduced NAD and FAD are pumped outside the membrane and begin to accumulate forming a concentration (proton) gradient. This lowers the pH and results in protonmotive force that serves to drive the hydrogen ions through protein channels called ATP synthase (ATPase) molecules. As hydrogen pass through ATPase the enzyme links inorganic phosphates present in the cytoplasm or mitochondrial matrix to ADP molecules. Once in the cytoplasm each pair of hydrogen is bound to oxygen to form water. The complete breakdown of sugar and production of new ATP using oxygen as the final electron and hydrogen acceptor is called oxidative phosphorylation.

In anaerobic respiration, the inorganic final electron acceptor is an ionic compound other than oxygen such as nitrate, nitrite, or sulphate. Anaerobic respiration generally produces less ATP than aerobic respiration. Fermentation is an anaerobic process that occurs in the cytoplasm of cells. In fermentation reactions, pyruvic acid produced by glycolysis either serves as a final electron and hydrogen acceptor from NAD forming *lactic acid* (lactic acid fermentation), or is decarboxylated with the resulting acetaldehyde to form *alcohol* (alcoholic fermentation). Other products can be produced depending upon the species, but all generate a net gain of only the two ATP molecules formed during glycolysis.

1.3. DETECTING AND IDENTIFYING MICROBES

A. INTRODUCTION

The current system for detecting and identifying microbes started in 1758 by Linnaeus a Swedish botanist. He published his first report in *System Nature*. Prior, different countries described organisms using different names. In his system, Linnaeus grouped similar inbred organisms in to species. He defined specie as a group of organisms that interbreed to produce viable offspring's. Many scientists found this definition unacceptable in cases of asexual organisms like bacteria. Consequently, scientists started to define species as a collection of strains. Similar species were grouped into genera; then family; then order.

The Linnaeus system assigns two names, the descriptive name which is always a noun or genus, and a specific epithet. Carl Woese further modified the Linnaean system by using morphology and biochemical tests to unravel the relationships among organisms. In 1976 he sequenced rRNA. Based on these techniques he created a new taxon that replaces the Linnaean taxon of kingdom were: Eukaryotic cells would contain eukaryotic rRNA and different tRNA, different lipid content and characteristics. Also in Carl Woese's system, other bacteria and archaea rRNA that differs from those of eukaryotic cells would be grouped as prokaryotic cells.

B. CULTURE PRESERVATION

Refrigeration is the most common method used to slow microbial growth and preserve cultures for short periods of time. Cultures can also be preserved by deep-freezing at temperatures between -50°C and -90°C in liquid nitrogen. Lyophilization (freeze drying) involves the removal of water from a culture under low atmosphere and temperature conditions. Lyophilized cultures can be stored as a dry powder for long periods of time and restored by mixing with liquid media.

C. MICROBIAL GROWTH PATTERN

Mathematical considerations should be made in the population growth. Bacteria reproduce by binary fission. In the process, they double their population each generation. Unlike some species that reproduces arithmetically by adding one cell at a time for each generation, most bacterial species doubles its population such that numbers can be calculated as 2n, wherein the value of n represents the number of generations. If a bacteria species had begun with more than one cell, to determine the population after a given period of time, one would use the formula: Nf = Ni X 2n , where Nf is the final number of cells, Ni is the initial number of cells and n is the number of generations. For example, a fresh, sterile culture medium is inoculated with 10 *E. coli* bacteria. The medium is placed in an incubator at 37 °C for 2 hours. Given that *E. coli* can divide every 20 minutes under ideal conditions, how many cells will be present in the broth at the end of the incubation period? Nf = 10 X 26. Since there are 6, 20-minute periods in 48 hours (3 generations/1 hour) Nf = 10 X 64 = 640 bacteria.

D. MICROBIAL GENERATION TIME

Generation time is the amount of time it takes for a cell to reproduce. Each different species has its own generation time. Some bacteria, such as *E. coli* and *Staphylococcus aureus* have very short generation times. Other microbes like *Mycobacterium leprae* may take as long as 10 days. Because many food-borne pathogens replicate very quickly, special care must be taken to refrigerate hot food soon after a meal to slow down microbial growth.

LAG PHASE: The lag phase occurs after microbes have been added to growth media and represents the period of time the organisms need to adapt to the new environment. Population growth at this time is slight, very close to zero.

LOG PHASE: The log phase represents the period of optimal population growth. Eventually, the microbes approach the upper limit to their continued growth called the carrying capacity (k). If the population grows beyond (k) it will run out of nutrients and space and may crash. At this point, bacterial population levels out and population growth nears zero again.

STATIONARY PHASE: The stationary phase may last for a long period of time. In a device called a chemostat used in the fermentation and pharmaceutical industries, bacterial growth is kept in the stationary phase. Ultimately, waste and dead cells begin to accumulate causing the death phase. The population declines during this phase though it does not completely crash. Spore formers can persist beyond this stage and can regenerate a population if conditions once again become favorable.

E. QUANTIFICATION OF MICROBIAL GROWTH

The *Most Probable Numbers* (MPN) technique use lactose broths to quantify microbial growth. After incubation, a 3-digit number is produced based on the number of positive tubes per set. The number corresponds to a MPN/100 ml of water on a statistical table. Second, *Indirect Methods* involve using metabolic activity, using measurements of waste production and nutrient depletion to determine population growth. Third, the *Dry Weight (biomass) Method*, organisms in broth is dried and their biomass measured. Fourth, the *Turbidity Method* uses spectrophotometer to determine optical densities due caused by microbial growth.

F. ENERGY, CARBON, AND ELECTRON SOURCES

Autotroph utilizes radiant or chemical energy. *Heterotrophs* feed by breaking the carbon-carbon bonds in already existing carbon compounds. *Photoautotrophs* utilize radiant energy from sunlight both to produce ATP and to biosynthesize organic molecules such as carbohydrates for energy storage. *Photoheterotrophs* gain carbon from pre-existing organic molecules and use radiant energy to drive the process of catabolism. *Chemoautotroph*s harvest energy from inorganic sources such as hydrogen, sulfur, and nitrogen. These organisms are also called *lithotrophs*. *Chemoheterotrophic* organisms harvest energy by oxidizing organic compounds; these organisms are also called *organotrophs.*

Molecular oxygen (O_2) oxygen bound in water and organic compounds are generally non-toxic to living things. Some forms of oxygen-containing compounds are excellent oxidizing agents that can kill or inhibit cells. Singlet oxygen ($1O_2$) is generally produced during aerobic respiration and by the reactions between molecular oxygen and light. Superoxide free radicals (O^{2-}) are produced during aerobic respiration and sometimes by anaerobes; these molecules are very strong oxidizing agents that must be degraded before damage can be done to the cell. Aerobic organisms produce enzymes called superoxide dismutase that chemically convert superoxide to hydrogen peroxide. (H_2O_2).

Obligate anaerobes do not produce these enzymes so they are poisoned in the presence of oxygen. Peroxide ions (O_2^{2-}) contained in hydrogen peroxide is degraded by peroxidase enzymes such as catalase. The Catalase Test involves placing a sample of microbe into a drop of hydrogen peroxide. If the microbe produces catalase, the sample will vigorously bubble. In the process, hydrogen peroxide is reduced to water and molecular oxygen. Most cluster-forming cocci in the family Micrococciaceae such as *Staphylococcus epidermidis, S. aureus,* and *Micrococcus* produce catalase, while chain-forming cocci such as *Streptococcus* and *Enterococcus* do not.

Hydroxyl radicals (OH^-) are formed as the result of exposure of water to ionizing radiation such as gamma or X-radiation, or the incomplete reduction of hydrogen peroxide. These are one of the most highly reactive molecules. However, they do not accumulate in aerobes due to the activity of enzymes such as superoxide dismutase and peroxidase.

G. OXYGEN REQUIREMENTS

Aerobes are organisms that require oxygen in some form as final electron and hydrogen acceptor during chemiosmosis/electron transport. *Obligate aerobes* such as, *Bacillus subtilus, Staphylococcus epidermidis* and *Pseudomonas aeruginosa* must have a supply of molecular oxygen, while *microaerophiles* such as: *Neisseria gonorrhoeae, N. sicca, N. meningitides* and *Helicobacter pylori* require oxygen in some other inorganic form like carbon dioxide. *Aerotolerant organisms* such as the *Lactobacillus acidophilus* and other lactobacilli do not utilize oxygen but have enzymes necessary to detoxify poisonous forms of oxygen. *Facultative anaerobes* do not use oxygen but do have the enzymes necessary to cope with free radicals such as superoxide and peroxides. *Obligate anaerobes* such as *Clostridium botulinum, C. tetani,* and *C. perfrenges* do not utilize oxygen in any form.

H. NITROGEN REQUIRMENTS

Nitrogen is a limiting resource that makes up about 14% of the dry biomass of any organism. It is a key component of amino acids and nucleic acids. Though roughly 79% of the gaseous atmosphere is composed of nitrogen gas (N_2), few organisms can utilize it in this form. Rhizobium can reduce nitrogen to a more useable form such as ammonia ($NH4^+$) which is usable through a process called nitrogen fixation. These organisms often form symbiotic relationships with plants.

I. TEMPRATURE REQUIRMENTS

Physical requirements like temperature can affect the three-dimensional shape of biological molecules such as proteins. Bacteria can be separated into several groups based on the temperature range best suited to their metabolism. *Psychrophiles* grow best at temperatures between -5 °C and +20 °C. This group includes microbes responsible for the spoilage of food in refrigerators. *Mesophiles* grow best between 15 °C and 45 °C. All major human and animal pathogens are Mesophiles. Some are *thermoduric*, meaning that they can withstand slightly higher temperature ranges. *Thermophiles* have an optimal temperature range between 45 °C and 80 °C. *Hyperthermophiles* such as some of the Archaea can live at temperatures between 65 °C and 105 °C.

J. pH REQUIRMENTS

Acidophiles are bacteria that grow best at a pH range between 0.0 and 6.5. *Neutralophiles* require a pH between 6.5 and 7.5. The pathogens of humans and animals belong to this group. Some Neutralophiles are more tolerant of pH changes. For example, *Helicobacter pylori,* a pathogen of the gastrointestinal tract, produces bicarbonate and urea waste products that neutralize stomach acid. This results in a gradual erosion of the mucosa and eventually an ulcer. Approximately 80% of stomach ulcers in humans are caused by *H. pylori* infection. Alkalinophiles require a pH between 7.5 and 14.

K. PRESSURE REQUIRMENTS

Water is essential to all living cells as the primary solvent in which chemical activities take place and as a reactant in metabolic reactions such as hydrolysis. Some microorganisms can produce resting stages such as endospore and cysts when in the absence of water, but all must have water in order to be metabolically active. *Osmotic pressure* is the pressure exerted on a cell by the movement of water toward the highest concentration of dissolved solutes across a *semi-permeable membrane*. Cells that can survive in high concentrations of salt are called *halophiles*. *Obligate halophiles* such as *Halobacterium*, a member of the Archaea, require high salinity. *Facultative halophiles* such as *Staphylococcus aureus* can survive in salt concentrations between 7.5% and 20%, allowing them to colonize the skin and nasal cavity of mammals— places too salty for most other microbial flora to survive. *Hydrostatic pressure* is the force placed on an object by the column of water above it. Water pressure increases by a factor of 1 atmosphere for each 10 meters of depth. *Barophiles* are microorganisms that have evolved to live in conditions of high hydrostatic pressure such as in deep ocean trenches.

L. USE OF MORPHOLOGY AND SEROLOGY IN IDENTIFICATION

Some of the procedures like gram stains and serological tests are used by taxonomists to identify and classify microorganisms include the use of physical characteristics which are based on morphology; biochemical tests; ability to grow on certain media. Finally, fermentation of the following: fats and lipids, starch, carbohydrates, amino acids, citrate, gelatin and gases produced as waste from metabolites. Serology is the study of serum. This study takes advantage of interactions between antibodies and antigens. Antigenic organisms produce antibodies. Antigenic materials include the following: proteins, ions, carbohydrates, and lipids.

M. USE OF PHAGE TYPING IN IDENTIFICATION

During *phage typing, bacteriophages* (or phages or viruses that infect bacteria) can be indirectly linked to bacteria in the same way that antibodies are specific to antigens. Phages form plaques when they infect lawns of bacteria. Once the process is complete, these plaques can be observed and quantified.

N. USE OF NUCLEIC ACIDS IN IDENTIFICATION

The process involves the analysis of nucleic acids and involves nuclei sequencing and the comparison of nucleic sequences.

O. USE OF TAXONOMY IN IDENTIFICATION

This process involves the use of *taxonomic keys* and the organization of morphological, biochemical, serological, and nucleic acids. Phage typing tests are used in identifying an unknown organism. Different microbes have different distinct characteristics; some characteristics are associated with only one species of bacteria and can be used to distinguish it. Some of the characteristics used include the following: (1). Appearance of colonies on plate. (2). Appearance of growth on agar slant. (3). Appearance of growth profile in a tube which can resemble pin point or punctiform structures, circular pin head or irregular forms, smooth or lobate borders forms, flat forms, and raised convex or irregular umbonate bodies.

Exzoenzymes are catabolic enzymes found in microbes. Different microbes have unique enzymes coded by its DNA; subsequently these enzymes can perform unique sets of chemical reactions. The determinination of these reactions can be used to identify microbes since exzoenzymes are made in the cell but can function outside the cell. Carbon and energy acquisition are used as the basis for the classification of its nutritional type. Carbon provides the backbone of all organic molecules since all living organisms need carbon nutrients to provide energy and building blocks for structure and reproduction.

MICROBIAL CULTIVATION BROTHS AND MEDIA

There are different sets of media used to differentiate gram positive and gram negative bacteria. First, there is the *selective media* which inhibit one kind of organism over the other. Second. *Differential media* distinguishes organisms based on visual difference (using indicator dyes). Carbohydrate broths can serve as differential media with the addition of pH indicators such as Phenol Red and Durham tubes to trap gas by-products of fermentation. Media such as *McConkey's, Hektoen, Columbia CNA* and *MSA* are both selective and differential so can be used to perform more than one test.

Obligate anaerobes can be cultured in special reducing media such as sodium thioglycollate or in anaerobe chambers and handled in anaerobe hoods. *Transport media* containing low nutrients or special buffers can be used to transport microbes from one place to another and keep them isolated from the outside environment. Some microbes require special conditions in which to grow. In the absence of these conditions they will not grow in normal culture media. For example, *Mycobacterium leprae* will only grow well in the body of the armadillo. Rabbits are generally used to culture *Treponema palladium*, while Viruses, Chlamydia, and Richettsia can be cultured in eggs, cell, and tissue cultures. Microbes that require oxygen content in between strict aerobic and anaerobic conditions such as *aerotolerant microaerophiles,* and capnophiles (requiring CO_2 concentrations between 3%-15%) like *Neisseria gonorrhoeae* can be cultured in a candle jar apparatus using chemical gas packs to create the needed gas requirements. Highly fastidious or hard to grow microbes can be cultured in enrichment media which contain a nutrient or nutrients that only one specie in a sample containing many can utilize(selective media). *Cold enrichment* is used to culture *Vibrio cholerae.* Process involves incubating a medium in a refrigerator (4 °C) to inhibit growth of enteric bacteria but allow *Vibrio* which can tolerate cold, to grow.

CULTURE TECHNIQUES: In order to be ably identify microbial species, it is important to isolate individual strains by producing pure (axenic) cultures of each species to be studied. There are several techniques for the isolation of individual species. *Streaking for isolation* involves separating cells one from another through a series of steps involving passing a sterile loop over a plate of artificial media divided into sectors. The loop is sterilized between each step insuring that fewer and fewer cells are passed to each sector. If done properly, streaking results in the separation of colony forming units (CFUs) of each species. *In the pour-plate technique,* CFUs are separated through a process of serial dilution. During this process, small samples of medium containing microbes are sequentially used to inoculate new sterile media. This reduces the population of cells in each new container by a factor of ten. Diluted samples are then spread on the surface of solid media and allowed to incubate. Individual colonies can then be aseptically transferred to sterile media for isolation and study. While some bacteria and no virus can be cultured in artificial media, most can. Broths are liquid media produced by mixing dry or powder components with water. For example, agar is a complex carbohydrate derived from red algae such as *Chondrus* (Irish moss) or *Gelidium*. Agar is supplied in a powdered form and must be melted to mix with water. It melts at 100°C and solidifies at 40°C but will not re-liquefy at room temperature.

Most bacteria cannot hydrolyze agar, so dissolved bacteria in broths in concentrations between 0.5% and 1.5% can serve as a solid base for their culturing. A defined (synthetic) medium is one in which the exact chemical composition is known. Chemically undefined media such as *brain-heart infusion* agar and *blood agar* contain ingredients that have not been measured. Media can be useful in the culturing of fastidious microbes that need additional nutrient content to survive. Complex media are those produced through the addition of nutrients from the digestion of beef, soybeans, milk, or blood. These can be a combination of both defined and undefined types such as McConkey's agar, and Columbia CNA agar. Selective media inhibit one group of bacteria while allowing others to grow. Examples include: Mannitol Salt Agar (MSA), which contains 7.5% salt allowing halotolerant Staphylococci to grow while inhibiting others. McConkey's and Hektoen agars contain bile salts to inhibit most gram-positive cells while encouraging the growth of gram-negative enteric rods. Differential media enable groups of bacteria to be separated by their ability to utilize nutrients or by their form of growth.

Blood agar can be used to separate microbes on the basis of their ability to lyse red blood cells and utilize hemoglobin. Alpha-hemolytic organisms like Streptococcus pneumoniae partially break red blood cells (RBC's) down producing an olive green color around the colonies, beta--hemolytic organisms such as Streptococcus pyogenes and Staphylococcus aureus completely break RBC's down producing a clearing of the agar, gamma-hemolytic organisms, such as Enterococcus faecalis and Staphylococcus epidermidis do not destroy RBC's but grow on the surface of the agar.

GRAM NEGATIVE BACTERIA GROWTH MEDIA

HEKTOEN AGAR: This media is selective for the growth of gram negative bacteria, particularly *salmonella spp* and *shigella spp.* Bile salts in the media give it its selective properties over gram positives which are susceptible to chemicals (bile salts) in the media which can inflict stress on the gram positive bacteria due to its peptidoglycan on the cell wall. Due to the presence of lipid bilayer, Gram negative bacteria are resistant to bile salts.

Hektoen contains sodium thiosulphate as a substrate for H_2S producers and lactose as a substrate for lactose fermenters. An organism that ferments lactose will produce acid wastes that are detectable by acid fuschin (the PH indicator) that are found in Hektoen. Consequently, lactose fermenters produce yellow to yellow colonies on Hektoen. Gram negatives do not ferment lactose and appear as green colonies (same color as agar plate). In addition, organisms that produce H_2S will deposit black precipitates or centers. Salmonella do not ferment lactose and do not produce H_2S. Proteus will produce H_2S in this media, and will ferment lactose.

McConkey's AGAR: This media is differential for lactose fermenters. The media contain selective factor like the dye Crystal Violet (detects alkaline PH), and bile salts. Gram positives are inhibited by this combination. McConkey's Agar also contains lactose and an indicator (neutral red). Lactose fermenters will produce bright pink to red color (same color as media). Non fermenters will produce colorless or transparent colonies. McConkey's Agar can be used to differentiate: *Escherichia coli, Enterobacter, Proteus, Salmonella, and Pseudomonas.*

IMVic (Indole, Methyl Red, Voges Proskauer, Citric Utilization). IMVic is a series of test for lactose fermenters; and H_2S, and urea hydrolysis for non fermenters of lactose. Indole is also present in the test. Some microorganisms can hydrolyze the amino acid, tryptophan that is present in the IMVic, into indole, pyruvic acid, and ammonia. The test is administered by growing organisms in broth rich in tryptophan (tryticase soy broth or TSB). After incubation Kovacs reagent is added (p-Dimethyl-aminobenzaldehyde). If Indole is present, the media will form a red dye called resinodole.

METHYL-RED: Is a pH indicator used to detect acid products in the test *Voges Proskauer* (VP). This test can identify the metabolism of glucose and looks for fermentation of mixed acids like formic acid, acetic acid, lactic acid, and succinic acids. VP can be performed by inoculating Methyl Voges Proskauer broth in two separate tubes (2 sets). After inoculation, methyl red will be added to detect presence of acid product. If acid is present, a red-orange color will form. If Acid is absent, yellow to light orange color will form.

BARRITTS SOLUTION: Barritts A (alpha-naphthol in alcohol), and Barritts B (KOH with creatine) can be used in the detection of non acid products. If no acidic products are present acetone added to the solution will react to form a red product. The reaction can take 15-30 min to develop.

CITRATE UTILIZATION: Citrate utilization tests the organism's ability to utilize citrate as sole carbon source. Some bacteria can cleave citric acid from sodium citrate (Simmons citrate media) to form pyruvic acid and carbon dioxide. CO_2 can react with sodium and water to form sodium carbonate (alkaline). The pH indicator used to detect this compound is *bromthymol blue* which changes from green (pH 6.8) to blue (pH greater than 7, 6). This test is commonly used to distinguish between Escherichia and Enterobacter.

HYDROGEN SULPHIDE (H_2S): Lactose Fermenters can be differentiated by the H_2S test which looks at ability for organism to produce H_2S from sulfur compounds SIM (Sulfur, Indole, and Motility) deep media. A semi solid media is used to perform the test. If organism produces H_2S it will react with an element of iron in media to produce FeS (Iron Sulphate) as a black ppt.

UREA HYDROLYSIS: Urea Hydrolysis test is used for non fermenters. Some organisms can hydrolyze urea to carbon dioxide and ammonia. During the test, organisms are inoculated in Urease broth containing the indicator phenol red. This indicator will change media from yellow to pink as the pH increases from 6.8 to 8.1.

CARBOHYDRATE FERMENTATION: Most organisms use carbohydrates as fuel. Some will metabolize aerobically or by fermentation pathway. In either case, the end products vary and include acidic end products, basic end products, and carbon dioxide gas. These end products can be detected and used to characterize the bacteria.

DURHAM TUBE APPARATUS: Organisms maybe identified by observing three types of carbohydrate fermented and whether they produce acidic or non acidic products. Durham tubes apparatus can be used to accomplish this and consist of a tube containing small amounts of phenol red carbohydrate broth. If organism is capable of fermenting carbohydrates to acid, there will be a color change from red to yellow. In addition, the Durham tube can be used to trap gas after incubation

NITRATE REDUCTION: Some organisms have the ability to utilize inorganic compounds other than oxygen as final electron acceptor. In the process they will reduce some compounds. Nitrate reduction test will examine the ability of bacteria to reduce nitrate. This ability is important in the environment for the effective functioning of the nitrogen cycle and can be summarized by the reaction:

$NO^{3-} = NO^{2-} + \text{Ammonia} + N_2 \text{ gas}$

Ability to reduce nitrate is tested by inoculating cultures in tubes with tryptic nitrate broth. Three events can occur when an organism is incubated with nitrate. First, nitrate is reduced to nitrite (if organism produces nitrate reductase). Second, nitrate is reduced to ammonia or nitrogen gas (if it has nitrate and nitrite reductase enzyme). Third, nitrate is left unaltered. Should this be the case, after incubation sulfanilic acid and alpha-napthylammine can be added to tubes. Both substrates test for the presence of nitrite (NO_2). Nitrite present will react with substrate to produce *red azo dye* indicating the organism had only the first enzyme in pathway. In the absence of red azo dye organism has both enzymes for reduction or none. These two options can be distinguished by adding zinc metal. Zinc reduces nitrate to nitrite. If pink or red azo color forms on addition of zinc, organism has no enzymes at all meaning zinc was responsible for the reduction. A colorless result indicates that organism reduced the compound completely.

OXIDASE TEST This test is useful in the identification of gram negative bacteria. Aerobic bacteria contain heme proteins called cytochromes which are involved in the electron transport chain. Cytochrome oxidase is an enzyme that contains an oxygen molecule that functions as the final electron acceptor. To test the presence of oxidase, a cotton swab containing phenylenediamine is moistened and added to the plate near the bacterial colonies. If the microbe contains cytochrome in the oxidized form it will react with the cotton swab to produce an intermediate pink color which will rapidly turn red and black.

GRAM POSITIVE BACTERIA GROWTH MEDIA AND BROTH

A. STAPHYLOCOCCI AND STREPTOCOCCI

Staphylococci and their relatives are gram-positive bacteria. Some gram positive rod shaped bacteria like *bacillus subtilus* can be identified with *Skim Milk Agar* which detects the presence of *casein* enzyme; *Starch Agar* which detects *amylase enzyme;* and *Spore Stain*. However, the key differential test for cocci shaped gram positive bacteria like *Staphylococcus* and *Streptococcus* is the Catalase test. The chemical reaction in the test can be summarized by the equation:

$2H_20 = 2H_2O + O_2$

As earlier mentioned, in most bacteria, hydrogen peroxide is a strong oxidizing agent that is produced as a byproduct in normal metabolic reactions. An enzyme, catalase, has evolved in gram positive bacteria to detoxify toxic free radicals before it causes harm. Accordingly, test for the presence for catalase is the basis for distinguishing *Staphylococcus* (catalase positive) from *Streptococcus*'s (catalase negative).

B. STAPHYLOCOCCI AND MICROCOCCIACEAE

Tests that distinguish *Staphylococcus* from *Micrococciaceae* include the use of salt tolerance. *Staphylococci* are facultative halophytes that survive media containing 7.5% salt. The Salt Agar used is the Mannitol Salt Agar or (MSA) media contains 7.5% salt. Results are in terms of tolerance to media. Tolerance is defined as growth on agar plate. *Staphylococcus aureus* is a major pathogenic strain of the genus. Its ability to ferment Mannitol can be tested by the Durham apparatus and involves streaking organism on MSA which contains Phenol Red, an indicator. Fermentation can change this media from pink to yellow. Furthermore, *Staphylococcus aureus* produces hemolysin, an enzyme which breaks down hemoglobin into blood. This presence of this enzyme can be tested for by streaking pure culture with pathogen on sheep's blood agar. After incubation, the colonies should be observed for area around individual colonies. This test forms the basis for differentiating *Staphylococcus aureus* from *Staphylococcus epidermidis*. Other tests include the following:

SHEEP BLOOD AGAR (SBA): *Staphylococcus aureus* is beta-hemolytic while *Staphylococcus epidermidis* is alpha-hemolytic on SBA.

PIGMENTATION: When grown on SBA, *M. luteus* develops yellow pigmented colonies, while colonies of *Staphylococcus aureus* remain off white.

COAGULASE ENZYME: The Coagulase test forms the definitive test for *Staphylococcus aureus*. Coagulase is an enzyme that causes blood to clot. When grown in blood plasma, *S. aureus* causes SBA to clot.

C. STREPTOCOCCUS AND ENTEROCOCCUS

Unlike *Staphylococci, Streptococci* are catalase negative. Serological tests are used to differentiate streptococci from serotypes A-O (this is Lance field type). Other tests include the following: Hemolysis, sensitivity to microbial agents, growth in bile esculin agar and hemolysis. *S. pneumonia* is a common infection in immune compromised individuals and has been implicated in numerous opportunistic infections. . *S. pneumonia* are alpha hemolytic. On the other hand, the hemolysis on SBA produced by *Enterococcus faecalis* varies between gamma and alpha hemolytic.

OPTOCHIN: Optocin is a chemotherapeutic agent known as *Ethyl hydrocuprein hydrochloride.* This chemical was formerly used as antibiotic but abandoned as treatment due to harmful side effect. Optochin discs cause zone of inhibition around confluent colonies of *Streptococcus pneumoniae*. Today, this forms the basis for its use as a major diagnostic for *S. pneumoniae*.

BEA (Bile Esculin Agar): This test examines the sensitivity of microbe to cell surface lyses due to bile salts. Organism can be inoculated into BEA plates. Streptococcus is sensitive to bile and will lyse on contact. *Enterococcus faecalis* will not lyse on contact with bile and will grow in the media. *E. faecalis* does this by hydrolyzing citrate found in bile esculin as ferric citrate. Reduction of iron also results in the formation of a black precipitate as *E faecalis* grows. *Streptococcus pyogenes* is beta hemolytic and causes septic sore throat, scarlet fever, puerperal fever, meningitis, necrotizing facialitis, wound infections, glomerulonephritis, and rheumatic fever and is responsible for 90% acute streptococcal infection and is sensitive to bacitracin.

CNA (Colistin Naxydilyic Agar): CNA is selective for gram positive bacteria. This media contains colistin which inhibits gram negative bacteria and is also differential for hemolysis because it contains blood. Some gram negative bacteria like pseudomonas can grow in this medium.

THROAT CULTURE: Primary component of throat normal flora include: alpha hemolytic organisms like Streptococcus mitis, Staphylococcus salaivarius. The presence of beta hemolytic S pyogenes is indicative of strep throat specimens are collected using a sterile swab used to inoculate McConkey's prior to streaks for isolation. The presence of gram negative lactose fermenters is indicative of disease causing microorganisms in the oral cavity.

D. DETECTING FOOD BACTERIA

Food substances should be tested for overall presence of coliform or enteric gram-negative bacteria that can be introduced into our bodies by food handling. Food serves as nourishment but can contain numerous microbes. While some microbes are beneficial, like those used in fermentation and yogurt production, others can cause food to spoil. Food poisoning falls into two categories: (1). Food infection, symptoms of the disease are caused by proliferation of active organism in intestinal tract. (2). Food intoxication, disease is due to the presence of toxins which produce symptoms.

E. DETECTING WATER BACTERIA

Water is an important reservoir for the transmission of infectious disease. In 1849 a British doctor, John Snow, was able to link the outbreak of cholera to well water used for drinking and cooking. He was able to show that the well water was contaminated by sewage. Eventually, the problem was solved by removing the pump handle from the well. The first US standards for drinking water were established in 1914. These standards were based on coliform evaluations. Today, before water is considered as potable (drinkable) it must be sanitized by passing through a treatment plant. During this time, testing is routinely carried out to detect indicator organisms (coliforms). The most important coliform is *E. coli* since it is abundant in human fecal matter. The most common method for screening fecal coliforms is the Membrane Filtration Technique, and the Most Probable Number Technique (MPN).

MPN technique uses a series of 3 groups and 5 replicate series (15 in all) of lactose broth and Durham tubes that are inoculated with different dilutions of water. After 48 hours incubation the number of tubes positive for lactose fermentation as indicated by the yellow color of dye, and visible gas bubble is counted. A 3 digit number (one digit per dilution from highest to lowest) is then used in comparison to a statistical table which gives the most probable number or estimate of the coliforms present in the water. The first presumptive test is followed by a confirmatory test. Positive samples from the highest dilution of lactose are streaked onto a plate of eosin. Methylene blue are incubated and checked for their presence of metallic green colonies. E coli produces these colonies on EMB, other coliforms like Enterobacter and lactose fermenting gram-negative rods produce purple colonies with pink centers. Furthermore, along the testing lines; green colonies with metallic sheens are inoculated in fresh tubes of lactose broth and a nutrient agar slant, and then incubated for 24 hours. If lactose test is positive, this is indicative of fecal contamination in water supply. National US Standards for quality of potable water were established in 1968 by the National Technical Advisory Committee (NTAC) and recommended by the US Environmental Protection Agency (EPA)

1.4. ECOLOGICAL RELATIONSHIPS

A. INTRODUCTION

Living things form ecological relationships with one another. Relationships range from direct competition for resources to close interdependency. In this kind of relationship, each organism suffers if the other is removed. *Antagonistic relationships* occur when organisms actively inhibit or kill one another. Parasites such as viruses and other pathogenic microbes kill host cells and tissues either for the purpose of their own replication to spread through the body of a host or to gain access to nutrients stored in host cells and tissues. Such relationships can also occur when one group deprives another of resources indirectly by replicating to the extent that they crowd all other species out (competitive exclusion), or directly by producing antimicrobial compounds such as antibiotics that inhibit the growth, or kill the competitor. *Synergistic relationships* occur when two or more species cooperate so each receives greater benefit than either would receive by living separately. Symbiotic relationships such as *mutualism* can exist such that neither species will thrive if separated from the other.

Biofilms are communities of microbes that form on the surface of objects such as rocks, the inside of pipes, toilet bowls, and teeth. During biofilms formation on teeth, a microbe such as *Streptococcus mutans* produces a sticky glycocalyx to trap food and allow adherence to a surface such as teeth. Other bacteria are attracted to the presence of the streptococci and begin to attach themselves to the glycocalyx as well. This phenomenon is called *quorum sensing*. In time, several different species of bacteria form a thick sticky mass or plaque. If the plaque is not removed from the teeth, it can harden to form tartar and the accumulated acidic metabolic waste of the bacteria can dissolve tooth enamel, leading to dental cavities. Many microbes, including Salmonella, *S. aureus*, and *Pseudomonas aeruginosa* can be involved in the formation of biofilms that enhance pathogenicity.

B. SYMBIOTIC MICROBIAL RELATIONSHIPS

Symbiotic relationships are very common in nature. These relationships are synergistic, antagonistic, or neutral depending on the amount of cooperation between members (symbioses). In mutualism, two or more species cooperate to the benefit of both as seen in termites and their cellulose-degrading protozoan, and bacterial gut inhabitants and the resident micro flora in and on the human body.

COMMENSALISM: Commensalisms occur when two or more organisms interact such that one benefits while not having any significant positive or negative impact on the other. Examples of this include the relationships between large predatory sharks and remoras (fish that attach them to the body of the shark) and the resident micro flora of human skin such as staphylococci, fungi, nonpathogenic mycobacteria, and corynebacteria.

PARASITISM: Parasitism occurs when two or more species interact in an antagonistic fashion where one species (the parasite) benefits to the detriment of the other (the host). Viruses, parasitic worms and insects, pathogenic fungi, and bacteria are all parasites that exploit host resources for their own benefit.

MICROBES ARE UBIQUITOUS

Living things adapt to environmental conditions like changes in pH, temperature, and nutrient levels. The human body, as an environment, hosts many different microbes. *Omnipresent* is the term use to describe the presence of many different microbes in an environment. *Ubiquitous* is used to describe a microbe that can exist in many different environments.

NORMAL FLORA

Normal micro biota (normal micro flora) are those microorganisms normally found in or on the body of a healthy individual. Both commensalistic and mutualistic species are represented. While some parts of the body are normally *axenic* (free of microbes), most of the body is inhabited by micro flora. Resident micro floras begin to develop at, and following birth. During a normal, healthy pregnancy, the womb is essentially axenic and microbes that might be present in the mother's body are shielded from the mother by the placental barrier. At birth, the infant passes through the birth canal, coming in contact with microbes for the first time. After about two weeks, the infant has developed normal micro flora in the gastrointestinal tract. Other microbes that ultimately become part of the normal micro flora are gained from exposure to air, horizontal transfer from other people and from food and drink.

ORIGIN OF NORMAL FLORA

Most normal micro flora are either commensalistic or mutualistic so they are generally not associated with disease. However, if conditions are right, some can be opportunistic pathogens. Conditions that can lead to this include host immunity suppression due to injury, prior illness or chemotherapy, changes in normal micro flora owing to microbial antagonism, or competition, or the introduction of a member of the normal micro flora into a new part of the body, such as the insertion of *S. epidermidis* into the urethra by nonsterile catherization.

1.5. GENETICS

A. INTERODUCTION

The term genome refers to the complete genetic makeup of an organism. All cells have a genome composed of Deoxyribonucleic Acid (DNA). Some viruses also contain DNA, but many have genomes composed of Ribonucleic Acid (RNA). However, while living cells contain both DNA and RNA, viruses contain either one or the other but not both. The structure of nucleic acid DNA is a complex, double-stranded polysaccharide composed of a backbone containing phosphate groups bonded to deoxyribose sugar. Two phosphate groups are covalently bonded to each ring-shaped sugar. One is linked to the third carbon (3') on the molecule, while the other is linked to the fifth (5') carbon forming a 3'-5' glycosidic bond. This confers directionality to each nucleoside since one is constructed (biosynthesized) from 3' to 5'and the other from 5' to 3'. The physical torsion on the molecule owing to this structure causes the DNA molecule to twist, taking on a shape called a *double helix*. Each sugar is bonded one of four nitrogen-containing bases. Each combined phosphate-sugar-nitrogenous base forms a unit called a nucleotide. Nucleotides linked together compose a nucleoside. Two of these bases, *adenine* and *guanine*, are called *purines* and have a double-carbon ring structure. The other two bases, *thymine* and *cytosine*, are called *pyrimidines* and have a single-carbon ring structure. Adenine on one nucleoside of the DNA molecule can form two hydrogen bonds with thymine on the other nucleoside. Guanine can form three hydrogen bonds with cytosine in a similar fashion. Base pairing insures that the exact coding during replication. The length of a DNA molecule varies by species and is generally not expressed in metric units. Length is expressed as the number of base pairs (bp, i.e. A-T, G-C) of nucleotides each molecule contains. Sequences of DNA base pairs are called genes.

B. PROKARYOTIC GENOME

Prokaryotic cells contain DNA (bacterial chromosomes) that are *haploid* (composed of a single DNA copy) and circular. Most cells have a single chromosome, but some species may have two. *Vibrio cholerae* and *Agrobacterium tumefaciens* are examples of bacterial cells having two chromosomes. The chromosome of a typical bacterial cell is free in the cytoplasm and located in an area called the nuclear region or nucleoid. The amount of DNA exceeds the actual volume of the cytoplasm. The chromosome is folded into loops about 50,000 to 100,000 bp in length. These loops are maintained by RNA and proteins called bacteriohistones. The molecule is further twisted by the enzyme gyrase (topoisomerase).

C. PLASMIDS

Plasmids are extra chromosomal rings of DNA found in some bacterial cells. These are considerably smaller than the bacterial chromosome ranging in size from a few thousand to several million bp. Plasmids contain genetic information that can enhance the microbe's ability to survive and pass it genetic structure to others. Plasmids are sometimes referred to as *factors,* based on the type of genetic information they contain. *Fertility (F)* factors are plasmids that carry genes necessary for a cell to transfer DNA to another compatible cell through a process called conjugation. *Resistance (R)* factors carry genes that allow a cell to be resistant to antibiotics or other antimicrobial compounds. *Bacteriocidin* factors carry genes for the production of toxins that kill other bacteria that might compete with the cell for nutrients and space. *Virulence plasmids* carry genes that enable a nonpathogenic bacterium to become a pathogen.

D. EUKARYOTIC GENOME

The eukaryote genome has more than one chromosome located in the nucleus. One exception is the mammalian red blood cell, which lacks a nucleus. In general, eukaryotic somatic (body) cells have two copies of each chromosome and are said to be diploid. Reproductive cells such as spores and gametes are produced through the process of meiosis and are thus haploid. Eukaryote chromosomes are linear, unlike the bacterial chromosome, which is circular. Eukaryote chromosomes are composed or "packaged" by strands of negatively-charged DNA which wrap themselves around positively-charged globular proteins called *histones*. The histones form clusters called *nucleosomes* that clump together to form *chromatin fibers* in the nucleoplasm or cytoplasm inside the nuclear membrane. When the DNA in a chromatin strand is being used during early protein synthesis, it is loosely packed and called *euchromatin.* When it is not being used, it is coiled into a tight package called *heterochromatin*. Prior to mitosis (the division of the eukaryote nucleus) and cytokinesis (division of the cytoplasm), the DNA in the nucleus is replicated and condensed into mitotic chromosomes that become visible under the light microscope. Each replicated strand is called a *chromatid* while still attached to its copy by a central point called the centromere. When the copies are separated during mitosis, each chromatid becomes an independent chromosome.

E. DNA REPLICATION

The replication of a DNA molecule involves polymerization of special energy-carrying nucleotides called triphosphate. The energy released by the enzymatic removal of two of the phosphates is utilized in the linking of each nucleotide to its neighbor on the growing DNA nucleoside. DNA replication begins at a specific area along the molecule called the origin of replication. At the origin, histones are removed to expose the DNA strand, and then the enzyme *helicase* untwists the replicating portion of the molecule and breaks the hydrogen bonds between complementary base pairs causing the formation of a replication fork in the direction of replication. Stabilizing proteins keep the separated strands from twisting back up. An enzyme called *RNA polymerase* (primase) begins the replication process by adding RNA nucleotides to each template nucleoside. A molecule of *DNA polymerase III* binds to each of the separated strands. Consequently, this enzyme adds nucleotide bases to their complementary bases on the template strand after the RNA primer sequence and proofreads to prevent improper nucleotides from being joined to the template. *DNA polymerase* is directional so it will only completely build and proofread the nucleoside that moves in the 5' to 3' direction. This is called the continuous (leading) strand. Following DNA polymerase III, a new enzyme called *DNA polymerase I* removes the RNA primers and replaces them with DNA nucleotides. The nucleoside that moves from 3' to 5' is called the discontinuous (lagging) strand since DNA polymerase III cannot continuously add nucleotides in that direction. Instead, *primase* adds RNA bases in several places along the growing strand, enabling DNA polymerase III to add DNA nucleotides between them. These completed DNA portions are called *Okazaki fragments*. DNA polymerase I replace the RNA with DNA along the chain, filing the gaps between Okazaki fragments, but leaves unconnected unjoined regions in the sugar-phosphate backbone or "nicks." To complete the strand, a new molecule called *DNA ligase* links the nicks together.

Furthermore, *DNA gyrase* twists the new double helix back into a super coiled form in the bacterial cell. *Bacterial DNA replication* is bidirectional since the chromosome is circular. It begins from a central origin and proceeds around the chromosome until the two polymerase enzymes meet. The tension placed on the separated strands by the untwisting activity of helicase is relaxed by the enzyme *topoisomerase* by cutting the twisting sections and re-joining them opposite to the direction of the super coil. Another aspect of the replication of bacterial DNA is the process of *methylation.* During replication, some of the nucleotides (usually adenine, seldom cytosine) along specific sequences on the new strand have methyl groups ($-CH_3$) added. This process is necessary for several reasons:

- Methylated sequences serve to block or turn on the transcription of mRNA along gene sequences, thus act as a control mechanism for genetic expression
- Methylated sequences may serve as initiators for DNA replication
- Methylated sequences are absent in viruses, accordingly, bacteria may seek out and enzymatically degrade bacteriophages prophage sequences
- Methylation may be involved in the process of DNA repair

F. DNA REPLICATION IN EUKARYOTIC CELLS

Eukaryote DNA replication proceeds in a manner very similar to that of bacteria, with the following exceptions: First. Eukaryotes utilize four different DNA polymerase molecules; *(a)* which initiates synthesis and places primers (bacteria use primase for this), *(s),* which elongates the leading strand, *(e),* which elongates the lagging strand, and *(g),* that replicates mitochondrial DNA (mitochondrial DNA is circular and naked in the mitochondrial matrix). Second, Eukaryote DNA requires many points of replication owing to its large size. Third, Eukaryote Okazaki fragments are far shorter than those of Prokaryotes. Fourth, methylation of plant and animal DNA occurs only on cytosine molecules.

G. TRANSCRIPTION

In genetics, the genotype directs phenotypic expression. All genes are not expressed all of the time. However, genotypes are not always expressed as phenotype. Two examples are: lactose catabolism in *E. coli* and ecophenotypic expression of pigment in *Serratia marcescens. E. coli* only produces the enzyme *b-galactosidase* (lactase) when lactose is present. When lactose is depleted or not present, the sequence of genes controlling enzyme production is shut down. *S. marcescens* produces the red pigment prodigiosin when incubated at a temperature range between 25 °C and 30 °C. When incubated at 37 °C the pigment is not produced or very little is produced. The "central dogma" of genetics states that each sequence of nucleotides on a segment of DNA that codes for the production of a protein is called a gene. In other words DNA replication precedes transcription, followed by translation.

The process of building a molecule of mRNA is called *transcription*, while the building of a new protein from the mRNA code is called translation. Ribosomes cannot construct polypeptides from the genetic code carried by DNA but can do so from RNA. Information flows from the DNA to messenger RNA (mRNA) to amino acid sequence of the growing polypeptide. Four different type of RNA can be transcribed from DNA. These are as follows:

- Primase primer RNA used to initiate DNA replication
- Messenger RNA (mRNA) used to carry the instructions about polypeptide structure to the site of translation
- Ribosomal RNA (rRNA) part of the ribosome, used in the construction of polypeptides
- Transfer RNA (tRNA) carry amino acids to the site of translation

Transcription begins when an RNA polymerase binds to a promoter site on the 5' to 3' DNA (blueprint) strand. A small polypeptide portion of the RNA polymerase molecule called the *sigma factor* recognizes the promoter site sequence. A short leader sequence of about 10 DNA nucleotides separates the promoter from the actual gene sequence. The *RNA polymerase* molecule untwists and separates the hydrogen bonds between the two DNA nucleosides. Triphosphate ribonucleotides (rATP, rUTP, rGTP, and rCTP) are joined to their complementary bases on the DNA blueprint strand (A-U, G-C). Energy to drive this process is supplied by the extra two phosphate bonds carried by each triphosphate ribonucleotides. Four different type of RNA can be transcribed from DNA: primase primer RNA used to initiate DNA replication

Eukaryote mRNA undergoes RNA processing (pre-translational modification) before translation. The 5' end of the mRNA transcript has a guanine nucleotide added during elongation. This is called *capping.* During termination, proteins remove the mRNA transcript and add 200 adenines to the 3' end. This is called *polyadenylation.* Furthermore, capped and polyadenylated mRNA are called pre-messenger RNA, since they contain intervening sequences of RNA that do not code for the placement of amino acids. These "junk" sequences are called introns and they separate usable portions called "expressed" sequences or exons. Introns are removed from the mRNA by small rRNA molecules called *spliceosomes* or *ribozymes.*

As the growing mRNA strand is synthesized, it detaches from the DNA blueprint strand. This process continues until RNA polymerase reaches a terminator sequence of guanines and cytosine's, followed by a repeating sequence of adenines. Since guanine forms three hydrogen bonds with the cytosine on the DNA template, it takes longer for the RNA polymerase to join these. A loop forms in the guanine-rich portion of mRNA putting strain on the adenine-rich portion behind it, and causing the molecule to separate from the DNA blueprint and releasing the RNA polymerase.

Another way transcription is terminated is called *Rho-dependent* since it depends on a protein called Rho located near the end of the mRNA transcript. The Rho protein moves along the mRNA until the termination sequence are reached. Afterwards, it separates the DNA blueprint from the mRNA transcript and the RNA polymerase enzyme. Eukaryotic transcription differs from that of bacteria in several ways: (1). RNA synthesis in eukaryotes occurs primarily in the nucleus with the exception of RNA produced in the mitochondrion or chloroplast. (2). Eukaryotes have three different types of nuclear RNA polymerase, one for the synthesis of mRNA, one for the major rRNA gene and one for tRNA and smaller rRNA molecules. (3). At least five different transcription factor proteins assist the binding of eukaryote RNA polymerase to promoter sequences (bacteria only use a single sigma factor). These are removed following initiation of transcription and replaced by proteins called elongation factors (not found in bacteria).

H. TRANSLATION

Prokaryotes often exhibit concurrent RNA transcription. In this process several RNA polymerase molecules attach to the initiation sequence one after another forming a polyribosome complex. In this way, multiple copies of the same mRNA molecule can be made from the same gene or set of genes. The genetic code used to produce proteins is carried by mRNA since ribosomes cannot read the DNA blueprint. Furthermore, there are only four DNA nucleotides, yet there are 21 naturally occurring amino acids found in the structure of proteins. Earlier, it was discovered that information about amino acid placement is not carried by single DNA nucleotides, but is instead carried by triplets of mRNA nucleotides called codons. 64 codon combinations are possible based on the original 4 DNA nucleotide triplet pairs. Of these, 61 code for amino acids and 3 (UAA, UAG and UGA) have no associated amino acids, thus serve as stop codons, since they cause ribosomes to stop the process of translation.

The mRNA code is "redundant," since with the exception of the amino acids methionine and tryptophan, there are multiple codons that can code for the same amino acid, with the first two bases of the codon specifying a particular tRNA and the third subject to "wobble" since it does not have to form a bond with a tRNA nucleotide for the amino acid to be placed correctly. Translation is the process cells use to synthesize polypeptides using the codon sequence on the mRNA as a template. In the bacterial cell, several related polypeptide sequences are carried on the same mRNA template. Each sequence on the mRNA strand has its own ribosome binding site and start and stop codons. Since transcription occurs in the cytoplasm, translation can begin even before transcription is complete. Eukaryotic mRNA differs from that of prokaryotes in that it undergoes *post-transcriptional modification* and carries instructions for the synthesis of only one polypeptide, and is not translated until after it has been transcribed completely modified, and has left the nucleus.

Transfer RNA (tRNA) is a sequence of ~75 ribonucleotides that fold to form a three-dimensional structure. Each tRNA has an acceptor stem that forms a temporary bond with one amino acid and an anticodon that can bind to its complementary codon on mRNA. Though there are 62 codons on mRNA, there are only about 40 tRNA molecules. Each tRNA anticodon can bind to an mRNA codon provided that at least the first two mRNA nucleotides are complementary to its first two nucleotides. This can occur because of "wobble," a phenomenon associated with the ability of nucleotides, and anticodons to bond to complementary nucleotide. This redundancy enables the cell to produce the proper polypeptide even if minor mutations (errors) occur in the DNA during replication or the mRNA during transcription.

I. RIBOSOMES

Though both prokaryote and eukaryote cells contain ribosome's differences do exist: (1). Prokaryote ribosomes are 70S in size, composed of a 30S small subunit and a 50S large subunit. (2). Eukaryote ribosome's are 80S, having a 40S small subunit and a 60S large subunit. The ribosome's in mitochondria and chloroplasts are, however, 70S like those of bacteria. (3). Two Prokaryote ribosomes are synthesized in the cytoplasm, while eukaryote ribosome subunits are synthesized in the nucleolus and assemble themselves in the cytoplasm or along the rough endoplasmic reticulum. Furthermore, the differences in the size and rRNA between the two types serve as a target for selectively toxic antimicrobials such as erythromycin that binds to the 23S rRNA portion of the bacterial ribosome (the eukaryote rRNA portion is 28S).

Prokaryote translation always begins with the amino acid *N-formylmethionine* (f-met), while eukaryote translation always begins with methionine (met). In both eukaryotes and prokaryotes, elongation of the polypeptide chain is powered by guanosine triphosphate (GTP) and terminates at a stop codon with the help of release factor proteins that breaks the bonds between the tRNA and final amino acid in the sequence allowing the ribosome subunits to detach.

J. GENE REGULATION

Most genes (~75%) are constitutive, meaning that they are expressed continuously by a cell. Others are regulated so that they are expressed only when needed. Some gene regulation occurs at the level of translation, so while mRNA is produced, it may not be used to produce proteins. Some mRNA molecules act as riboswitches, altering their shape in response to changes of pH, temperature or nutrient concentration to either allow or block the binding of ribosomes. Short interference RNA (siRNA) or antisense RNA is an RNA molecule that is complementary to mRNA, tRNA, or DNA. The siRNA functions by binding to its complementary nucleotide base to silence it (make it become inactive).

K. THE OPERON

Prokaryotic cells have linear sequences of DNA called operons. The operon is composed of a promoter sequence, followed by an operator gene, followed by one or more structural genes that act as blueprints for proteins. The operon is controlled by a regulator gene found elsewhere on the chromosome. Operons can be inducible (turned on by a substrate) or repressible (turned off by a product). In the inducible lactose (*lac*), the operator gene is blocked by a repressor protein when the cell is not in the presence of lactose. When lactose is present, it acts as an inducer by binding to the repressor protein, thus preventing it from attaching to the operator.

RNA polymerase can then bind to the operator and transcribe the mRNA molecule. Three different proteins are synthesized. When all of the lactose in the cell has been catabolized, the repressor protein binds to the operator and shuts down the operon. In the repressible tryptophan (*trp*), the structural genes involved in tryptophan biosynthesis are transcribed continuously as long as the cell needs the amino acid. When a sufficient concentration of tryptophan has been produced, the amino acid will bind to a repressor protein causing it to bind to the operator gene and shutting the *trp* operon down.

L. TYPES OF MUTATIONS

A mutation is a change in the nucleotide base sequence on a DNA molecule. The most common form is the *point mutation*, which is a change in a single nucleotide on one side or the other of the molecule. Common point mutations include *base pair insertion, deletion, or substitution.* Purine for Purine substitution (A to G or G to A) is called *transition.* Purine to pyrimidines or vice-versa (A to C or T, G to C or T) is called a *transversion.* Insertions and deletions can cause *frame shift mutations.* This occurs when the sequence of amino acids in the final polypeptide product is different, thus producing different proteins or nonfunctional polypeptides.

If the point mutation has no effect on the polypeptide, it is called a *silent mutation.* This occurs due to the redundancy of the genetic code. Inversion, duplication, and transposition of multiple nucleotides are called *gross* (large-scale) *mutations* and occur both in prokaryote and eukaryote cells. Eukaryote cells can also undergo chromosomal mutations. The most common chromosomal mutation is *non-disjunction*, a failure of chromosomes to separate during meiotic division. A major feature of non-disjunction is that one of the daughter cells will have one less chromosome that the other. If these are human cells that mature into gametes and participate in fertilization, the resulting offspring will have a genetic disorder such as *Down's or Turner's syndrome.* In plants, non-disjunction can result in changes such as the oversized fruit of cultivated strawberries (natural strawberry fruits are small and bitter).

M. MUTAGENS

Mutagens or mutagenic agents are physical or chemical agents that induce changes in the genetic code. Natural spontaneous mutations occur regularly among cells. These result from errors during DNA replication as well as recombinant events that occur when segments of DNA from other chromosomes or introduced from parasites such as viruses are added to the strand.

N. PHYSICAL MUTAGENS AND FREQUENCY

These include radiation, which can alter DNA in two different ways. First, ionizing radiation, such as X-ray and gamma radiation energize electrons cause's genes to leave atoms and molecules forming highly reactive ions. This can cause DNA molecules to break down and triggers mutations. Second, nonionizing radiation such as ultraviolet light causes the breaking of bonds between purines and pyrimidines when two pyrimidines molecules of the same type (T or C) are adjacent to one another on a nucleoside. These *pyrimidines dimmers* distort the sugar phosphate backbone and prevent proper replication and transcription. Third, nucleotide analogs have a similar chemical structure to a normal nucleotide (as in thymine and 5'-bromouracil) and compete with the normal nucleotide during DNA replication, causing point mutations. Some nucleotide altering chemicals such as nitrous acid alter the structure of a nucleotide. Nitrous acid removes the amine (nitrogen-containing) group from adenine, converting it to a guanine analog, resulting in a base-pair substitution. Fourth, chemicals such as ethydium bromide, benzopyrene from smoke and yellow and red acridine dyes can cause *frame shift* mutations in DNA as DNA polymerase copies the alter strand, adding or deleting base pairs around the bulge formed by the bound mutagen.

The natural mutation rate for cells is about 10^{-6}, meaning that a mutation may occur spontaneously once every one million times a DNA molecule is replicated. In terms of spontaneous mutations in base pairs, the rate is about 10-^{10} (one in ten billion) and in genes along a chromosome, there are normally about 10^{-7} (one in 10 million). Mutagenic agents increase the rate at which such mutations occur. Most mutations are harmful to the cell. If these result in the death of the cell they are called *lethal mutations*. Beneficial mutations give the cell characteristics others of its type do not have, allowing it to survive in changing environments or make use of nutrients others of its type cannot. The accumulation of beneficial mutations results in the evolution of new species.

O. DETECTION OF MUTAGENS, CARCINOGENS, AND MUTANTS

In positive selection, only those mutant cells that can survive in a medium containing a selective agent such as penicillin can survive. In negative selection, nutritional mutants called auxotrophs cannot grow on a minimal medium lacking a key nutrient. The mutants are identified by the replicate organism direct agar contact (RODAC) technique. The *Ames test* utilizes a histidine *auxotroph* of Salmonella to determine if a chemical agent is a mutagen. Though some spontaneous back mutations (a reversion back to the strain of

Salmonella that can synthesize histidine) can occur. Frequent occurrence on the minimal plate *after* the addition of the test chemical is an indication the chemical is a mutagen.

P. RECOMBINATION

This is the exchange of nucleotide sequences between two homologous DNA molecules (identical or nearly identical to one another). Recombination occurs during meiosis in eukaryotic cells. During this process, short sequences of DNA on chromosome tetrads are exchanged enzymatically. The three types of horizontal gene transfer in bacteria are: transformation, transduction, and conjugation.

Q. HORIZONTAL TRANSFER AMONG PROKARYOTIC CELLS

Transformation occurs naturally in bacteria that are competent, meaning there are alterations of the cell envelope that enable the cell to absorb naked DNA in the surrounding environment. In 1945, Avery, McCarty, and McCloud demonstrated that this "transforming principle" was DNA. Genera that have naturally competent members include the following: *Streptococcus spp, Staphylococcus spp, Haemophilus* spp, and *Pseudomonas*. Some bacteria, such as *Escherichia coli,* can be made competent under laboratory conditions.

R. TRANSDUCTION

In *generalized transduction*, random host-cell DNA is carried by the defective (transducing) phage. In *specialized transduction*, specific genes and gene sequences are carried. Some bacteria, when infected by a specialized transducing phage, become pathogenic since the genes for virulence (ability to cause disease) are carried by the phage. This process is called *lysogenic conversion*, since the infected bacteria are not forced to enter into the lytic viral replication cycle. Examples of bacteria that become pathogens in this way include the following: *Clostridium botulinum, Staphylococcus aureus, Legionella pneumophila, Escherichia coli* O157:H7, and *Yersina pestis*.

S. CONJUGATION

Conjugation involves the transfer of an entire plasmid. During this process, the F^+ plasmid undergoes rolling circle replication, meaning that it is replicated as a linear single nucleoside rather than a complete circular strand of DNA during replication of the chromosome. After passing through the *pilus* into the F^- recipient cell, the complementary nucleoside is synthesized and the plasmid is linked into circular form by ligase. *Hfr* conjugation occurs when a plasmid from the F^+ donor, previously recombined with the chromosome to produce a new Hfr^+ cell, is partially copied along with chromosomal genes by rolling circle replication. After this process, the DNA fragment is completed and recombined with the recipient chromosome. Since all of the plasmid DNA was not transferred, the recipient remains an F- cell and cannot participate in further conjugation with other cells.

T. TRANSPOSONS AND TRANSPOSITION

The American geneticist Barbara McClintock, through studies using corn seeds, showed that some genes have the ability to move from one chromosome to another, thus produce variability in phenotypic expression that does not adhere to classic Mendelian ratios. This is the case since the insertion of such segments turns genes for color on and off. She called these segments of DNA transposable genetic elements (transposons) or, more commonly, "jumping genes." McClintock won the Nobel Prize for her discovery. These are examples of simple transposons. More complicated transposons contain *palindromic sequences* (nucleotide sequences that read the same both forward and backward, such as AAGGAA) at each end, bounded by *inverted repeat* (IR) sequences on each side. Complex transposons include not only the *transposase gene* in the insertion sequence, but other genes as well, bounded by insertion sequences. *R-factors* (genes that carry information about resistance to antibiotics) and cell marker genes are often transposons. Transposons have been discovered in many organisms like pathogenic bacteria such as *Salmonella typhimurium,* and protists such as *Trypanosoma* (pathogens of trypanosomiasis), and *Plasmodium* (the agents of malaria). Transposons are also responsible for variation in the chemical structure of the five classes of human immunoglobulin's involved in humeral immunity to disease.

1.6. VIRUSES

A. VIRAL GENOME

The viral genome contains either DNA or RNA, but not both. While even the simplest bacterial cell has a genome composed of hundreds to thousands of genes, viruses contain very few. The genetic information carried by a viral genome is only capable of providing what is necessary for replication, thus a virus is incapable of independent metabolic processes. The types of viral genetic material can be double-stranded DNA (dsDNA) like:

- *Poxviridae*
- *Herpesviridae*
- *Papillomaviridae*
- *Polyomaviridae*
- *Adenoviridae*
- some *Hepadnaviridae (*hepatitis B)

Double-stranded RNA (dsRNA) like *Reoviridae*; single-stranded DNA (ssDNA) like: some *Hepadnaviridae*, and *Parvoviridae*; single-stranded RNA (ssRNA) like:

- *Arenaviridae*
- *Astroviridae*
- *Bunyaviridae*
- *Calciviridae*
- *Coronaviridae*
- *Filoviridae*
- *Flaviviridae*
- *Herpesviridae*
- *Orthomyxoviridae*
- *Paramyxoviridae*
- *Picornaviridae*
- *Retroviridae,*
- *Rhabdoviridae*
- *Togaviridae*

B. VIRAL MORPHOLOGY

Viruses are much too small to be seen with any light microscope. The largest smallpox virus is more than 0.5 times smaller than *E. coli* and 50 times smaller than a human red blood cell. In 1892, Dmitri Ivanowsky demonstrated that the tobacco mosaic virus was a "filterable" agent of disease, since it could pass through a porcelain glass filter designed to trap very small bacterial cells. The filtrate of infected sap from tobacco leaves could pass the disease to healthy uninfected plants. Wendell Stanley isolated and characterized this virus in 1935. The name *virus*, the Latin term for "poison," became standard for these pathogenic agents by the late Nineteenth Century, replacing the phrase *contagium vividium fludium*, also Latin for contagious living fluid.

C. VIRAL CAPSID

The capsid, or protein coat, surrounding the viral nucleic acid core is one of the factors used in viral classification. The capsid is composed of individual protein subunits called capsomeres. Some capsids are composed of one protein type, but others can have multiple capsomeres proteins. Viral morphology can be helical (rod-shaped), like tobacco mosaic virus, (Ebola and Marburg), or icosahedra (20 evenly shaped triangular vertices) like polio, rhinovirus, herpes, adenoviruses; or complex (many shapes) like bacteriophages, rabies, and smallpox.

D. BACTERIOPHAGES

Bacteriophage, like T4, is an example of a complex viral morphology. Enveloped viruses surround themselves with plasma membrane taken from a host cell during the release stage of viral replication. Between the virus and the envelope there are viral matrix proteins. The envelope is modified during replication by the addition of viral glycoproteins, collectively called "spikes." Viral spikes are the structures that enable enveloped virions to be released or "bud" out of the host cells and bind to specific cell markers on new host cells. Examples can be seen in *neuraminidase* (budding factor) and *hemagluttinin* (attachment factor) proteins on the envelope of influenza viruses. Spikes can also be found on nonenveloped viruses. They are attached directly to the nucleocapsid. An example of a virus with spikes is the adenoviruses.

E. VIRAL CLASSIFICATION

Note that unlike the multiple-part replication cycle of bacteria, viral replication occurs as a single step. Phases of this process include the following:

ECLIPSE PHASE: This is the period of time following viral adsorption and penetration and prior to release.

LYSOGENY: Some viruses like *Bacteriophages lambda* lacks tail fibers but attaches to a host cell via molecules at the base of the tail. This is a lysogenic virus that can incorporate its dsDNA with that of its host cell, *E. coli.* The prophage can remain dormant and even be replicated and passed to new daughter cells via fission. Induction to enter the lytic cycle occurs eventually, and is triggered by some environmental change or physical event such as exposure to ionizing or nonionizing radiation, or to carcinogenic chemicals. Some bacteria can undergo lysogenic conversion when infected by a prophage. In this phenomenon, phage genes are expressed that give rise to toxins and other pathogenic compounds without the induction of the entire prophage genome. Many bacteria such as; *Corynebacterium diptheriae, Yersina pestis, Clostridium botulinum* and

Escherichia coli only express pathogenic characteristics as a result of lysogenic conversion.

F. REPLICATION IN ANIMAL VIRUSES

Entry of viruses can occur by direct penetration of the protein coat and insertion of the viral genome. This is the case in Polio and other nonenveloped viruses. This is followed by fusion of the viral envelop with the host cell membrane as is the case with measles and mumps viruses, or by stimulation of endocytosis of the entire enveloped virus like in herpes and the nonenveloped adenovirus. Those viruses that penetrate via membrane fusion and endocytosis must then undergo uncoating either in the cytoplasm, or while within the endocytitic vesicle. Host cells enzymes cause this to occur. The mechanism that triggers this process is not well understood.

G. REPLICATION OF DOUBLE STRANDED VIRUSES

Pox viruses replicate in the cytoplasm only, while the genome of hepatitis B is first transcribed to RNA, then the RNA template is used to generate new dsDNA using reverse transcriptase, an enzyme carried by the virus. Double stranded DNA viruses (dsDNA) like the Herpes, and Human Papilloma Viruses (HPV) also use this strategy when replicating.

H. REPLICATION OF SINGLE STRANDED VIRUSES

In Single Stranded viruses (ssDNA) such as the *parvovirus,* replication of the complementary strand occurs in the nucleus, but the complementary strand is not incorporated into the nucleocapsid during assembly.

I. POSITIVE SENSE, SINGLE STRANDED RNA VIRUSES

The (+) ssRNA viruses such as *polio viruses* and *rhinoviruses* have RNA that can act immediately as mRNA to synthesize viral proteins. New (+) strands are synthesized from a (-) strand, and then assembled as nucleocapsid prior to release.

J. NEGATIVE SENSE, SINGLE STRANDED RNA

(-) ssRNA viruses such as *filoviruses, reoviruses* and *arena* viruses must first synthesize new (+) strand following uncoating. The (+) strand can then be used to synthesize new complementary (-) strands in a manner similar to the way mRNA is used during translation to synthesize proteins.

K. VIRAL RELEASE FROM CELLS

In animal viruses, nonenveloped viruses are released by cell lyses, but enveloped forms are released by budding. Budding occurs when the nucleocapsid migrates to host cell membrane, and is surrounded by a portion of host cell membrane from the nucleus, endoplasmic reticulum, or outer membrane. Furthermore, during synthesis, viral protein spikes such as *neuraminidase* and *hemagluttinin* are added to the host membrane.

L. VIRAL LATENCY

Some animal viruses such as *Herpes Zoster* (chickenpox, shingles), *Herpes Simplex* I and II and HIV undergo latency and persistence and have the ability to remain in the body for extended periods of time without expressing themselves in a lytic cycle. This process is called latency and occurs in two ways: In the case of Herpes viruses, they produce lytic cycles when infecting mucosal or epithelial cells, but have the ability to reside in the ganglia of nervous tissues without killing the cells. During this time they migrating to the cells they are specific for after being stimulated by some environmental factor such as exposure to radiation or reduced host resistance due to disorders like gastroenteritis, influenza, or AIDS.

Other viruses like the HIV virus become a provirus (viral DNA incorporated with a host cell chromosome) and is held inactive by a repressor protein for long periods of time. When stimulated by environmental or host stimuli as is the case with disorders and disease, the proviral DNA is used to transcribe viral RNA, which begins the replication cycle. Persistent viruses are those that are retained in the body in small numbers that continually replicate. The accumulation of tissue damage over long periods of time plays a major role in pathogenicity. Measles viruses, for example, can persist in nervous tissue for decades, eventually leading to a disorder called *subacute schlerosing panencephalitis.*

1.7. INFECTIOUS PARTICLES AND DISEASE

A. INFECTION

Infection is the movement of microbes inside the host. Contamination refers to the presence of microbes on a surface or tissue. Infection occurs when a microorganism contacts a potential host. Colonization occurs when the infecting agent multiplies in or on the body. Infection and colonization do not, however, always result in disease. Portals of entry for the agents of infectious disease are the skin, mucus membranes, placenta, and the parenteral route. Intact skin is composed of several layers of dead, keratinized cells called the epidermis. Beneath this layer is the dermis, composed primarily of connective tissues and associated with fixed macrophages. Hair follicles, sebaceous (oil-producing) glands, and sudoriferous (sweat) glands open to the outside and can sometimes act as portals into the deeper layers of the skin. Examples of microbes that can enter and/or cause infection through intact skin include the following: dermatophyte (skin-loving) fungi such as *Trichophyton, Pitisporidium,* and *Microsporidium*, bacteria such as *Propionibacterium acnes* and helminth worms such as *Enterobius* (pinworms).

The parenteral route of infection involves break in the skin such as cuts, scrapes, puncture wounds, bites, and burns. Examples of infectious agents that enter the body via this route include the following: the rabies virus, *Staphylococcus aureus*, *Clostridium perfrenges, Pseudomonas aeruginosa,* and insect vectors that transmit pathogens such as *Plasmodium, Leishmania,* and *Trypanosoma.* Mucus membranes are found in the respiratory, gastrointestinal, and genitourinary tracts, as well as the conjunctiva of the eye. Respiratory pathogens such as: influenza viruses, Rhinoviruses, and Ebola, as well as bacteria such as: *S. pneumoniae, H. influenzae, L. pneumophila* and *Y. pestis.* All can enter through the mucus membranes of the respiratory tract, as can *B. anthracis*. All of these can be transmitted by aerosol droplets released during coughing and sneezing. Many of these microbes can enter the respiratory tract via the nasolacrimal ducts when a person rubs their eyes. Organisms such as: *C. jejuni, S. typhimurium, E. coli, H. pylori, V. cholerae and Shigella* use the gastrointestinal route, carried by vehicles such as food and water were transmission is generally via fecal-contamination. Examples of organisms transmitted sexually include the following: *Treponema palladium, Neisseria gonorrhoeae, Chlamydia trachomatis,* Human Papilloma Viruses, Herpes simplex II and HIV. In addition, these pathogens can infect through the mucus membranes of the genitourinary tract. Some pathogens can be transmitted nosocomially such as urinary tract infections caused by *Proteus mirabilis, P. vulgaris* and *E. coli,* as well as the normally nonpathogenic *S. epidermidis.*

B. VIRIODS

Some examples of viriods include the Potato Spindle Tuber Viroid (PSTV), which is a naked, circular piece of RNA that causes disease in plant tissues. Viroids are pathogens of plants, but do not cause disease in other organisms. There are viroid-like agents that infect fungi and some that might be involved in some human diseases.

C. PRIONS

Some diseases were once referred to by scientists as "slow viral infections" such as scrapie in sheep, chronic wasting disease in deer, bovine spongiform encephalopathy ("mad cow" disease) and *Creutzfeldt-Jacob* disease in humans. In later years, these diseases were shown to be as a result of very small protenaceous infective particles (prions). In 1982, Stanley Prusser discovered that a very simple prions protein (PrP) seemed to be responsible for diseases such as those mentioned above. He recognized that there were two stable forms of PrP, one composed of alpha helices and found in nerve cells, and another having beta helices and found only in diseased mammals. He suspected that the mutated PrP could overwhelm healthy PrP, leading to cell death and the development of large vacuoles in brain tissue as found in spongiform encephalopathy.

D. ROLE OF ADHESION IN INFECTION

Adhesion (attachment) factors enable a microorganism to attach itself to host cells, tissues or other surfaces. These factors include ligands (adhesins) such as those used by *E. coli* to attach to the mucus membranes of the gastrointestinal tract, capsules and slime layers used in the production of biofilms, such as dental plaque, and the attachment proteins on viral spikes.

E. INFECTIOUS DISEASE

Infectious diseases occur when infection and colonization results in changes in the state of health. In epidemiological terms, a broad term for disease is *morbidity. Mortality* is death due to disease or injury. Infectious disease is caused by the activity of invading microorganisms that can be spread from one host to another. Disease can also occur due to damage the body inflicts upon itself as a result of the attempt to combat infecting agents.

F. OUTCOMES OF INFECTIOUS DISEASE

These manifestations include symptoms of the disease as related by a patient to a physician. These tend to be subjective, such as headache, nausea, and pain and cannot be measured directly. Many different diseases can be associated with the same set of symptoms. Signs are clinical manifestations of disease that are visible, including: vomiting, diarrhea, coughing and sneezing, fever, petechiae (reddish streaks or marks on the skin or mucus membranes), and changes in normal pigmentation such as jaundice and lesions. The combination of signs and symptoms is called the *disease syndrome*. Some diseases may go undetected since no signs or symptoms are visible. Asymptomatic diseases, such as *Trichmonas vaginalis* in males and occasionally *Salmonella typhi* can go undetected, though they can be spread to others. Sub clinical infections by viruses such as measles and bacteria such as *S. pyogenes* may persist for many years and the infected individual may become an unintentional carrier of the disease.

G. ETIOLOGY AND PATHOLOGY OF DISEASE

Etiology refers to the causation or cause of disease, while pathology refers to the study of disease. *Pathogenesis* is the development of disease. Not all disease is due to the activity of microbial pathogens. Some diseases are inherited like: muscular sclerosis; endocrine, like hyper- or hypothyroidism; mental, such as epilepsy and senility. Other diseases are degenerative like: immunologic disease such as allergies and rheumatoid arthritis. Additionally, other diseases are neoplastic, such as cancers. Diseases that have no known cause are said to be *idiopathic*. Robert Koch was the first doctor to develop protocols for the identification of the etiological agents of disease. His postulate provided a framework for medical science to identify most of the bacterial causes of disease and has been modified to work with viral pathogens as well. Koch's postulates do not work well with microbes that grow poorly on artificial media such as *M. leprae*, when disease is the result of more than one pathogen, as is the case with liver cancer since it is caused by infection of liver cells by both hepatitis B and D viruses rather than each independently and when more than one pathogen may be independently responsible for the same disease, such as the many agents of pneumonia and meningitis.

H. MICROBIAL VIRULENCE FACTORS

Pathogenicity is the ability an organism to cause disease. Pathogenicity is composed of two factors: infectivity, or the ability to infect and colonize a host and virulence; or the ability to cause host cell damage. Infectivity is measured as infectious dose (ID), meaning the number of microbes necessary to initiate infection, colonization and disease. Highly pathogenic forms such as the Ebola virus can infect a host if only one virus comes in contact with skin or mucus membranes, while others such as the spores of *Bacillus anthracis*, require 8000-10,000 spores to cause a serious illness. Virulence can occur along a spectrum where highly pathogenic organisms always cause disease while less virulent forms may not cause disease at all or act as opportunistic pathogens.

I. SOURCES OF INFECTIOUS DISEASE

The "Four F's of Infectious Disease": (1). Fingers, or improper hand washing or failure to wash hands regularly is one of the most commonly avoidable ways to prevent the spread of infectious disease. (2).Fomites, or any inanimate object a microbe can inhabit on a transient basis that can come in contact with a person, such as table and countertops, cups, dishes, towels, sponges, improperly sterilized laboratory or surgical equipment, gloves, doorknobs, drinking fountains or toilet seats. (3). "Flies" a general term describing arthropod vectors of disease. Diseases are spread either mechanically as microbes are picked up on the body surface and carried elsewhere or biologically when the arthropod takes a blood meal from an infected reservoir, then spreads the pathogen to new hosts when it takes new blood meals. (4). Feces, or human and animal wastes harbor large microbial populations, many of which could be pathogenic or act as opportunistic pathogens when spread to food and water owing to improper sanitary techniques or contamination of water supplies caused by flooding or breaks in sewer lines.

J. ANIMAL RESERVOIRS AND HUMAN CARRIERS

Humans can be carriers of infectious disease, not only when ill, but also when seemingly healthy. Asymptomatic carriers retain pathogens but do not manifest the disease syndrome. This could be the result of prior illness or a healthy immune system that fails to eliminate small numbers of the pathogen that have become "hidden," such as in *S. pyogenes* infections behind the tonsilar tissue, HIV and Herpes infections that have become latent, *Salmonella* residing in the gall bladder or cystic duct, or due to the presence of microbes that cause illness in one host but not another, such as *Trichmonas vaginalis* infections that are generally asymptomatic in males but result in vaginitis in females. Sub clinical carriers may have an active infection that continues in a reduced form in a part of the body other than the target tissue normally associated with the illness. One example of this is the persistent infection of tissues associated with the nervous system caused by the measles virus, and results in subacute schlerosing panencephalitis.

K. NON LIVING RESERVOIRS

Soil, water, and food are all nonliving reservoirs of infection. Soil can harbor potential pathogens of many kinds, ranging from *Bacillus anthracis* to *E. coli* O157:H7, *Mycobacterium leprae* to *Pseudomonas aeruginosa*. Water can serve as a reservoir and vehicle for *Vibrio cholera, E. coli, Cryptosporidium parvum, Entamoeba histolytic, Giardia lamblia,* and many other pathogens. The first outbreak of *Legionnaires disease* in the 1970s was the result of a plugged air conditioner condenser drain that allowed *Legionella pneumophila* to reproduce and be spread as aerosol droplets in the recirculated air of a Philadelphia hotel. Meat, milk, and vegetables can all harbor pathogens and serve as vehicles for transmission of infectious disease either directly or when contaminated owing to unsanitary food handling techniques.

1.8. MICROBIAL MASS ACTION PRINCIPAL: OUTBREAK COEFFICIENT

An "outbreak" can be defined as a sudden eruption of a disease; in contrast, an "epidemic" is defined as an outbreak of disease with widespread occurrence at a point in time. Previously (Olisa, 2002) an "outbreak coefficient" (ω) was derived using standard existing formulas for the general reproductive rate ($R_0 = \beta XD$); and incidence ($I=\beta XZ$), where (β) is the transmission coefficient. This concept is novel. In previous studies, (Blaser, and Newman, 1989; Nokes, and Anderson, 1988; Baker, 1989), the basic reproductive rate of an infectious agent was used to determine the thresh hold result in an epidemiological model. Furthermore, these investigators noted that disease would persist if $R_0 > 1$. For an infectious agent, R_0 can be determined in the presence of other confounding variables such as two or more pathogens. By combing the empirical and theoretical formula from these studies, improvements were made to the equation for computing disease incidence when mixing was homogeneous. This idea was first proposed by Busenberg and Castillo-Chavez (1991). Based on these findings, homogeneity can be used to address the issue of mixing and its impact on R_0 by creating a model that addressed the nature a pathogen disseminates in the population. In the proposed model, cohorts such as age, sex, and social behavior have little or no impact on herd immunity. This models operability relies on factors that impact the innate biology of the infectious agent like infective dose and ways spread. In the past, others have developed real time prediction models. Meester, de Koning, de Jong and Diemann (2002), proposed a real-time predictive model for historical cases of Classical Swine Fever epidemics.

By definition, biological agents (infectious agents) are microbes capable of causing disease to humans. Different biological agents have different infective doses (ID). Id_{50} is the amount of pathogen that can cause disease in 50% of the population in question at a point in time. One basic characteristic of infectious agents is their low $Id_{50.}$ In addition, infectious agents can be transmitted within a population in multiple ways. In nature, he most highly infectious agents spread asymmetrical (transmission is random, and homogeneous). Infectious agents are not selective and are unresponsive to immunization and treatment. With these assumptions, models predicting the prevalence of infectious agents would be non-linear (Nokes, and Anderson, 1988). Accordingly, mathematical models formulated by interaction and mixing of microbe and host are ultimately dependent on the number of ways the infectious agent is disseminated. In this case, the Id_{50} becomes a direct reflection of the innate biological characteristics that impacts the rate of infection (Busenberg and Chavez, 1991).

The "mass action principal" can be defined as the net rate at which new cases of an infection arise, and is proportional to the density (or number) of susceptible individuals (X), times the density of infectious persons (Z), times the probability of transmission (β) from infectious to susceptible individuals (Nokes, and Anderson, 1988). When interaction is homogeneous, incidence rate (I), can be then formulated as follows:

$I = \beta XZ$ (1)

Where β is the *probability of transmission* or the *transmission coefficient.* β is the probability that an infectious agent will transmit disease. Incidence rate is a direct estimate of the probability, or risk, of developing a disease during a specific period in time. R_0 represents the basic reproductive rate of infection. R_0 can be described as the number of secondary cases of infection derived by one primary case, and is formulated as

$R_0 = \beta XD$ (2)

Where D is the length of time the primary case is infectious to others, and X is the number of susceptible individuals. As before, R_0 is dependent on the typical course of infection, the social and demographic makeup of the community, and the biology of the infectious disease. For infection to persist, R_0 would have to be ≥ 1. Solving the equation for X in equation (2), we get:

$X = R_0/ßD$ (3)

To address individual mixing, it was found that transmission coefficient is directly proportional to the number of ways an infectious agent is disseminated. As mixing or dissemination increases, the rate of transmission also increases. This statement can be expressed as:

$\beta \propto Y$ (4)

Where Y_2 is the number of ways that an infectious agent can be disseminated or contribute to spreading throughout a population (e.g., via air, food, and water). The infective dose represents the probability for the infectious agent to infect and cause disease in half the exposed population. Accordingly, transmission coefficient is inversely proportional to the infective dose:

$\beta \propto 1/Y_1$ (5)

Where Y_1 is that agent's Id_{50}. As the Id_{50} decreases, transmission increases.

$\beta \propto Y_2/Y_1$ (6)

Subsequently,

$\omega = \beta(Y_2/Y_1)$ (7)

Where ω is the “outbreak coefficient,” and β the transmission coefficient, is equal to 1

1.9. INFECTION CONTROL

A. INTRODUCTION

MICROBIAL CONTROL METHODS: The goal of an aseptic condition is to totally remove microbial organisms or suppress their reproduction or metabolism (antisepsis). Control methods used could be achieved physically, or using: temperature, radiation, chemical, or with the use of disinfectants and antiseptics. Both physical and chemical methods can adopt the use enzyme activity to denature proteins, thus shutting down microbial metabolism. Physical and chemical methods can also inhibit microbial cell permeability of the plasma membrane thereby interfering with the selective transfer of substances in and out of the cell. Some substances may directly affect genetic material in the microbe to disrupt both metabolism and reproduction.

A number of diseases like dysentery have been shown to contaminate hands from toilet seats. For the most part allied health worker scrub hands to reduce the threat of disease. Transient microbes are found on surface of skin and are acquired from the environment. Resident microbes are indigenous to the body and are found in the pores of skin and inside the body. Ignatz Semmelweis, a Viennese physician, and Oliver Wendell Holmes showed that the number of women who die from puerperal fever caused by streptococcal infection, decreased after hand washing.

ELEVATED TEMPERATURE: Elevated temperatures increases rate of reactions, denatures proteins (enzymes), and causes irreversible alterations of the three dimensional structure of enzyme protein. However, the use of elevated temperatures is not always effective. Some gram positive organisms are thermoduric which means that they are heat resistant (more than gram negative) due to large amounts of peptidoglycan on cell walls. In addition, spores tend to be heat resistant.

THERMAL DEATH POINT: Thermal death point is used to measure resistance or susceptibility to temperature elevation. Thermal death point can be defined as the lowest temperature to kill an organism: in 10 min at pH 7.0. Microbial Death Rate (MDR) is higher at higher temperatures. To kill same amount of microbe, disinfectant requires 4 min at 45°C; 12 min at 20°C.

EFFECTS OF ULTRAVIOLET (UV) RADIATION: UV radiation is a non-ionizing radiation that affects genetic material of the cell like DNA. UV radiation causes damages to nitrogenous bases of DNA like thymine and cytosine's. The radiation can cause the two to bond together forming a thymine and cytosine dimmer. These dimmers cannot form reactions with other bases in DNA during cell division and these can cause lethal mutations and photo reactivation which is the use of light by some organisms to repair damages to DNA. Examples can be seen in the following microbes: *Serratia marcescens*, and *Micrococcus radiouridans*.

UV can be considered as a disinfectant and not a sterilizing agent. Factors that determine how effective UV light is include the following: (1). Wavelength, maximal lethal wavelength is 265 nm. The closer a wavelength is to 265, the greater the maximum killing of UV light. Lamps can generate about 253.7 nm. (2). Time of exposure to UV light.

DISINFECTANTS AND ANTISEPTICS: Disinfectants are agents used on inanimate object and surfaces because they are harsh no tissues. Antiseptics on the other hand are safe to use on tissues. Some agents are *sterilizers* meaning they can eliminate all life forms. Other agents are *bacteriostatic* and inhibit bacterial growth, or the agent may be *bactericidal*. Bacteriostatic agents kill bacteria not spores or viruses. Selection on bacteriostatic or sterilants depends on whether the need is to provide aseptic or bactericidal conditions. The lipid outer layer of gram negative bacteria will make them less susceptible to chemicals and resistant to chemical control. Gram positives will be more susceptible to chemical agents.

High-level germicides kill all pathogens, including endospores. Intermediate-level germicides kill fungal spores, vegetative bacterial cells, cysts and inactivate viruses, but cannot kill endospores. Low-level germicides kill vegetative bacterial cells, protozoa, fungi and inactivate some viruses, but are ineffective against endospores, cysts, very resistant pathogens such as mycobacteria and most viruses.

B. PHYSICAL METHODS OF CONTROL

HEAT: One of the most effective ways of killing microbes is with the use of heat. When used effectively, it denatures proteins, disrupts plasma membranes, and oxidizes biological molecules. It can inactivate viruses and kill endospores. Heat can be applied either in dry form, as in flaming and baking; or moist, as in steaming, boiling or autoclaving. The thermal death point is the lowest temperature at which bacteria die in a broth incubated for 10 minutes at a pH of 7. The decimal reduction time (D) represents the time it takes for 90% of a population of microbes to be killed by a particular method of microbial control, such as autoclaving.

Moist heat is formed when water heats up quickly but cools slowly. In liquid form it can retain and deliver heat energy much more efficiently that dry heat alone since molecules in a liquid are much closer together than those in a gas. Boiling (raising water temperature to 100 °C) kills most vegetative cells within 10 minutes at sea level. Water boils at a lower temperature at higher altitudes or pressure, this characteristic can be used to effectively boil water for longer periods of time cost-effectively to achieve the same level of disinfection on some non-enveloped heat resistant viruses, and the cysts of protozoa. Bacterial endospores are very resistant to boiling at short periods. For example, the spores of *Clostridium botulinum* can be boiled for 5-20 hours and still remain viable. For this reason, boiling should not be considered an agent of sterilization.

AUTOCLAVES: Autoclaves boil water at higher pressures and temperature for extended time frames using steam. The heat energy in steam can dissipate quickly into the atmosphere. Water under pressure has a higher boiling point, and increases the amount heat delivered to a microbial population. An autoclave is a chamber that uses steam under pressure to sterilize media, glassware, surgical implements, and other materials that are not sensitive to heat. At standard operating temperature of 121 °C and pressure (15 lb/in2), it takes about 10 minutes (though standard operating time is generally 15 minutes) to kill vegetative cells, endospores, cysts of protists and inactivate viruses. When operating correctly, an autoclave can deliver twice the heat energy to the surface of an object than steaming alone. Autoclaves also contain sterility indicators, such as autoclave strips made of spore ampoules. *Bacillus stearothermophilus* spores are used in spore ampoules and strips since the endospores of this bacterium are very *thermoduric* and will only be killed if the autoclave operates properly. Autoclaves cannot be used to sterilize powders, oils or any material or medium Examples include: egg media, whole blood and many carbohydrate broths that are sensitive to heat. Also, since some bacterial exotoxins can withstand autoclaving, bandages sterilized in this manner must be thoroughly rinsed in sterile water prior to use.

PASTEURIZATION: Pasteurization as a process reduces microbial populations in liquids such as milk and juices, but does not sterilize. Pasteurization is used primarily to kill and inhibit the growth of pathogens found in dairy products such as *E. coli*, *Brucella melitensis, Mycobacterium bovis,* and *Listeria monocytogenes.*

Standard (batch method) pasteurization raises the temperature of the fluid in large containers to 63 °C for 30 minutes. *High temperature-short time* (flash) pasteurization can be achieved when passing a fluid through tubes heated to 72 °C for 15 seconds. *Ultra-high temperature pasteurization* is the process of raising the temperature of milk to 134°C for 1 second. All three techniques produce approximately the same effect in terms of the reduction of microbial populations

DRY HEAT: Dry heat can be used on powders, oils and other substances that cannot be sterilized using moist heat can be sterilized with dry heat. However, it takes greater temperatures and longer application times to achieve the same effect. Baking, flaming and incineration are all methods for the application of dry heat.

1.10. ANTIBIOTICS AND VACCINES

A. INTRODUCTION

Historically, early Egyptian physicians used molds found in bread to treat some diseases even though they had no idea of the existence of microbial and anti-microbial activity. Furthermore, the sixthteenth century physician, Aureolus Paracelsus, treated syphilis with heavy metals like mercury and antimony. In addition, ancient Africans and South Americans discovered that the bark of the Cinchona tree could be used to treat malaria. In later years, the name quinine was derived by Thomas Sydenham (1624-1689) from the original Quechua (Inca) word for the cinchona tree bark, "Quina" or "Quina-Quina," which roughly means "bark of bark" or "holy bark." Subsequently, using this information, French researchers Pierre Joseph Pelletier and Joseph Bienaimé Caventou were able to extract "quinine" from the Cinchona bark.

Decades later, the German scientist, Paul Ehrlich (1854-1915), often referred to as the father of chemotherapy developed an antitoxin for diphtheria and syphilis. Well into the end of the First World War; the British physician, Alexander Fleming (1895-1964) identified the antibiotic in *Penicillium chrysogenum*. His associates, Earnest Cain and Howard Flory later developed techniques to purify penicillin G from molds thus giving birth to modern antibiotics as we know it. Some antibiotics are known to have adverse reactions or allergic reactions due to interference with normal host defenses. They can also be disruptive to normal micro flora. Some examples of antibiotics with toxic side effects include: Streptomycin, Sulfonamides, Tetracycline, and Chloramphenecol. Other criteria for selecting antibiotics are metabolism of drug by patients, duration of treatment, type of pathogen, interaction with other drugs, pathogens resistance to antibiotics, chemotherapeutic index, and *Minimum Inhibitory Concentration* (MIC) defined as the minimum amount of drug needed to limit or inhibit growth of pathogen (not necessarily kill) at the least amount of time. This is a time series event.

Chemotherapeutic Index =

Maximum dose tolerated by patient / Minimum Dosage Needed Clear Infection

In a clinical setting, the prescription of right antibiotics for treatment is important. Failure to do so may lead to death. One of the most rapid, accurate and cost effective ways to determine which antibiotics to administer is the *Kirby-Bauer* sensitivity technique. To perform this technique, organisms isolated from patients are streaked for confluent growth in large blood plates. A variety of antibiotic impregnated discs are dispensed manually or with the use of a disc dispenser onto the surface of the culture plate. During incubation, the organism will grow around the discs of antibiotics which it is susceptible. Size of zone of resistance will reflect the relative resistance or susceptibility of the organism to the antibiotic. Infection control can be achieved by action of antimicrobial agents. Microbial death does not occur all at once when cells are treated with antimicrobial compounds. Cells are killed in constant percentages at a constant rate.

B. CELL WALL AND CELL MEMBRANES INHIBITORS

Antibiotics that interfere with cell wall synthesis break down or prevent the synthesis of the cell wall and expose the cell membrane to the osmotic conditions outside. This can lead to plasmolysis or lyses. Physical or chemical removal of the phospholipids or the envelope of enveloped viruses can prevent them from attaching to host cells since the viral spikes necessary for adsorption are removed. Nonenveloped viruses are less likely to be affected since their spikes are located on the surface of the capsid. Antimicrobials can also damage proteins and nucleic acids and disrupt disulfide and hydrogen bonds that maintain the three-dimensional shape of a protein causing it to denature and become nonfunctional.

CELL WALL SYNTHESIS INHIBITORS

PENICILLIN: This is a bactericidal, narrow spectrum, semi-synthetic drug derived from the penicillin mold. This antibiotic can break down bacterial peptidoglycan and is useful in treating Staphylococcus spp, Streptococcus spp, and Spirochetes. It can be taking orally and is not destroyed by acid environments of the stomach. Microbes become resistant to this drug by producing using pencillinase (beta-lactamase) to destroy the integrity of its beta lactam rings.

AMPICILLIN: Was discovered in 1961 and are a beta-lactam antibiotic, and a semi-synthetic drug derived from penicillin. It functions as a competitive inhibitor of the enzyme transpeptidase which is needed by bacteria to make their cell walls. Unlike penicillin, it has broad spectrum activity. Like penicillin it can be inactivated by beta-lactamase.

CEPHALOSPORIN: Is a broad-spectrum, beta lactam antibiotic that is resistant to pencillinase, and causes fewer allergic reactions than penicillin. It is usually administered intravenously since they are sensitive to the acidic environment of the stomach.

BACITRACIN: Is named and derived from Bacillus spp. structurally, the antibiotic is one of the few existing polypeptide antibiotics that has a narrow spectrum, and is effective against Staphylococci spp and Streptococci spp as well as Neisseria gonorrhoeae. It is usually administered topically. Bacitracin interferes with the dephosphorylation of the C55-isoprenyl pyrophosphate, a molecule which carries the building blocks of the peptidoglycan bacterial cell wall outside of the inner membrane. Another example of peptide antibiotics produced by pathogens is Nisin secreted by *Lactobacillus lactis*.

VANCOMYCIN: Vancomycin was first isolated from soil samples containing *Streptomyces orientalis*. It is very toxic, and difficult to administer. Furthermore, this antibiotic has a narrow spectrum of activity and can be used to destroy pencillinase producing *S. aureus,* and to treat Streptococcal endocardiatis. Some new strains of *Enterococcus faecalis* have evolved to be resistant to Vancomycin (VRE). Most gram-negative bacteria show resistant to Vancomycin because their outer membrane is impermeable to large glycopeptide molecules that make up Vancomycin. Resistance to Vancomycin is a growing problem, particularly within health care facilities such as hospitals since it is the last-line antibiotic for serious Gram-positive infections. Vancomycin-resistant Enterococcus (VRE) emerged in 1987. Vancomycin resistance emerged in more common pathogenic organisms during the 1990s and 2000s. Some of the pathogens that have emerged resistant to VRE include the following: Vancomycin-intermediate *Staphylococcus aureus* (VISA), Vancomycin-resistant *Staphylococcus aureus* (VRSA), and Vancomycin-resistant *Clostridium difficile*. The cause of resistance has been linked to the agricultural use of avoparcin.

One mechanism of resistance to Vancomycin appears to be alteration to the terminal amino acid residues of the NAM/NAG-peptide subunits known as D-alanyl-D-Alanine. Vancomycin is known to bind to these subunits. Vancomycin should be administered intravenously for systemic therapy since it does not cross through the intestinal lining. It is a large hydrophilic molecule which partitions poorly across the gastrointestinal mucosa. The only indication for oral Vancomycin therapy is in the treatment of *pseudo membranous colitis*, where it must be given orally to reach the site of infection in the colon. Vancomycin acts by inhibiting proper cell wall synthesis in Gram-positive bacteria.

CELL MEMBRANE INHIBITORS

POLYMYXINS: Are polypeptide antibiotics produced by *Bacillus polymyxa* with a narrow spectrum of activity. They are normally used to treat Pseudomonas infections and cause severe side effects like kidney and brain damage.

POLYENES: These are anti-fungal drugs produced by Streptomyces. They target ergesterol, a cell membrane component of fungi. Some examples include the following: Nystatin which are used to treat vaginal and intestinal infections caused by Candida albicans; Amphotericib B functions to disrupt cell membranes of fungus permitting access of other drugs, and is used synergistically with Flucytocine to treat histoplasmosis systematically.

AZOLES: These are broad spectrum antifungal agents that are inhibited by alcohols and used as sprays or topical ointments. Some examples include the following: Clotrimazole and miconazole which are topical agents used to treat cutaneous mycosis (dermatophyte like ring worm, athletes foot fungus, and Candida albicans; Metronidazole can be used to treat gastrointestinal infections and hepatic diseases caused by *Entamoeba histolytic* and *Giardia lamblia* and urinary tract infections caused by *Trichmonas vaginalis.*

C. ANTIBIOTICS THAT INHIBIT PROTEIN SYNTHESIS

STREPTOMYCIN: These are aminoglycoside antibiotics produced by Streptomyces. They were discovered in 1944 and have a narrow spectrum of activity. This antibiotic is mainly used to treat gram negative infections like those caused by Pseudomonas spp. They have toxic side effects that damage the kidney and auditory nerves and function by distorting 70S ribosome's so that mRNA is incorrectly read resulting in the synthesis of defective proteins.

ERYTHROMYCIN: One of the most common narrow spectrum antibiotics used in the treatment of penicillin resistance *S. aureus*. It inhibits protein synthesis by preventing mRNA from moving on the surface of ribosomes.

TETRACYCLINE: Broad spectrum antibiotics produced by Streptomyces. Side effects include discoloration of infants when taken by mother during fetal development. There potency is inactivated by dairy products, iron containing foods and alcohol. They function by preventing the attachment of tRNA to ribosome's, consequently, blocking protein synthesis.

CHLORAMPHENECOL: This is a broad spectrum antibiotics produced by Streptomyces. It primarily interferes with protein synthesis and can be used to treat Salmonella infections. One side effect is aplastic anemia. It's beneficial over other antibiotics because of the small size of its molecules which can reach areas of the body that other antibiotics cannot reach.

D. ANTIMICROBIALS THAT INHIBIT NUCLEIC ACIDS

CIPROFLOXACIN: Fluoroquinolone broad spectrum antibiotic that inhibits the activity of microbial DNA gyrase. It can be used effectively to treat *Bacillus anthracis*, *Neisseria gonorrhoeae*, and *N. meningitides*.

RIPHAMPIN: Rifampin is effective against Mycobacterium infections. Functions by inhibiting the transcription of mRNA, and is known to have toxic side effects.

NALIDIXIC ACID: Nalidixic acid is often used to treat urinary tract infections. This antibiotic causes the degradation of DNA in gram negative bacteria.

TRIMETHOPRIN: Trimethoprin block nucleic acid synthesis by competing for active sites on enzymes necessary for folic acid synthesis. They are administered synergistically with sulfonamethoxazole to treat infections caused by gram positive bacteria like *Streptococcus pyogenes*.

FLUCYTOSINE: Is an analog of the nitrogenous base cytosine. It functions by inhibiting nucleic acid synthesis in fungi and is sometimes used synergistically with Amphotericin B to treat systemic infections of Candida albicans and Cryptococcus neoformans.

E. METABOLIC INHIBITORS

SULFA DRUGS: Sulfa drugs are coal tar derivatives that contain sulfur. They have been in use since the 1930s prior to antibiotics. Sulfanilamide competitively competes for PABA, which is a metabolite for the production of folic acid in some bacteria. This drug is commonly used to treat *N. meningitidis* since they can pass through membranes of the meninges in the central nervous system.

ANTIVIRAL COMPOUNDS Antiviral compounds such as Acyclovir (ZOVIRAX) is used to treat Herpes infection and works by inhibiting viral DNA polymerase. Others like Azidothymidine (AZT) blocks reverse transcription of retroviruses like HIV. AZT does not cure, but rather slows the progress of the disease. Patients can build resistance against AZT. Protease inhibitors prevent the synthesis of viral particles and are normally used synergistically with AZT as combination therapy. Consequently, the drug can cause toxic side effects.

F. HUMAN ANTIBIOTICS

Most, if not all pathogens scavenge iron from transferrin using either cell wall bound iron-binding proteins, or reductase (*Streptococcus pneumoniae*), or by secreting low molecular weight iron-acquisition molecules like siderophores (*Escherichia coli).* In other pathogens like viruses and plasmodium, the parasite that causes malaria dock on transferrin-iron complexes on host cells (red blood cells in the case of plasmodium, or CXC signal transducing receptors on T- cells in the case of HIV) as a way to attach cells and gain platforms for energy independent entry into host cell by endocytosis. Yet, other microbes utilized iron as cofactor in various metabolic apoenzymes. To prevent this loss of iron to microbes, the body secretes molecules like lactoferrin to reclaim the iron from pathogens. Lactoferrin is an important natural antibiotic found in milk.

Natural antibiotics like HNP-1 (α-defensin), lactoferrin, lysozymes, and interferon are cysteine containing oligopeptides that function in two ways. First, they function by depriving pathogens of iron. Second, they bind and inactivate enzymes on cell wall, and membranes of microbes. Examples of microbial enzymes affected by natural antibiotics are: transpeptidase, and signal transducing serine or threonine kinases. In the process, the allosteric impact of binding due to cross-linking cysteine molecules results to the structural and functional breakdown of microbial cell wall integrity.

G. FACTORS EFFECTING QUALITY AND GRADE OF ANTIBIOTICS

Environmental conditions like temperature and pH both affect how well antimicrobial agents work. Warm disinfectants generally work more quickly than cold ones and this activity is also enhanced by more acidic pH. Other chemical disinfectants, such as bleach (sodium hypochlorite) work better at lower pH. Excess accumulations of organic matter such as blood, urine, vomit, feces and the polysaccharide layers of biofilms can lessen the effectiveness of heat and radiation and can also inactivate some chemical disinfectants. Thorough cleaning of the surface prior to application of the disinfecting agent increases it ability to penetrate, and come in contact with microbes, and reduce their populations.

One factor that influences the diffusion of antibiotics is its m*olecular weight* (different molecular weights diffuse at different rates), size of inoculums of sample, and the density of bacteria. To better determine an antibiotics impact on multiple drug resistance (MDR) it is necessary to use Kirby Bauer interpretation charts. When using the chart, the diameter of the zones of inhibition is measured in millimeters. The size of the zones of inhibition forms the basis for comparing antibiotics.

1.11. IMMUNOLOGY

A. INTRODUCTION

The human body has three basic types of defense mechanism against microbes. The first line of defense for the body is the skin and mucous membranes which form physical barriers. Second and third lines of defense lie within the body, and consist of blood base and water soluble biochemicals and other cells. Collectively, these cells and biochemical work *in sync* to kill and destroy pathogens that infect the body. The second line defense is called the innate system because they are present at birth. Most of these cells are found in blood plasma and include iron binding molecules like transferrin and lactoferrin. Other such as defensins, dermicidins, lysozymes, and phagocytic dentric cells are *cysteine containing peptides* of about 40 amino acids that are secreted by either or both the epidermis outer layers of the skin (dermicidins, lysozymes and defensins) or mucus membranes (lysozymes and defensins).

B. INNATE IMMUNITY

Innate immunity is the basis for the second line of defense in humans because their development is not dependent on contact with pathogens. Their activities are relatively non-specific and the spectrum of activity is broad. Cells that make up the innate immune response include the following: (1). *Leukocytes,* these are divided into two groups, the *granulocyte*s, so called because they have large granules that absorb stain. Examples of granulocytes include the following: *basophiles, eosinophils*, and *neutrophils*. Eosinophils and neutrophils can phagocytize pathogens and excite the blood to attach an invading microbe through a process call *diapedesis.* Granulocytes are more uniform and consist of *lymphocytes* (very small) and *monocytes* (relatively large). Monocytes migrate out of blood to form macrophages which are phagocytic to bacterial, parasites, and fungi. Most *lymphocytes* are involved in *adaptive immunity* except the *natural killer* (NK) lymphocytes which produce, secrete toxins that kill viral cells. Other non-specific chemical defenses include the following: *compliments*, which are a set of serum proteins; *opsonins*, which are chemotactic factors that indirectly trigger *inflammation* and fever; *interferon*, these are proteins released by host cells to nonspecifically limit the spread of viral particles; and *defensins* and *lysozymes*.

C. ADAPTIVE IMMUNITY

The third line of defense is called the adaptive system because its activity is specific and unique to species of pathogen that invaded the body. The adaptive system responds to antigens. Components include the following: lymphocytes (with the exception of NK cells), there are two types: *B-lymphocytes* and *T-lymphocytes*. They are so named because of the proteins found on the cytoplasmic membranes known as immune proteins. The glycoprotein molecules, known as *clusters of differentiation* or CD, are further used in their identification.

B-LYMPHOCYTES: Also known as B cells are plasma cells that are produced in the red bone marrow in adults. They function to fight exogenous antigens and secrete soluble plasma proteins called antibodies or immunoglobulin's (Ig) into blood or lymph. Body fluid like blood and lymph are called humore so B cells make up the humeral immune response. Ig are made up of heavy and light chains (due to their relative molecular weights) which contain hyper variable regions that serve as antigen binding sites, and an Fc or fragment of crystallization which serves as a receptor for binding host cell membranes. There are five classes of antibodies namely IgG, IgM, IgA, IgE, and IgD.

Antibodies function to neutralize toxins or physiologically active proteins by allosteric impact. They can also block attachment surfaces of molecules in viruses and bacteria and parasites like plasmodium, depriving them of entry into target cell. Antibodies also opsonize (enhanced phagocytosis). That is they stimulate phagocytosis since neutrophils and macrophages have receptors for the Fc receptor of IgG molecules. Antibodies also catalyze killing by oxidation through the production of hydrogen peroxide and other oxidizing agents that kill bacteria. Antibodies also bind to each other or agglutinate; hence they are used as diagnostic tools in laboratories to detect infection.

T-LYMPHOCYTES: These are produced in the red bone marrow in adults and mature under the influence of the thymus. T cells gradually replicate and generate T Cell receptors (TCR). T cells act directly against antigens and do not produce antibodies, thus they participate in cell mediated response. There are three types of T cells: (1). Cytotoxic T cells (T_cCells). (2). Helper T cells (T_H Cells), which help in regulating activity of B Cells, and (3). Cytotoxic T cells. There are two sub populations of T cells: T_H 1, which assist Cytotoxic T cells and; T_H2 that function with B cells. Helper T cells secrete soluble proteins call cytokines which regulate immune response. Some examples of cytokines include: interleukins, which regulates leucocytes, there are about 27 in all; interferon which are antiviral proteins; growth factors that stimulate stem cells to divide; Tumor necrosis factor (TNF) secreted by macrophages and T cells to kill and regulate tumor cells and inflammatory responses; and chemokines which regulate and signal leukocytes inflammatory responses.

D. NATURAL ACQUIRED IMMUNITY

Active acquired immunity occurs when the body is exposed to pathogens in the environment. *Passive acquired immunity* occurs when newborns acquire immunoglobulins like IgG's from their mothers, which pass through the membranes of the placenta from the mother's blood stream. *Artificially acquired active immunity* occurs when physicians initiate immunity using vaccines to administer foreign antigens. Furthermore, this forms the basis of immunizations against infections disease. Finally, *artificially acquired passive immunity* is induced when antibodies are administered to speed up the pace of adaptive defense.

1.12. BIOINFORMATICS AND COMPUTATIONAL BIOLOGY

Bioinformatics (sometimes referred to as computational biology) uses computer, engineering the natural sciences like biochemistry, molecular biology, systems biology, mathematics, and statistics to develop algorithms and software used in solving complex biological and systems problems. The goal of bioinformatics is usually to attain cost-effective research. Cost effective since nano-technologies replace often expensive and unnecessary human labor used in gene and protein analysis for diagnostics and therapeutic research. Increasingly, since innovations in: human and microbial gene sequencing, molecular diagnostics, and vaccine and peptide antibiotics research, bioinformatics is being preferred over other techniques as more a more cost-effective process for achieve desirable outcomes.

Comparatively, bioinformatics offers a more practical approach than computational genomics or proteomics which is more hypothesis driven and based on the *incremental approach* to rational process evaluation. Often, the process involves the use of modeling. Rapidly, increased information available in databases of genes and gene function has greatly fueled bioinformatics and computational biology as well as basic research in biology. Consequently, there has been a meteoric surge and improvement in computational proteomics and genomics. Unlike the past decade, there are fewer limitations on the availability of high quality information in databases. Furthermore, there are numerous applications to bioinformatics. However, while some of the applications are extremely sensitive and effective, they are not cost-effective or feasible. It's important to make this distinction when planning for a pharmaceutical intervention or programs that involves large scale manufacturing. Admittedly, bioinformatics and computational genomics and proteomics are most cost-effective when used in Quasi-experimentation designs. In other words, evaluation and assessments processes for qualitative research (quasi-experimentation or non-experimental) are more cost-effective than those that are qualitative experimentation (experimental), this is in part because quasi-experimentation uses theory and facts to make comparisons. Furthermore, the evaluator (researcher) do not have control over the experiments, rather the experiments occur in natural settings. A good example of this setting are those found in clinical diagnostic laboratories or processes to implement best practices in the field.

Conversely, in research settings, the evaluator (researcher) has control in terms of sample selection, size, treatment, and environment. In situations like these, threats to data validity increases in pre-test, post test, and control groups, bringing to question increasing difficulties associated with data interpretation. Experimentation or evaluations to explain these questions can add to experimental cost. Nonetheless, some of the established and cost effective uses of computational biology in biotechnology and pharmaceutical industries are in the analysis of gene and protein structures.

1.13. EPIDEMIOLOGY

Epidemiology is the study of where disease occurs and how it spreads within populations. Epidemiological studies involve the gathering of data related to a disease, and analysis of the trends seen in this information. Data is reported in the form of tables, graphs, and charts that allow patterns to become visible. Occurrence can be categorized not only by frequency, but also geographic distribution.

Endemic diseases occur continuously in localized populations at a relatively slow but steady frequency, such as malaria along the gulf and southern east coasts of the U.S., Western Africa, Central and South America, India, Sri Lanka and Southeast Asia. These areas all have favorable climatic conditions to support the *Anopheles mosquitoes* that serve as vectors for the several Plasmodium species responsible for the disease. The trypanosomes *Trypanosoma gambiense* and *T. rhodesiense*, agents of African trypanosomiasis (African sleeping sickness), are endemic to parts of Africa that support tsetse *fly* vectors, while *Trypanosoma cruzi*, the agent of American trypanomaisis (*Chagas' disease*), is endemic to North, Central and South America since these regions are home to the "cone-nosed" reduvid bugs of the genus *Triatoma* that are its vectors.

When SARS appeared in the Americas in the outbreak of 2003, it appeared in a few cases in Toronto, Canada and a few in some U.S cities, but then disappeared. Epidemic diseases appear within a population, and then rapidly spread outward. In reference to the SARs example, for a disease to be considered *epidemic*, the observed number of cases must significantly exceed the recorded frequency of the disease based on regular case reporting. If epidemics of the same disease occur within different countries at the same time, the disease is considered to be a *pandemic*. Examples of pandemic diseases include the 1918-1919 outbreak of influenza H1N1 and the current AIDS pandemic. The outbreak of SARs cited in the example cannot therefore be considered a pandemic.

Sporadic diseases occur infrequently and may be scattered throughout the world. In order to be able to classify the category of disease, it is necessary to provide specific information about incidence. This data is gathered by case reporting performed routinely by infectious disease specialists at the local, state, federal, and international levels. Data about the most important pathogenic diseases is used to generate a list of notifiable diseases reported on a weekly basis to the Centers for Disease Control and Prevention (CDC) in Atlanta, Georgia.

Analytical epidemiology involves a thorough investigation of the disease, including data from descriptive studies to determine the etiological agent, its mode of transmission and potential methods of prevention. These studies are often introspective since they follow a disease outbreak and require examination of infected versus uninfected populations to determine the root causes, predisposing factors and possible routes of disease transmission.

Experimental epidemiology involves using hypothesis testing to determine the cause of disease, or methods of treating diseases that are already known. Koch's Postulates can be applied to this type of study when the agent is microbial, or modified if the agent is viral or a fastidious intracellular parasite.

Other types of infections, like *nosocomial infections* are acquired by patients while in health care facilities such as hospitals and clinics. *Nosocomial diseases* are among some of the most common and costly medical problems today, accounting for ~90,000 deaths annually in the United States alone. *Exogenous nosocomial* infections are the result of pathogens being spread by patients as they are shed from various portals of exit while the patients are in the health care facility. *Endogenous nosocomial* infections are the result of *opportunistic pathogens* already present in or on the body of the patient and brought on by conditions present at or the direct result of activities at the health care facility. *Iatrogenic nosocomial* infections are spread by health care workers, generally as the result improper sanitary conditions, failure to follow universal precautions, or contaminated invasive surgical or patient care equipment.

Reduction in nosocomial infection requires conscious effort to maintain good antiseptic and aseptic conditions and techniques. Some commonly used universal precautions include the following: wearing gloves, changing gloves, washing hands between patients, never handling any sterile apparatus that might contact patient skin, proper disposal of biohazardous materials, isolation of contagious and susceptible patients, and regular sanitation of hospital garments.

The establishment of infection control committee's officers should also be considered an important step in finding and eliminating the root causes of such infections. Local and state health authorities should routinely report disease outbreaks to national and international epidemiological agencies like the CDC and WHO. This is vital in the tracking of infectious disease. Public health agencies must play a major role in disease education and surveillance, as well as in the work to limit the spread of infectious diseases in their local populations by enforcing guidelines established to insure the purity of water supplies and reduction of food-borne illness among food suppliers and restaurants. These agencies should work to reduce the number of disease-carrying vectors such as mosquitoes and ticks, as well as the reservoirs such as rodents and wild animals that come into contact with members of the public.

1.14. EPIDEMIOLOGIC TRANSITION THEORY: IMPACT ON INFECTIOUS DISEASE

A. INTRODUCTION

The General *Theory of Epidemiologic Transition* was first theorizes in 1977. The theory argues that periodic changes in health status and disease in different populations can be attributed to demographic and socioeconomic policies and conditions, and that disease cases result in population change. Furthermore, in emerging economies, general social and economic development projects can be expected to influence mortality (Omran, 1977). In a previous report, Rogers and Hackenberg, (1987), suggest that mortality due to infectious disease had been partially and significantly reduced by economic development in the western hemisphere. However, they noted that this trend is reversed in developing economies.

In previous Epidemiologic Transition Theory studies, the independent impact variable was identified as economic development, and demographics. Economic indices can be measured by the gross domestic product (GDP) and national census data (Brass 1980), while the dependent variable, infectious disease mortality; can be measured by new and old cases of disease. These epidemiologic changes can measured by disease incidence or the rate of disease per year and life expectancy (Ruzicka, 1983), and Zavala, 1992). In these studies, the GDP data was acquired from the US census bureau while the mortality data was acquired from the CDC&P. Furthermore, investigators had a general consensus and agreement about the relationship between causes and of the independent variables used. Prior to this landmark study (Omran, 1977), there had been speculations, mainly by skeptics, that the Epidemiologic Transition Theory lacked credibility.

At present, based findings from numerous studies, theories in epidemiologic transition appear to be generally accepted. However, a few investigators (Gaylin, and Kates, 1997) have published reports that suggest the theory only provide partial explanation for socioeconomic transition. In this reports, it is recommended for the performer to use interval measurements, like those from the *biological agents index* excel spreadsheets, and to define disease based on both clinical and laboratory diagnosis, and the use of a non-experimental research design (longitudinal, and retrospective), and multiple regression analysis to determine causality. (Note that correlation and causality are not the same. Statistics for correlation cannot replace causality)

B. ROLE OF INSTITUTIONS IN EPIDEMIOLOGIC TRANSITION

The Epidemiological Transition Theory has some important implications in macroeconomics and epidemiology. Traditionally, world governments develop socioeconomic policy, and have the mandate to implement multinational policy for disease eradication. These multinational governmental platforms include the Pan American Health Organization (PAHO), World Health Organization (WHO), World

Bank, Africa Union (AU), and others. It is therefore not surprising that most of the data used in epidemiological transition studies come from these multinational nongovernmental institutions. The Pan American Health Organization (PAHO) is a regional/international public health agency that works to improve health and living standards in the US and the Americas (Alleyene, 2002). In the past, PAHO and other nonprofit agencies have been involved in several US public health initiatives ranging from the recent hurricane Katrina disaster to US-Mexico border infectious disease surveillance (Neff, 2004; Kuiken, 2005; Giesecke, 1996; Elias et al, 1990), and the implementation of a community network of laboratories for testing human disease in collaboration with the world health organization (Meijer et al, 2005; Van Man et al, 1998).

Furthermore, by mandate, the PAHO has regional influence in the Americas and serves as the World Health Organization representative in the US. In North America, the PAHO have been chartered by the United Nations to function as a linkage institution between the US, Canada, and Mexico on domestic and international border public health related issues (Aziz, and Wright, 2005; Garrette, 1997; Weinberg et al, 2003). In addition, PAHO along with the WHO has been tasked to assist in the assessment of the economic impacts of policy and disease in the Americas (Fairchild, 2004; Mukherjea, 2003; Adams, and John Paul II, 2005; Stehr 2005; Nelson et al, 2005). PAHO is headed by an executive committee that is composed of nine member states of the organization. A council or general elections is responsible for electing committee members for three terms during conferences. The committees usually meet twice yearly. During this time, two standing sub-committees, one for women, health, and development, and the other for Planning, and Programming, jointly develop policy and economic strategy for the organization.

From previous publications, it is evident that most of the clients in the PAHO surveillance programs come from Canada and the US, Central Caribbean, and South America countries, as the UN (Garrette, 1997; Fox et al, 2005; Guzman, 2005). In addition to the surveillance of AIDS and other communicable diseases, PAHO coordinate family medicine and other non communicable disease policies in collaboration with the UN (Nicoll et al, 2005; Scorgie, 2002; Ojeda, 2003). At present, according to published reports, the PAHO functions to integrate biomedical technology in its current programs as a way to improve its services in public health, and initiate public health interventions in the region (Alleyene, 2002). In general, public health situations and national disasters determine these initiatives. Furthermore, resources are donated by member nations and funds trickle down to corporations, and academics for various programs (Alleyene, 2002).

Other institutions with similar programs and organization include the world Health Organization (WHO), and Centers for Disease Control and Prevention (CDC&P), which is an agency of the US Department of Health. Its main task is disease control and prevention through disease surveillance, immunization, diagnostic laboratory regulation, and health education. Over the years, the CDC publishes a *weekly morbidity and mortally report* for the nation in collaboration with the US census bureau

1.15. HEALTH PROMOTION

Health promotion can be defined as the process of empowering individuals to gain control over their health. The ultimate goal of health promotion is to increase the quality of living of people. In the United States, this is achieved in two main ways: (1). Through *behavioral or life style change*, and or (2). *Environmental modification.* Some of the basic prerequisites for health promotion include the following: political stability, education, nutrition, healthy environment, increased standards of living, availability of natural resources and social equity.

Furthermore, health promotion, once achieved, can only be sustained through aggressive efficient advocacy and mediation to enable the promotion process. Accordingly, the process will involve coordination of both government and private sectors, and the utility of various information, and biomedical technologies, as well as linkage institutions like the mass media and advocacy groups. Families, workforce, and individuals stakeholders in communities have to be identified and mobilized during mediation. Furthermore, health personnel have a major responsibility to mediate between the interests of the public versus the best practices for promoting health in the public.

In addition, health promotion strategies and programs adopted should account for the local needs of individual countries and differing social, cultural, and economic systems. The processes should also involve the building of healthy public policy, creating health awareness, and limiting health consequences through: legislation, fiscal policy measures, organizational change, and the creation of a supportive environment since changing patterns of life, work, and leisure impact health significantly. Finally, health promotion should involve the strengthening of community action through economic development, the development of personal skills, the reorientation of health services towards the establishment of improved healthcare systems and a systematic approach towards the assessment of these health programs.

REFERENCES

1. **Adams, G, J-. P. Paul II.** 2005. Politics. *Economist.* **375.**8421: 6-6.
2. **Alleyene, G.** 2002. Pan American Health Organization's first 100 years: Reflection of the director. *American Public Health Association.* **92.**12:1890-1894.
3. **Albala, C., F. Vio, and M. Yanez** 1997. Epidemiological transition in Latin America: A comparison of four countries. *Review of Medical Child.* **125.**6:719-27.
4. **Aluru, S.**, 2006. ed. *Handbook of Computational Molecular Biology.* Toronto CA: Chapman & Hall.
5. **Armstrong, G.L., L.A. Conn, and R.W. Pinner.** 1999. Trends in infectious disease mortality in the United States during the 20th Century. *JAMA.* **281.**1: 61-6.
6. **Aziz, M, and A. Wright.** 2005. The World Health Organization / International Union against tuberculosis and lung disease global project on surveillance for anti-tuberculosis drug resistance: A model for other infectious disease. *Clinical Infectious Disease;* **41.**S258-262.
7. **Bauman, R.** 2007. *Microbiology* (2nd ed.). San Francisco, CA, USA: Pearson, Benjamin, and Cummings. pp. 1-435.
8. **Baldi, P, and S. Brunak.** 2001. *Bioinformatics: The machine learning approach,* (2nd ed.). Cambridge, MA, USA: MIT Press.
9. **Barnes, M.R, and I.C. Gray.** 2003. eds., *Bioinformatics for Geneticists,* (1st ed.). Hoboken, NJ, USA:Wiley.
10. **Barennes, H, *et al.*** 1996. Efficacy and pharmacokinetics of a new intrarectal quinine formulation in children with *Plasmodium falciparum* malaria. *Brit J Clin Pharmacol* **41.**5: 389.
11. **Baxevanis, A.D., and B.F. Ouellette.** 2005. eds., *Bioinformatics: A practical guide to the analysis of genes and proteins,* 3 rd ed. Hoboken, NJ: Wiley.
12. **Baxevanis, A.D., G.A. Petsko, L.D. Stein, and G.D. Stormo.** 2007. eds., Current protocols in bioinformatics. Hoboken, NJ: Wiley.
13. **Brass, W., 1980.** Policies for the Reduction of Mortality Differentials. *Pop. Bulletin.***19:**3-27.
14. **Center for Disease Control & Prevention**.1991. Treatment with quinidine gluconate of persons with severe *Plasmodium falciparum* infection: Discontinuation of parenteral quinine. *Morb Mort Weekly Rep* **40(RR-4).** 21–23.
15. **Claverie, J.M., and C. Notredame.** 2003. *Bioinformatics for Dummies.* Hoboken, NJ: Wiley.
16. **Cristianini, N, and M. Hahn, M.** 2006. Introduction to computational genomics, Cambridge, UK: *Cambridge University Press.*
17. **Durbin, R., S. Eddy, A. Krogh, and G. Mitchison**. 1998. *Biological sequence analysis.* Cambridge, UK: Cambridge University Press.
18. **Elias, C., B. Alexander, T. Sokly.** 1990. Infectious disease control in a long-term refugee camp. The role of epidemiologic surveillance and investigation. *American Journal of Public Health.* **80.**7: 824-828.
19. **Fairchild, A.** 2004. Policies of inclusion. *American Journal of Public Health.* **4.**4:528-539.
20. **Fox, J., B. Coffey, J. Mintert, T. Schroeder, L. Valentin.** 2005. The response to BSE in the United States. *The Magazine of Food, Farm, and Resource Issues.* **20.**2:103-107.
21. **Garrette, L.** 1997. Infectious disease pathogens know no Borders; Surveillance will be key Tool in coming Battle. *Nations Health.* **27.**1:20.
22. **Graziella, C., F. Mesele, and J. Vallin.** 2005. Epidemiologic transition theory exception, Retrieved in 2007. *www.demogr.mpg.de/Papers/workshops/020619_paper40.pdf.*
23. **Giesecke, J.** 1996. Surveillance of infectious disease in the European Union. *Lancet.* **348.**9041: 1534.
24. **Guzman, M.** 2005. Deciphering dengue: The Cuban experience. *Science* **5740.**1495-1497.
25. **Gilbert, D.** 2004. Bioinformatics software resources. Briefings in bioinformatics, *Briefings in Bioinformatics,* **5.**3:300-304.
26. **Johnson, B., H. Anker, F. Meleney.** 1945. Bacitracin: a new antibiotic produced by a member of the *B. subtilus* group. *Science* **102.**2650: 376–377.
27. **Keedwell, E.** 2005. Intelligent Bioinformatics: The Application of Artificial Intelligence Techniques to Bioinformatics Problems. Hoboken, NJ: Wiley.
28. **Kuiken, T.** 2005. Pathogen surveillance in animals. *Science.* **309.**5741:1680-1681.

29. **Magill, A, C. Panosian.** 2005. Making antimalarial agents available in the United States. *New Engl J Med* **353.**4:335–337.
30. **Meijer, A., M. Valette, J-C. Manuguerra, P. Perez-Brena, J. Paget, C. Brown, K. van der Velden.** 2005. Implementation of the community network of reference laboratories for human influenza in Europe. *Journal of Clinical Virology.* **34.**2: 7-96.
31. **Mount, D.W**. 2002. *Bioinformatics: Sequence and genome analysis* New York, NY, USA: Spring Harbor Press.
32. **Mukherjea, A.** 2003. Stopping AIDS global patents, local effects, and the management of national borders. *Radical Society: Review of Culture and Politics.* **30.**2:1-18.
33. **Murray, C.J, and A.D. Lopez.** 1997. Alternative projections of mortality and disability by cause 1990-2020: Global burden of disease study. *Lancet.* **349.**9064:1498-504.
34. **Nelson, A., J. Tam, Y. Ly-Mee, J. Breese, C-H. Kin-Hung Poon, I. Kin-Sing, T-C. Mast, P.K. Chan, U. Parashar, F. Tai-Fai, R. Glass**. 2005. Hospital based study of the economic burden associated with Rotavirus. *Journal of Infectious Disease.* **9:** S64-S70.
35. **Nelson, A., J. Tam, Y. Ly-Mee, J. Breese, C-H. Kin-Hung Poon, I. Kin-Sing, T-C. Mast, P.K. Chan, U. Parashar, F. Tai-Fai, R. Glass**. 2005. Estimate of Rotavirus disease burden in Hong Kong: Hospital based surveillance. *Journal of Infectious Disease*. **192:** S71-S79.
36. **Neff, M.** 2004. HHS Funds disease surveillance system along U.S.-Mexico border. *American Family Physician.* **69.**2: 254-254.
37. **Nicoll, A., J. Jones, P. Aavisland, J. Giesecke.** 2005. Proposed new international health regulations. *British Medical Journal.* **330.**7487: 321-322.
38. **O'Donnell, M.** 1989. Definition of health promotion: Part III: Expanding the definition. *American Journal of Health Promotion.* **3**:3:5.
39. **Omran, A.R. 1977.** Epidemiologic transition in the United States: The health factor in population change. *Population Bulletin.* **32.**2: 1-42.
40. **Ojeda, N.** 2003. Underutilization of reproductive healthcare services by women who are ineligible for employer-subsidized socialized Medicare. *International Feminist Journal of Politics.* **5.**1:20-47.
41. **Pachter, L, and B. Sturmfels**. 2005. *Algebraic statistics for computational biology.* Cambridge, UK: Cambridge University Press.
42. **Pevzner, P. A.** 2000. *Computational Molecular Biology: An algorithmic approach* Cambridge, MA, USA: MIT Press
43. **Raleigh, V.** 1999. Trends in World Population: How will the millennium compare with the past. *Human Reproduction Updates.* **5.**500-507.
44. **Rogers, R.G, and R. Hackenberg.** 1987. Extending epidemiologic transition theory: a new stage. *Soc Biol.* ***34.**3-4:234-43*
45. **Ruzicka, L.T.** 1983. Mortality transition in the third world countries: Issues for research. News international union science study *Population.* **17.**60-82.
46. **Scorgie, F.** 2002. Virginity testing and the politics of sexual responsibility. *Implications for AIDS Intervention.* **61**.1:55-75.
47. **Serow, W.J., M.E. Cowart, Camezon.** 1998. Epidemiologic transition theory and aging: Hispanic populations of North America and the Caribbean. *Journal Health and Human Services Administration.* **20.**3:333-47.
48. **Simon., Bernard.** 2002. A Border Giveth and a Border Taketh Away. *New York Times.* **151**:52085: 1-2.
49. **Stehr, M.**, 2005. Cigarette tax avoidance and evasion. *Journal of Health Economics.* **24:**2:277-297.
50. **Van Man, N., L-T. Luan., D. Trach, N. Thanh, P. van Tu, A-D. Nguyen, T. Fischer, B. Ivanoff, J. Gentsch, R. Glass.** 1998 Epidemiological profile and burden of rotavirus diarrhea in Vietnam: 5 years of sentinel hospital surveillance, 1998-2003. *Journal of Infectious Disease.* **192.**127-132.
51. **Waterman, M.S.** 1995. *Introduction to Computational Biology: Sequences, Maps, and Genomes.* Boca Raton, Florida, USA: *CRC* Press.
52. **Weinberg, M, S.L. Waterman, A. Carlos, V. Falcon, P. Morales, L. Lopez, C. Peter, A. Gutierrez, E. Gonzalez, A. Flisser, R. Bryan, E. Valle, A. Rodriguez, G. Hernandez, C. Rosales, J. Ortiz, M. Landen, H. Vilchis, J. Rawlings**.2003. The US-Mexico border infectious disease surveillance project: Establishing binational border surveillance. *Emerging Infectious Disease.* **9.**1: 97.

53. **Woodward, R, and W. Doering** 1944. The total synthesis of quinine. *J Am Chem Soc* **66**:849
54. **Zavala De Cosio., M.E.** 1992. The demographic transition in Latin America and Europe. *Notas Poblacion.* **20.**11-32.

PART II: BEST PRACTICES

Chapter 3

COST EFFECTIVE PROCESS IMPLEMENTATION FOR BIOLOGY AND INFORMATION SYSTEMS

INTRODUCTION

Information on best practices communicated in this chapter is merely a recommendation and not in any means the "only practice." Having said this, recommendations are based on the goal to achieve cost effective, and not necessarily cost-beneficial outcomes (**see Part 1; Chapter 1; Section 11**). Methods recommended are not based on ongoing research, but proven methods with agreeable and measurable outcomes. In other words, best practices are feasible, affordable, and have favorable outcomes. One audience that can benefit from this chapter are non-governmental agencies or corporations in the private sector who implement national government projects, or work collaboratively with governments and international political unions like the United States Government, United Nations (UN), European Union (EU), Africa Union (AU), World Health Organization (WHO), and Non Governmental Organizations (NGOs).

Increasingly, government, non-government, and international institutions that mange infectious disease programs in developed and pluralistic economies utilize new public management strategies to regulate, and evaluate scientific intervention. These cost-effective measures have had great successes; nonetheless, a major problem with infectious disease program implementation has been the identification, and mobilization of participants **(Part 1; Chapter 1; Section 7-8).**

At the present time, it is evident that in Africa and the Middle East some infectious disease programs have been difficult to evaluate, specifically, socio-economic programs. In the US, cost associated with providing some antimicrobial prophylaxis and vaccines against pandemic infections to various states are considered too high and unaffordable. Most antibiotics and vaccine manufactures have indicated that they simple do not have the technological capability to manufacture sufficient doses. In part, this is based on old technologies, and practices that are time consuming and labor intensive. As a result of scarcity, the US population has been segmented by the state public health authorities. With respect to vaccines distribution, different demographic sectors have been scrutinized to determine who gets what and when. This form of profiling has been the subject of great controversy in the United States especially when "less important groups" justifiably, have argued that, as tax payers, nothing short of an equitable distribution of medical resources and vaccines during outbreaks would be acceptable to them. Circumstances such as these can be avoided with the introduction of new cost effective manufacturing practices like, but not limited to, the use of computational biology. **(Part 1; Chapter 2; Section 12)**

Another solution to this crisis would be for government to adopt New Public Management strategies **(Part 1; Chapter 1; Section 2).** Historically, the first shift to outsourcing by governments to nonprofit organizations probably began at the end of the Second World War by the US during reconstruction of Europe and Japan. During this time most programs were the results of the marshal plan **(Part 1; Chapter 1; Sections 1-3).** At the present time, the United States, and other industrialized countries like Britain and France have important roles to play in infectious disease program implementation at the communities and rural level worldwide. Realistically, this role is limited to finance, education and technology transfers. Presently, international financial institutions question the relevance and credibility of most governments in Asian, Africa, and South America, especially their abilities to manage funds for public health interventions in fiscally responsible ways. The United Nations on its part has been increasingly ineffective mainly because in most cases, its charter prevent them from outsourcing to private and nonprofit organizations. Perhaps they lack the mandate to do so, regardless, the UN should reform and consider outsourcing services since they lack the innovation to research, develop, and implement cost effective technologies, or the ability to utilize existing technologies without intellectual property infringement of existing private sector technology. One solution to this problem would be for the UN and similar organizations to adopt New Public Management Strategies.

Interestingly, in countries like Africa, the epicenter of infection control; China and India, the emerging economic super powers, and Saudi Arabia tend have more success in program implementation. Perhaps, in part, this is the case because they supply African countries with affordably financial credit as well as with goods and services. It appears, the AU finds good prospects with the trade-off between quality of goods and services with low cost, and low quality. This does not have to be the case. With New Public Management strategies, technology transfer, and the inclusion of the AU and grass roots communities in the implementation process, a balance can be achieved, and infection control can be reached. Furthermore, the first step for all government stakeholders would be to increasingly outsource, regulate, and evaluate the private sector and non-profit organization. The paradigm should shift to the involvement of the private sector since they can innovate.

Disease eradication in emerging economies is vital to achievement of desirable economic development outcomes. One assumption is that the desirable outcome should involve the reduction of new and old cases disease (incidence and prevalence). Accordingly, economies of scale, rather than supply side economics may be the underlying force in the determination of sales, and costs associated with manufacturing. In order to achieve efficiency, proper human and material resource management and quality should be maintained and improved in pharmaceuticals and diagnostics products and in the manufacturing process **(Part 1; Chapter 1; Section 11).**

Furthermore, the implementation of best practices for managing platforms in biotechnology requires the use of bioinformatics and computational biology **(Part 1; Chapter 2; Section 12).** This form of New Public Management tends to use molecular biology, software engineering, biochemistry and other disciplines to perform cost saving, yet effective experimentation and or quasi-experimentation for validating experimental null hypothesis. In earnest, while fundamental principles of computational biology remain unchanged, basic, and clinical research tend to ask different questions. This is, in simplistic terms, a case of the need for qualitative data by clinicians, and quantitative data by academicians. Industrialists on the other hand spend more time connecting dots and searching for applications to meet cost beneficial end points. In some cases, the roles have been switched. In modern times both industry and academia work collaboratively towards the common goal of implementing government programs. Specifically, academics tend to validate industrial applications, like, but not limited to efficiencies of new drugs, and the diagnostics equipments.

Local grass roots indigenous non-profit organizations are needed for program implementation and advocacy. Non-national, non-profit organizations should be encouraged to play increasing roles in training. Ironically, unlike China, and India, that provide low cost labor in both manufacturing and information technology, Africa has the distinction of having the more abundant mineral resources which is key for global manufacturing. In modern times, AU members control these resources and decide who gets what when and how. Since war, democracy, economic development, and the spread of infectious disease are all correlated, outcomes of one can easily affect the other. Rationally, this single factor is a cause for concern. Consequentially, This Chapter will introduce an alternative new cost effective technology—Computational Biology. Based on actual successes, this chapter will detail how computational biology can be used to substitute existing and more costly technologies for the purposes of pharmaceutical manufacturing, clinical and public health diagnostics, infectious disease surveillance and analysis.

BRAUNMYCIN® OLISFERROL™ RESEARCH AND DEVELOPMENT

OBJECTIVES

Upon completion of this section, performers will:

- Select, design, adopt, and implement cost-effective exploratory research to identify patterns and relationships between biochemical and physiological process in bacteria
- Use biological and information systems to develop non-specific peptide antibiotics and vaccines against bacterial and non-bacterial pathogens in general.
- Understand the role of experimentation and quasi-experimentation in computational biology research process
- Understand the threats to validity in computational biology research

A. INTRODUCTION

Peptide antibiotics work by binding and inactivating microbial cell wall enzymes that assist cell synthesis and signaling **(Part 1; Chapter 2; Section 10)**. Peptide antibiotics also interfere with microbial cell membrane attachment, and/or infection and in the process preventing energy free processes like endocytosis. One thing all peptide antibiotics have in common is a unique *X-Cys-X* iron binding moiety. This suggests that iron may play a role in the events previously described. Perhaps the most efficient antibiotics are those produced naturally by human innate immunity mechanisms **(Part 1; Chapter 2, Section 10)**.

Interestingly, interferon were first observed during research to improve the smallpox vaccine by two Japanese virologists, Yasu-ichi Nagano and Yasuhiko Kojima at the former Institute for Infectious Diseases, University of Tokyo. At the time, the scientists characterized interferon as *facteur inhibiteur* by fractionation and homogenation using an ultracentrifuge. Their work was published in 1954 in the French journal de la Société de Biologie. In later years, other papers appeared based on this earlier work. By 1957, British virologist Alick Isaacs and the Swiss researcher

Jean Lindenmann, at the National Institute for Medical Research in London coined the term *interferon* while working with the influenza virus. Mechanisms for bacterial resistance to human antimicrobial peptides are known (Peschel, 2002), consequently, capitalizing on this information, computational biology provides the investigator more flexibility when engineering new therapeutic protein molecule since there are no genetic codon or genetic *in frame* restrictions for synthesis.

B. DISCOVERY AND PREPARATION OF BRAUNMYCIN / OLISFERROL (PEPTIDE ANTIBIOTICS)

The most cost effective antibiotics are those produced using computational biology techniques. This is by no means the only way. Other alternative methods include cloning and fermentation. Regardless of technique, peptide antibiotics offer unique advantages over other types of antimicrobials because they can function as vaccines or antibiotics. **(Part 1; Chapter 2; Section 10)**. Vaccines can be used in disease prevention while antibiotics are used in disease management. To best illustrate this point, compare and contrast six peptide antibiotics and their limitations (**Table 2**).

	211 221 231
Lysozyme	XX**IADAVACAKRVVR**XXXXXXXXXXXXXXX
Defensins	X X X**RYGTCTYQGR**XXXXXXXXXXXXXXXX
Interferon	**IQSIQKSVETIKEDM** XXXXXXXXXXXXXXX
Lactoferrin	XX**YSGAFKCLRDGAGDVAFIRESTVFEDLS**
Lantibiotic	XXXXXXX**HCSIHVSL**XXXXXXXXXXXXXXXX
Olisferrol	XXXXXXXXCXXXXXXXXXXXXXXXXXXXXXX

Figure 1. Comparison of purified iron-binging moiety of selected human peptide antibiotics.

Table 2. Comparative analysis of Braunmycin with other human peptide antibiotics.

Description of braunmycin products in comparison with markets trend

Properties	*[acdefg]Lysozymes	*[acdefg]Defensins	*[acdefg]Interferon	*[abcdefg]lactoferrin	[cef]Lantibiotic	Olisferol™	[cf]Bacitracin
Cysteine containing Peptide	yes	yes	yes	yes	yes	yes	yes
Microbial Target	non specific	non specific	viruses degenerative cells	non specific	gram positive bacteria	non specific	*S. aureus; S. pyogenes* *Neisseria gonorrhoeae*
Market Cost (retail) and quantity per dose(USD in 2007	$ 800 /0.05mg	$ 250 / 0.1mg	$ 800 / 0.05mg Avonex® ;Rebif® ;CinnoVex®	$ 20 / 250 mg		$ 0.99/ 0.005mg ($ 999.99/ 5mg	$ 0.05 / 0.005 mg ($ 5 / 500 applications)
Registered Trademarked names	_	_		_	Nisin *	braunmycin®	BMD®
therapeutic category	Supplement	Supplement	antibiotic/chemotherapeutic	Supplement	antibiotics	antibiotics	antibiotics
Date Patented in the US	_	_	_	_	2004	2007	_
Most efficient dosing method	_	_	intravenous	oral	topical & oral spray	intravenous; oral spray vaginal spray	topical cream
Use	research	research	therapeutic	therapeutic / supplement	food preservation; therapeutics / supplement	therapeutic; veterinary food preservation;	therapeutic veterinary
Source	skin/mucus membrane	skin/mucus membrane	T cells/macrophages	plasma protein	*Lactococcus lactis*	Synthetic Amino Acids	*bacillus spp*
Cross-links with Cysteine residues on bacterial cell wa	yes	yes	_	yes	yes	yes	yes
Known interference with bacterial cell wall synthesis	yes	yes	_		yes	yes	yes
Known interference with viral cell membrane attachment	_	_	yes	_	_	yes	_
Known interference with cell wall iron reductase	_	_	_	yes	_	yes	_
Known interference in transpeptidase activity	yes	yes	_	_	_	yes	yes
Known interference with threonine and serine kinases	_	_	yes	_	_	yes	_
Manufacturing process	_	_	recombinant DNA	recombinant DNA	cell culture	computational biology	cell culture

* not stable in high pH environments

[a] When ingested are susceptible to degradation by chemotrypsin, pepsin and trypsin proteases

[b] When ingested, are too large to be absorbed into blood

[c] Hydrophobic; are difficult to deliver to infected blood vessels

[d] Naturally secreted by human cells but difficult to deliver artificially to infected human cells

[e] difficult to administer to patients

[f] not cost-effective to manufacture

[g] short shelf life

While initiating manufacturing best practices, the performer should carefully plan to adopt the strategic approach to manufacturing vaccines and antibiotics. One way to implement such a strategy would be the adoption of the incremental approach to research and development. The process requires for the performer to establish null hypothesis based on the desirable outcomes. For example (Table 2), an antibiotic that can withstand acidity, and degradation enzymes in the stomach environment would be preferably and cost effective. Another desirable outcome would be a vaccine or antibiotic with long shelf life. In addition, a low molecular weight antibiotic that is capable of absorption into blood stream via intestinal and or secretary membranes would be preferred. Few technologies enable these accomplishments, fortunately, with computational biology; the investigator is able to use molecular biology, software design, macroeconomics, and bioengineering, at the very least, to achieve these goals (Figure 1). Based on the examples, investigators at Biological Agents Corporation (BAC) were able to develop Braunmycin ® Olisferrol™ (BAC, El Paso, TX), an oligo peptide antibiotic that defies the problems stated earlier(also see US Patent 7,244,702, 2007).

C. EXPERIMENTAL DESIGN

Cell membrane bound iron-molecule receptors play extremely important roles in transporting iron, and iron containing molecules in bacteria. This property of the cell wall means that changes in its function or structure can greatly impact the physiology of the organism since cell membrane directed iron-uptake and pathogenesis go hand in hand (Wooldridge et al, 1993).

Functionally, a major membrane bound reductase in bacteria known to reduce Fe^{3+} is the flavine reductase (Pierre et al, 2002). Structurally, in gram-negative bacteria, the transport of iron across the inner membrane is a periplasmic protein dependent process that requires an ATP-binding cassette (ABC) transporter, which consists of ligands binding proteins, membrane permease, and ATPase **(Figure 2).** In *E. coli*, the binding of iron-hydroxamate compounds to their cell wall solute binding protein triggers ATP hydrolysis providing energy to change the conformation of membrane permease, and allowing ferrisiderophores, hemin, or iron to pass through the inner membrane (Braun, 2001). Numerous reports on *E. coli* describe the specialized nature of outer membrane siderophores, iron, and antibiotics active transport channels. Gram-positive bacteria do not have an outer membrane, therefore, the TonB; ExbB complex is not associated with transport in these microorganisms. There have been few reports characterizing solute binding ligands of cell wall iron-molecule receptors.

Table 3. Experimental Flow Chart

FLOW CHART

	START			FINISH
				Drug Tragets
	Staphylococcus aureaus	***Streptococcus pneumoniae***	**Potential Drug Targets**	**Found in:**
1	highly pathogenic	Less pathogenic		TB parasite
		Easy to manipulate		Malaria Parasite
				HIV
			X-Cys-X Ironbinding Reducateses identified	H5N1
2	Available genomic information on iron-acquisition and transport	Available S. aureus information on iron-acquisition and transport used to identify and characterize novel iron-binding cell-wall reductase		MRSA S. pneumoniae iron-dependent Cancer

In *Staphylococcal spp,* the protein cell wall receptors function as a glyceraldehyde-3-phosphate dehydrogenase (G-3-P-D) and mediate the uptake of iron from transferrin (Modun et al., 1999; Modun et al, 2000; Modun et al, 1998). In recent reports, an ABC multiple transporter of Zn^{3+}, Fe^{3+} and Cu^{2+} was characterized in *S. pyogenes* (Janulczyk et al, 1999). With respect to hydroxamate siderophore utility and ion permease associated antibiotic resistance, an iron-hydroxamate transporter in *Staphylococcus aureus* has been identified and characterized (Sebulsky et al, 1994).

Streptococcus pneumoniae remains a major disease causing pathogen in neonatal worldwide. Increases in the multiple drug resistant strains have been reported to be susceptible to albomycin. At present, little is known about molecular mechanisms for iron-transport, and substrates for existing iron-transporters of *S pneumonia* (brown et al, 2002). Previous studies show that mutations in ABC type manganese permease genes of *S. pneumoniae* lead to penicillin resistance (Novak et al, 1998). With respect to the utilization of lactoferrin, transferrin, heme, and hemoglobin as iron sources, a specific lactoferrin binding protein, PspA, of *S. pneumoniae* was identified and characterized (Hakanson et al, 2001; Hammerschmidt et al, 1999). In contrast to other mucosal pathogens, neither transferrin nor lactoferrin can support the growth of *S. pneumoniae* in iron-deficient medium (Schryvers et al, 1999). Previously, a pneumococcal hemin binding protein and its solute ligand was identified (Tai, 2003), these pneumococcal strains were shown to lack in ability to produce siderophores (Tai et al, 1993). Furthermore, mutants that were unable to utilize heme as an iron source showed reduced virulence (Tai et al, 1997).

In other reports, the pneumococcal iron acquisition gene was characterized as the major iron-transporter used in growth (brown et al, 2002). Based on these findings, structurally, microbial iron acquisition reductase would need to extend from microbial cell walls and glycocalyx (capsules) in order to function effectively (**Figure 3**).

D. SUMMARY OF APPROACH

When developing an experimental research design, the investigator should consider including experimentation with high causal power. That is, it should contain a control or standard with more observation in the pretest. Furthermore, changes to look for on testing should include positive or negative changes to the treatment compared to the control. An even stronger design would contain time series events like growth curves. To better illustrate, in a previous study to identify and characterize novel iron-acquisition proteins in *Streptococcus pneumoniae*—the etiological agent and leading cause of neonatal pneumonia, otitis media, and pneumoniae in HIV/AIDs patients— investigators can use albomycin, an iron containing antibiotic, and two iron uptake mutant strains of *S. pneumoniae*, one a construct (*pia*A-), and the other a spontaneous mutant (*alb*$^-$) (Olisa, 2007). Both controls in this example have been introduced to reduce misspecification and spuriousness of using one control.

Spuriousness could be intervening, and or an alternative variable. Consider the case where Braunmycin ® (BAC, El Paso, Texas) (**Table 2**; **Figure 1**). The information derived from peptide alignment computational biology studies can be used to deduce and improve synthesis of the synthetic product like Olisferrol, a microbial iron-acquisition antagonist. As mentioned earlier, in past studies, investigators have shown that microbes scavenge Fe^{3+} from human transferrin. To accomplish this feet, iron-binding molecules found in pathogens may be retractable, to say the very least, in order for them to navigate and bypass the complex glycocalyx networks in their own capsules (**Figure 3**). In response, the host (humans) use lactoferrin iron binding molecules to regain the iron from microbes (**also see Part 1; Chapter 2; Section 11**).

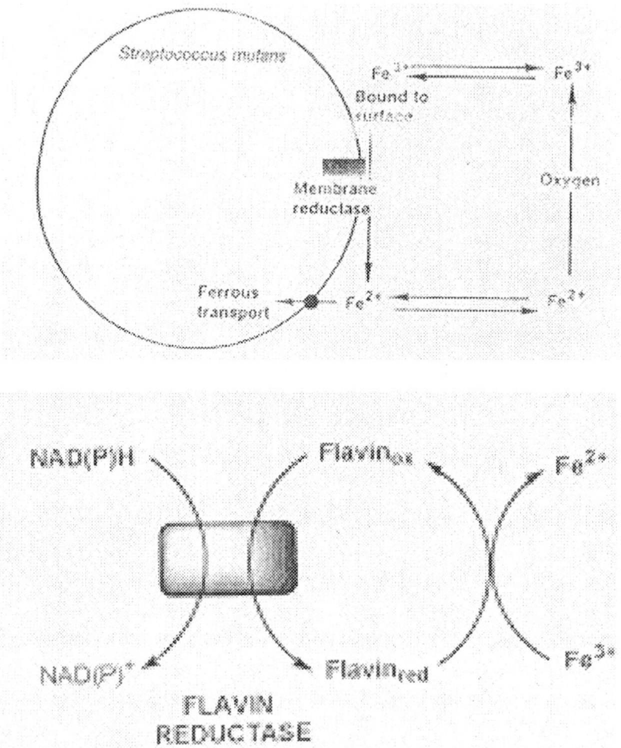

Byers et al, 1999, In Metal Ions in Biological Systems, p45-56
Pierre et al, 2002, Rev BioMetals 15: p341-346

Figure 2 Model for ferric iron reduction in Streptococcus spp

An established fact is that virulence and growth in pneumococcus reduce when microbes are deprived of heme (Tai et al, 1993, 1997), and that growth in some pathogens fail, and their capacity for disease infliction diminished when environmental iron (III) supply or uptake capability is terminated.

Observations made from studies with bacteriophages (viruses), protein toxins, and iron-containing antibiotics, show they lose their bactericidal effects in *Escherichia coli* after *fhu*A (a ferric-heme uptake transporter) is mutated (Braun, 1998). With this presupposition, BAC developed Braunmycin® [*Olisferrol*™ (X-Cys-X)] (BAC, El Paso, TX) using computational biology. In-vivo, Olisferrol has been designed to generate neutralizing and opsonizing antibodies that target conserved and physiologically active cell membrane, and wall, iron-binding protein in "iron-seeking" pathogens.

To purify iron-binding proteins, the investigators at BAC used, Braunmycin8567 ($C_6H_{12}FeNO_6$) (US Patent US Patent 7,244,702, 2007), a nitrilotriacetic acid iron complex (NTA-Fe^{+3}), that was linked to specially adapted polystyrene beads (Xenopore, Hawthorne, NJ). BAC adapted this protocol for the purification of lyophilized human apo-Transferrin **(Figure 11)** and Fe^{3+} receptors found in the cell-wall of *Streptococcus pneumoniae* Rx1 strain. Results from mass spectrphotometric amino acid sequencing, proteomic online database analysis of Fe^{3+} -binding moieties in *S. pneumoniae*, and on Fe^{3+} -binding moieties in human transferrin provided the biochemical rationale for using amino acid alignments to formulate *Olisferrol*™ as a non specific antibiotic.

Biochemically, *Olisferrol*™ (X-Cys-X), is a synthetic form of Braunmycin®, is dimeric, and a partially hydrophilic 30 amino acid oligopeptide with MW of approx 3 kDa, and with biochemical properties comparable to those of human apo-Transferrin. Compared to other DNA, RNA, or molecular vaccines, *Olisferrol*™ has some of the following advantages:

- Is resistant to protease degradation.
- Is affordable ($ 1,000 / mg [vaccine grade: $ 3, 000 / mg]
- Is easy to administer (human dosing concentration estimated at 3-5µg / 0.5ml, based on FDA approved dosing model for the Flu vaccinc, about 1000 vaccinations of *Olisferol*™ can be administered at that price range)

Furthermore, Olisferrol has been engineered to contain bi-ionic (metallic) properties to increase its shelf-life at 25 °C. Olisferrol is manufactured with: no cloned products; minimal risk of infectious proteins (<99.9%); minimal risk of infectious DNA (<99.9%); minimal risk of infectious RNA (<99.9%); minimal risk of infectious viruses (<99.9%); minimal risk of chemical toxins (<99.9%); minimal risk of chemical toxins (<99.9%).

Interestingly, about 80% percentage of the synthetic 30 amino acid in *Olisferrol*™ include amino acid formulation derived from, and conserved in microbial Fe^{3+} receptors. In conclusion, *S pneumoniae* is gram positive diplococci that scrupulously need Fe^{2+} for growth and virulence. Iron is abundant in the environment were it exists in the ground state (Fe^{3+}). The molecular mechanism for acquisition of Fe^{2+} from this supply, as well is substrate is unclear. Previously, investigators presented an identification of the pneumococcal Iron-Acquisition gene, *pia*A, (Olisa et al, 2000), In *Abstrt. B-22, p.45 100th Gen Meeting ASM.* Since then others: Brown et al, (2002), have extensively characterized *pia* and two other iron uptake systems, *namely,* pneumococcal iron-uptake system, *piu*, and pneumococcal iron transport system, *pit*. Subsequently, it has been shown that Fe^{3+} (α-Braunmycin) or Fe^{2+} (β-Braunmycin) nitrilotriacetic complex, ($Fe^{3+/2+}$-NTA)] can be mounted on 3-98 μ polystyrene beads, and used in iron-affinity chromatography to purify iron binding protein receptors. In this case, 50-μL Braunmycin per 500-μL extract yields 1-50 ng of any cell or membrane bound iron-binding protein.

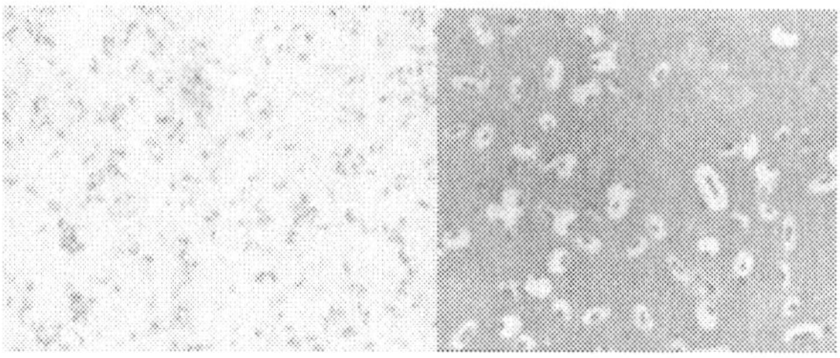

Capsule stain: Courtesy of M. J. Leboffe, City College of San Diego

Figure 3: Gram and capsule stain on Streptococcus pneumoniae.

Additionally, this information can be used to determine the molecular mechanisms for pneumococcal Fe^{++} acquisition from environmental Fe^{3+} supply and to determine the role pneumococcal cell wall iron-reductase play in Albomycin and multiple drug resistance. In a similar study, BAC investigators use albomycin and spontaneous alb^- *S. pneumococcal* strains as known markers for multiple drug resistance and iron-reductase activity to investigate, identify and detect the a novel iron-acquisition gene piaA, olisferrol.

E. OUTLINE OF APPROACH

- Computational genomics
- Reverse genetics of pia.
- Antimicrobial susceptibility assays
- Growth analysis under Fe^{2+} and Fe^{3+} repleted synthetic conditions.
- Growth analysis using Fe^{3+} containing and Fe^{2+} dependent metabolic inhibitors.
- Affinity chromatography of cell wall extract using an Fe^{3+} affinity column
- Glyceraldehyde–3–dehydrogenase (G-3-P-D) reductase assays
- SDS PAGE MALDI-TOF MS / MALDI-CID MS to determine mass finger print, amino acid content, and identity of PiaA
- Computational proteomics
- pia sequence alignment of Rx1, alb- and piaA-

F. COMPUTATIONAL GENOMICS

Computational Biology can be used to detect and identify pneumococcal Iron-acquisition gene, *pia*A or an iron-binding protein. The original approach uses *Staphylococcus aureus* iron regulated gene (SirA, SirB) which was previously identified (Heinrichs et al, 1999. J. Bacteriol, vol 181.5p 1436-1443). Amino acid sequence of *Sir*A and *Sir*B was obtained from National Library of Medicine using ENTREZ program. A search for *Sir*A homologue in the NIH unfinished *S. pneumoniae* database using BLAST search was conducted. The effort identified a segment of *S. pneumoniae* DNA sequence from the NIH unfinished sequence library which shares homology with SirB. DNA sequence of fragment *pia*ABCD was obtained, and open reading frames identified using ORF program in the National Library of Medicine website (Olisa, 2000; 2002). Using the deduced amino acid of *pia*ABCD, further search for homology in the bacterial gene bank using BLAST program was conducted. Results show that *pia*ABCD gene shares 71% homology with Irp1B of *C. diphtheriae*; 64% amino acid sequence homology with FepD in *Escherichia coli* and *Yersinia enterocolitica* (Olisa, 2000).

G. REVERSE GENETICS OF pia

The first step in reverse genetics will be to develop and design PCR primers for the genes expressing *pia*, then to clone and knock out *pia* to create a *pia* defective mutant. Using plasmids (pCRBlunt, and, pGEM). Afterwards, a natural method can be used to transform Rx1 and induce natural competence in *S. pneumoniae* (Rx1). Natural competence is the process by which bacteria naturally takes up foreign DNA from the environment. In the case of *S. pneumoniae*, electroporation cannot be used to achieve transformation since it interferes with recombination. *S. pneumoniae* can take in single stranded DNA to create competent Rx1.

Previously, investigators at BAC grew Rx1 in Todd Hewitt Broth (THB) containing 0.5% yeast extract, 0.1 % CaCl2, 0.01 % bovine serum albumin. The mixture was incubated to O.D600 of 0.05; samples were subsequently collected every 30 minutes for two hours and stored in 10% glycerol at -70°C until use. A total of twelve collections were made. A Hind III digest of construct was incubated with a 0.1 dilution factor of competent Rx1, mixture was incubated at 37°C at 5% CO_2 for 1 hour after which selection was carried out in Todd Hewitt Agar (THA) containing 5% Sheep blood, and 0.12 μg/ml Ampicillin.

```
MAF (20 mer)
           485                    504
            |                      |
GCTGGATCCGCAGCTTTTGGAATGGGTAA
   BamHI

MAR (21 mer)
         1326                    1306
          |                        |
TCAGAATTCGGACCCCCGATTATTGCAGTA
   EcoRI
```

Figure 4. PCR Primer Design

For DNA analysis (**Figure 4,5,** and **6**), investigators can use PCR to amplify *pia* gene in *pia*A$^-$ alb$^-$ and in Rx1 strains to determine its integrity. Results show the inability of PCR to amplify 1.4 kbp piaA gene in *pia*A$^-$ and alb$^-$ strains. These results imply that *pia* gene in mutants are not homogeneous to *pia* in wild-type. (Olisa et al, 2002, NCBI accession number AF338658). During experimentation, the standard Kirby Bauer antimicrobial disk diffusion susceptibility assay using Muller Hinton Blood Agar was used to isolate alb$^-$. Furthermore, investigators performed growth analysis with iron to characterize Rx1, alb$^-$ and *pia*A$^-$ based on their phenotype. During this process, lag phase analysis was performed after deferralating 1/3 THB with Chelex-100, media was repleted with heme and iron (II) chloride.

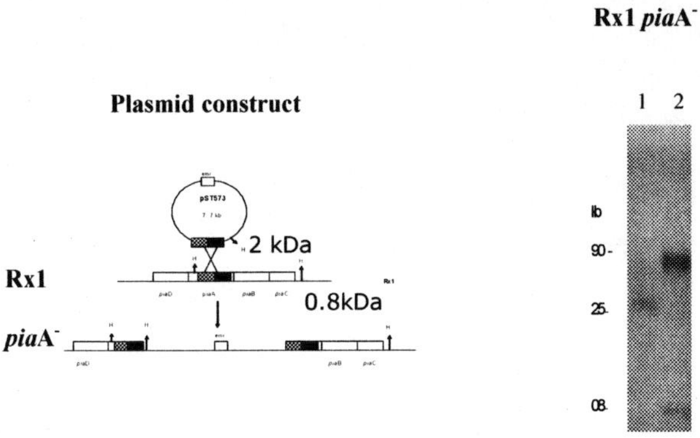

(a) (b)

Figure 5. (a) Gene map showing path for transformation and recombination of *pia* gene in Rx1. (b) Autoradiogram showing outcome of (a) using Southern blot analysis of chromosomal DNA isolated from *pia*- and parental strain Rx1. Probing was performed with ^{32}P radiolabelled piaA internal fragment. Lane 1: 2.5 kb Hind III digest from genomic Rx1 DNA; lane 2: 0.8 kb, and 8.2 kb Hind III digest of Rx1 (piaA$^-$) genomic DNA. The audioradiography is representative of the results of three independent experiments.

```
Rx1      GAAATTGAAGTGGGGATAATTACTGCAATAATCGGGGGTCC*******************
1059
PiaA-    GAAATTGAAGTGGGGATAATTACTGCAATAATCGGGGGTCCGAATTCGAGCTCGGTACCC 448

Rx1      **********************************************************
PiaA-    GGGGATCCTCTAGAGTCGACCTGCAGGCATGCAAGCTTGGCGTAATCATGGTCATAGC 506
```

Figure 6. DNA sequence analysis of 1.4 kb and 1.2 kb fragments generated with PCR primers *pia*AF / *pia*AR for Rx1 and *pia*AF/*pia*AR for piaA$^-$ strains respectively. Sequence analysis was performed using Sanger dideoxy-mediated chain termination method. Alignment shows point of insertion of recombinant pJDC9 at 378 bp, and a deletion in piaA$^-$ mutant between 378 and 630 due to insertion mutagenesis. Bold characters depict sequence portion of multiple cloning sites and inserted erythromycin resistant gene of vector.

H. GROWTH ASSAY

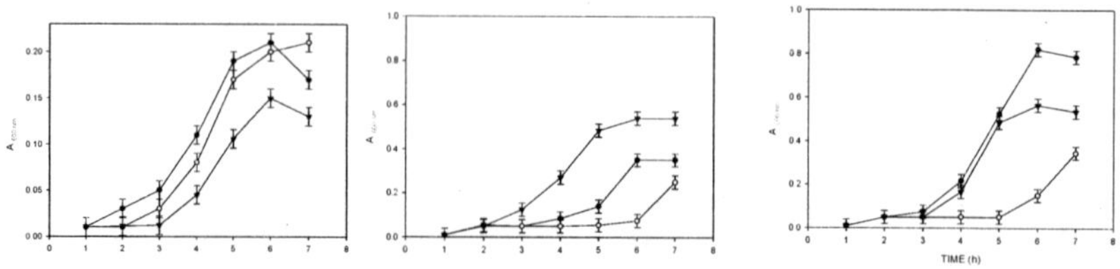

(a) (b) (c)

Figure 7. Growth of Rx1, alb⁻ and piaA⁻ mutants measured by optical density: **(a).** 1% THY broth; **(b).** 1% THY-Chelex broth; **(c).** 1% THY-Chelex 10 μM + ferrichrome. Key for **(a)** to **(c)** filled circles (●), parental Rx1 strain, circles (○), piaA⁻, filled triangle, (▼) alb⁻. Results represent the average of triplicate independent experiments. $p > 0.01$.

I. ANTIMICROBIAL ACTIVITY SPECTRUM ASSAY

Spontaneous albomycin resistant mutant of Rx1 (alb-) used was isolated using Kirby Bauer technique. Albomycin is a seryl-RNA antagonist (Stefanska et al, 2000), that is effective against multiple drug resistant bacteria (Gauze et al, 1955). In this experimental design, the investigators used albomycin to characterize cell-wall iron (III) binding activity in *alb*- and *pia*A- and Rx1 strains of *S. pneumoniae*. Crystal structure of albomycin in complex with FhuA of wild-type *E. coli* has been described (Ferguson et al, 2000). Mutations in iron uptake genes *fhu*ABCD, in *E. coli*, or *fhu*CBG genes of *S aureus* can result in albomycin resistance (Sebulsky et al, 2000; Kadner et al, 1980) and reduction in peptidase N activity (Braun et al, 1983).

Table 4. Summary of antimicrobial spectrum analysis of drug resistant: clinical; research and vaccine strains of *Streptococcus pneumoniae.*

Pneumoccocal Strain	Antimicrobial Susceptibility (± 3 mm)										
	streptonigrin	albomycin[C]	Erythromycin[D]	Tetracycline	chloramphenecol	Penicillin	Ampicillin	TMP/SXT	Cephalothin	Optochin[E]	Size of piaA[f] PCR product
Rx1	S	S	S	S	S	S	S	S	S	S	1400
[b]piaA-	R	R	R	R	R	S	S	S	R	S	No product
[a]alb-	R	R	R	R	R	S	R	R	R	R	No product
[h]MDR Clinical Isolate	R	S	_	R	R	R	R	R	R	S	No product
[g]MDR Clinical Isolate	R	S	_	R	R	R	R	R	R	S	No product
Pn-7 Vaccine Strain	S	S	S	S	S	S	S	S	S	S	1400
ATCC 603	S	S	S	S	S	S	S	S	S	S	1400

[d] Derived from Rx1 by insertion mutagenesis of <u>pia</u>A using 8.3 kb pJDC9 containing erythromycin resistant gene and a 0.8 kb internal <u>pia</u>A insert.
[c]Based on measurements of zones of inhibition to 0.005-µg/µl albomycin per 5-mm diameter filter paper disk.
[d] Based on measurements of zones of inhibition to 0.001-µg/µl erythromycin per 5-mm diameter filter paper disk.
[e]Optochin was used as diagnostic tool to confirm identity of *S. pneumoniae*.
[f] PCR performed using primers piaAF and piaAR
[g/h] Gift from Howard University, College of Medicine/University of Michigan, Clinical Microbiology Laboratory

Results represent mean from triplicate independent experiments. p= 0.03

J. REDUCTASE ASSAY

Based on the observation that *alb*⁻ and *pia*⁻ mutants grew with longer lag time in presence of heme (an Fe^{3+} containing molecule) compared to growth in an iron (II) chloride (an Fe^{2+} containing molecule), further growth analysis with Fe^{3+} containing and Fe^{2+} dependent metabolic inhibitors were performed (**Figure 7;Table 4**). Specifically, late log phase analysis was performed in Chelex-100 treated THB media. Synthetic growth media (Ca^{2+}, Mg^{2+}, Zn^{2+}, Cu^{2+}, Mn^{2+}, Mg^{2+}, 1/3 THB) was repleted with different sources of Fe^{3+}(aposiderophores). Albomycin, an Fe^{3+} containing antibiotic and streptonigrin, an F^{2+} dependent antibiotic. Based on observations, the investigators assumed that iron (III) cannot not be internalized by mutants. Consequently, investigators performed a reductase assay to see if reductase activity was occurring on the protoplast level, or in the cell wall in conjuncture with iron acquisition (**Figure 8**).

To perform this assay, both protoplast and cell wall fractions of Rx1, *alb*⁻ and *pia*⁻ were extracted and treated with G-3-P-D. To extract cell wall and protoplast, cells were grown overnight in low iron environment in deferralated THB. Chelex-100 was used to deferralated medium using plastic ware. Pneumococcal cells were treated in phosphate buffered saline in the presence of phenyl-methyl-sulphanyl fluoride, benzamidine, and EDTA and sucrose for 12 to 18 hours at room temperature. Supernatant was collected after centrifuge, and stored at –20°C until use. The results show reductase's present in cell wall, oxidized G-3-P-D. The extent of oxidation was quantified spectrophotometrically at A_{325}.

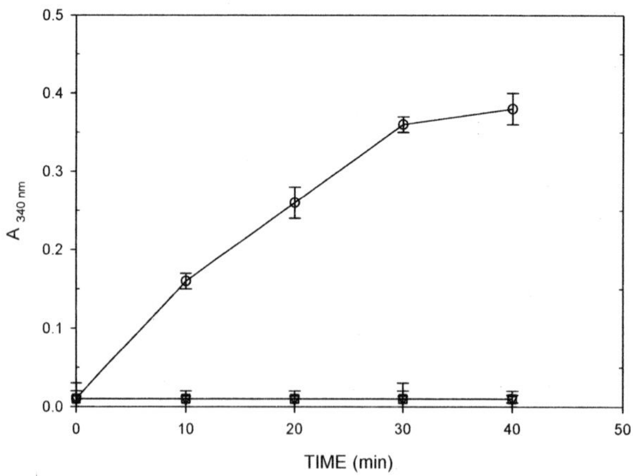

Figure 8. Pneumococcal cell-wall glyceraldehyde-3-phosphate reductase assay measured by optical density (A_{340nm}). Key: circles (○), parental Rx1 strain; triangle (∇), piaA⁻, filled square (■), alb⁻. Results represent the average of triplicate independent experiments. $p > 0.01$.

K. BATCH AFFINITY CHROMATOGRAPHY

Batch affinity chromatography and gradient SDS PAGE gel electrophoresis was performed to create high resolutions of cell wall protein extracts, and to determine molecular weight for batch affinity chromatography. For this purpose, investigators developed a synthetic siderophore, (Olisa, 2003; US Patent 7,244,702, 2007), and mounted it on a larger 100 micron polystyrene bead. Cell wall extracts were incubated with column for 12 to 23 hours and eluted with imadazole. Elute was used to perform 4% to 16% gradient gel electrophoresis. The purified protein was mixed and preheated with loading buffer at 70°C for 10 min, and centrifuged 1,000 x g to remove debris. Electrophoresis was carried out at 100V in the presence of a reducing agent. Results showed that four proteins were expressed under low iron conditions.

After albomycin susceptibility, and ferrichrome utility analysis, results led investigators to perform iron (III) binding activity assays using cell wall extracts of Rx1, *alb*$^{-}$, and *pia*A^{-} . To achieve this, cells were grown in iron deficient media. Cell wall proteins were extracted with buffer containing DMSO, benzamidine and sucrose. 600 μL of cell-wall extracts were incubated with Fe^{3+}-NTA or α-Braunmycin™ (BAC, El Paso, USA), and mounted with linker on polystyrene beads, or Xenobeads™ (Xenopore, Hartford, USA) for 12 to 18 hours at room temp. To visualize, BAC investigators ran extracted 5 to50 ng on a 4 to 12% SDS-PAGE, and stained with a silver staining protocol. **Figure 9a** shows the biochemistry of Fe $^{3+}$ -NTA **Figure 9b** shows loss of iron (III) binding activity in *alb*- and partial loss in *pia*A- MALDI analysis determined the identity of the 50 kDa and 37 kDa fragments to be Ef Tu and G-3-P-D.

SDS isolated protein were digested with trypsin to create polypeptides. Mass spectrophotometers were used to analyze short peptide molecules with greater efficiency. To achieve this, the desired protein was cut out, of gel, destained, dehydrated (NH_4HCO and acetonitrile), dried, and rehydrated (with trypsin). Digested peptides were recovered with acetonitrile, trifluroacetic acid, and NH_4HCO. Recovered peptides were concentrated in a vacuum centrifuge and re-hydrated three times over. MALDI-TOF MS was used to analyze unseperated trypsin digested pneumococcal peptides for molecular mass and relative abundance using techniques described by Wong et al, (1999). To achieve this, pulsed UV light (from laser) was used to fragment peptide molecules into ions for mass spectrphotometric analysis (TOF). Ions were derived by perpendicularly bombarding peptide molecules with a beam of energetic electrons (an N_2 laser). Prior to ionization, peptides were mixed with α-cyano-4-hydroxycinnamic acid to create an ionization competent matrix. For analysis, *investigator selected only cysteine containing peptides*. Post source decay (PSD) occurs in the analyzer. To achieve this, ions are sequential deflected through a vacuum containing static and oscillating high voltage electromagnetic fields. In these fields, ions are sorted into a spectrum based on their masses (diameter), velocities, and charge.

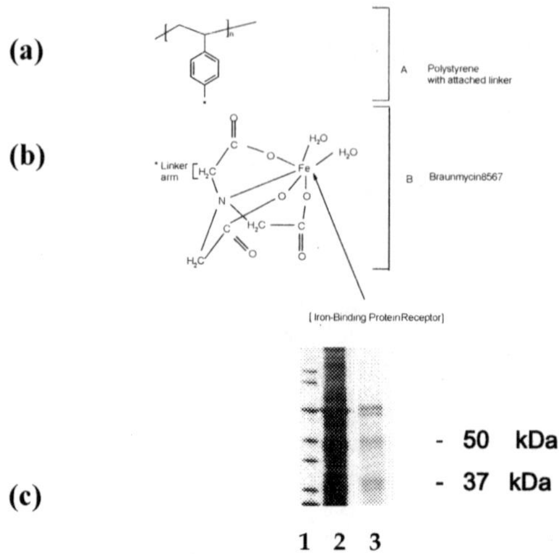

Courtesy Olisa, (2003; 2004). United States Library of Congress Copyright; United States Patent & Trademark Office Official Gazette.

Figure 9. Biochemical structure of Fe^{3+}-nitrilotriacetic acid bead: **(a).** polystyrene with attached linker; **(b).** Braunmycin8567 construct showing 6 coordination binding chemistry of iron (III) to oxygen and the position of the linker arm of the compound. **(c).** Gradient sodium dodecyl sulphate polyacrylamide gel electrophoresis (SDS PAGE) and silver stain analysis of cell wall extract of S. pneumoniae purified using iron (III) affinity beads ($C_6H_{12}FeN0_6$). Lane 1: marker; lane 2: crude cell-wall extract; lane 3: 50 ng elute from Rx1 parental strain showing 50 (Ef Tu), and 37 (G-3-P-D) kDa products. The set of gradient SDS PAGE gels shown here is representative of the results of three independent experiments.

L. MALDI TOF/CID ANALYSIS

To identify bound protein, investigators used MALDI-TOF- MS (Olisa, 2003; US Patent 7,244,702, 2007), to generate mass finger print of bound protein after trypsin digestion. To sequence and search NCBI databases for protein identity, investigators at BAC performed MALDI-CID-MS (Olisa, 2003; US Patent 7,244,702, 2007), on monoisotops of 50 and 37 kDa fragments, Results from NCBI database searches show their identity to be significantly homologous to Ef-Tu and G-3-P-D of *S. pneumoniae* implying that Ef-Tu is membrane bound in Rx1 (see **Table 5** and **6**). Collectively, the presence of 37 kDa G-3-P-D suggests that pneumococcal cell-wall iron binding proteins function as iron-reductase and participate in substrate level phosphorylation (**Part 2; Chapter 2, Section 5**).

Additionally, the presence of cell wall bound Ef Tu implies that iron regulates signal transducing process in pneumococcus. Collectively, results further suggest that multiple drug resistant isolates have somehow substituted and compensated for the iron utility. Perhaps, other divalent ions have substituted iron (III). In the course of this investigation, MALDI-CID MS was used to separate and identify peptides. Collision induced dissociation (CID) of peptides was used to induce side-chain cleavages which can be used to distinguish amino acid residues.

In summary, two iron-binding proteins: a 50 kDa and 37 kDa have been purified according to techniques described by Wong et al, (1999). Mobile phase (Xe gas) ions (from MALDI-TOF) were mixed with 2,5dihydrobenzoic acid and placed in a collision chamber. This matrix was used to resolve ionized molecules into large crystal needles to enhance the structure of the spectrums. Results show a highly hydrophilic cysteine iron-binding moiety was identified in these peptides. Characterization of the cysteine moiety show they are homologous to various reductase, iron response proteins, transporters, and signal transducing proteins in both prokaryotic and eukaryotic cells. (**Table 5** and **6**).

M. COMPUTATIONAL PROTEOMICS

To conduct amino acid sequencing, a database search was performed using protein database software available on world-wide web at pubmed. These programs are able to generate matches to peptides from known proteins based on molecular mass. Investigators used ion masses generated by MALDI-PSD or CID MS to conduct the search at NCBI data bases.

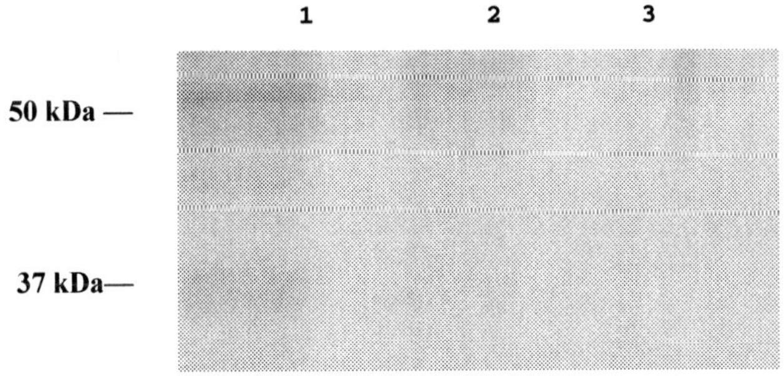

Figure 10. Gradient sodium dodecyl sulphate polyacrylamide gel electrophoresis (SDS PAGE) and silver stain analysis of specific cell wall extract in S. pneumoniae purified using iron (III) affinity beads ($C_6H_{12}FeN0_6$) cell wall extracts are absent in piaA$^-$ and alb$^-$ mutant strains. **Lane 1**: 50 ng elute from Rx1 parental strain showing 50, and 37 kDa products; **lane 2**: pia-, no product; **lane 3**: alb-, showing no product. The set of gradient SDS PAGE gels shown here is representative of the results of three independent experiments.

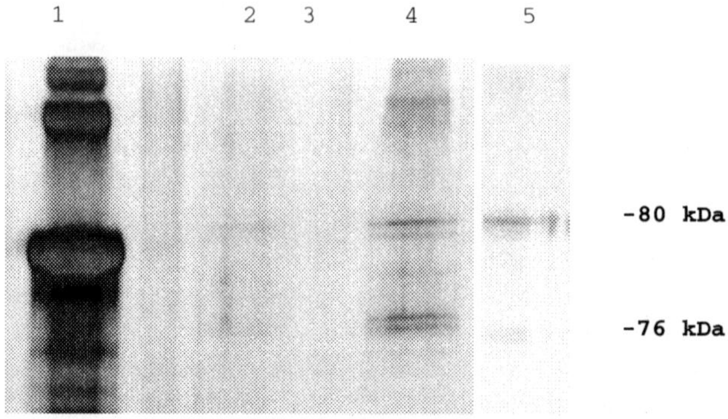

Figure 11. Gradient sodium dodecyl sulphate polyacrylamide gel electrophoresis (SDS PAGE) and silver stain analysis of human transferring purified using iron (III) affinity beads ($C_6H_{12}FeN0_6$). **Lane 1**:5 μg / μl Human Transferrin (HTf); **lane 2**: purification of 0.25 μg / μl HTf with $C_6H_{12}FeN0_6$ showing 76- 80 kDa elute; **lane 3:** purification of 0.25 μg / μl HTf with naked polystyrene**; lane 4:** purification of 50 μg / μl HTf with $C_6H_{12}FeN0_{6.}$ **lane 5**: Positive controls The set of gradient SDS PAGE gels shown here is representative of the results of three independent experiments.

Table 5. Summary of proteins identified from MALDI TOF/ MALDI CID (MS/MS) and gradient SDS PAGE of S. pneumoniae cell-wall extracts.

MW[c] (kDa)	Pneumococcal[b] protein identified	Identity/ positive (%)	NCBI accession no.	Mr/pI (Da)	Start-end position	Sequence[d]
50	Elongation factor[f], ef-tu	100/100	11612448	866.4	121-127	EHILLSR
				1,030.5	228-237	GTVASGRIDR
				1,107.5	258-267	AVVTGVEMFR
				1,192.5	387-398	TVGSGMVTEIEA
				1,235.6	258-268	AVVTGVEMFRK
				1,330.7	26-38	TTLTAAITTVLAR
				1,545.8	294-308	GQVIAKPGSINPHTK
				1,620.7	49-62	DYASIDAAAPEERER
				1,667.8	269-284	GQVIAKPGSINPHTK
				1,692.7	79-93	HYAHIDAPGHADYVK
				1,794.8	19-25	SKPHVNIGTIGHVDHGK
				1,842.9	242-257	VNDEIEIVGIKEETQK
				1,859.9	63-78	GITINTAHVEYETEKR
				2,032.8	324-338	HTPFFNNYRPQFYFR
				2,160.8	41-55	**VDMVDDPELLELVEMEIR[a]**
				2,392.0	56-78	**DLLSEYDFPGDDIPVIQGSALK[a]**
45	Phosphoglycerate kinase	100/100	15900413	1,542.8	349-359	**SIIGGGDSAAAAINLGR[a]**
				1,013.5	57-62	**AILFSHLGR[a]**
				1,884.6	162-179	SINTACSSSNDAIGDAFR
				2,196.2	141-161	ALPNMASGNVAMRFGANGVCK
				2,199.2	104-124	FGVIVASGIGGIKEIEDQVLR
				2,329.4	336-358	SFTGHLLGAAGAVEAIVTIEAMR
				2,489.5	230-252	NGFVMGEGSGMLVLESLEHAEKR
				2,823.0	19-35	VVVTGYGVTSPIGNTPEEFWNSLATGK
				3,232.7	36-64	IGIGGITKFDHSDFDVHNAAEIQDFPFDK
				3,359.6	253-284	GATILAEVVGYGNTCDAYHMTSPHPEGQGAIK
				3,672.6	253-287	GATILAEVVGYGNTCDAYHMTSPHPEGQGAIKAIK
40	Glyceraldehyde-3 phosphate dehydrogenase	91/91	15901835	839.4	47-63	YDTTQGR
				1,168.6	117-128	VVITAPGGNDVK
				1,222.7	216-227	AIGLVIPELNGK
				1,242.7	21-31	IQNVEGVEVTR
				1,289.6	252-263	NVTVDEVNAAMK
				1,399.8	20-32	**RIQNVEGVEVTR[a]**
				1,691.9	32-46	INDLTDPVMLAHLLK
				1,950.1	216-234	AIGLVIPELNKLNGKLDGSAQR
				2,059.9	309-325	VVSWYDNEMSYTAQLVR
				2,466.4	228-251	LDGSAQRVPTPTGSVTELVAVLEK
				2,916.8	21-46	IQNVEGVEVTRINDLTDPVMLAHLLK
				3,602.8	264-297	AASNESYGYTEDPIVSSDIVGMSYGSLFDATQTK

[a] Protein identity determined by database analysis using mascot software, www.matrix-science.com (Matrix sciences USA) on MALDI-CID generated ions. All other sequences determined by profound software, www.genomicsolutions.com on MALDI-TOF mass fingerprints.
[b] Partial amino acid sequence determined by significant (profound ≥ 29; mascot-score ≥ 28) database matches of mass spectra and fragment ion masses generated to peptides of known proteins.
[c] MW values indicate average masses (all other masses are monoisotopic). p>0.05
[e] Protein detection dependent on physiological state of bacterial cell. Sensitivity of detection assay is increased when overnight cell well extracts are incubated with 98 μ diameter beads coated with ≥ 10^{-8} moles of iron.
[f] May function as cell-wall localizing post translational chaperone proteins.

Table 6. Selected homologues of S. pneumoniae cell-wall iron (III) binding proteins.

Protein[a] identity	Size (AA)	Homologues	Protein[b] function	identity[c]/ positive (%)	NCBI accession no.
Oligopeptide transporter (AliB)	652	Cor. diphtheriae	iron-regulated lipoprotein	46/61	1076002
		Cor. diphtheriae	iron-receptor protein	42/46	38233233
		Cor. diphtheriae	iron-regulated lipoprotein (DtxR)	46/61	2276374
		Sta. epidermidis	iron-binding protein	81/81	27467301
		Sta. epidermidis	ferrichrome transport ATP-binding protein	75/100	27467339
		Sta. epidermidis	ferrichrome ABC transporter	42/48	27467436
		Rho equi	iron-dependent regulatory protein	70/80	10334814
		Rho equi	IupA	66/77	40287615
		Myc. bovis	IDER	60/70	31793883
		Myc. bovis	Ferrochelatase hemz	80/100	31792680
		E. coli	Heme-binding lipoprotein	73/84	4062407
Elongation factor (Ef-Tu)	275	Synechocystis sp.	ferripyochelin binding protein	77/88	16329663
		Synechocystis sp.	ferrichrome-iron receptor	63/81	16329191
		Myc. bovis	Ferrochelatase hemz	100/100	31792680
Phosphoglycerate kinase	398	Cor. diphtheriae	iron-sulphur protein	46/59	38234895
		Sta. epidermidis	iron-binding protein	50/54	27467301
		Sta. epidermidis	ferrochelatase	85/100	27468430
		Str. uberis	lactoferrin binding protein	36/38	34978672
Glyceraldehyde-3 phosphate dehydrogenase	335	Rho equi	IupA	52/57	40287615
		Myc. tuberculosis	sirR	70/70	15609925
		Yer. enterocolitica	Irp5 protein	60/100	2765198
		E. coli	iron-compound receptor	61/61	15803576
		Yer. enterocolitica	Ferrocheletase	100/100	40287616
		Bor. pertussis	Hemin binding protein	66/80	33591574
		Rho equi	IupB	100/100	40287616
Ribosme S9	130	Str. uberis	lactoferrin binding protein	60/70	34978672
Conserved protein (unassigned protein)	109	Str. uberis	lactoferrin binding protein	44/55	34978672
Ribosome S10	102	Str. uberis	lactoferrin binding protein	85/85	34978672

[a] Pneumococcal (S. pneumoniae TIGR) proteins were identified by MALDI TOF and MALDI CID partial sequencing. Scores ≥ 37% DNA alignment homology formed basis for protein selection.
[b] Protein functions as submitted to NCBI databases.
[c] Percentage identity/positive is based on DNA sequence alignment ≥ 37% at a $p > 0.05$ using NCBI BLAST software at available *at www.ncbi.nlm.nih.gov* .

N. DISCUSSIONS

GENETIC ANALYSIS OF pia⁻ and *alb*⁻ MUTANTS

*S. pneumoniae pia*ABCD nucleic acid sequence, used in this study, was previously submitted to the gene bank of the National Center for Biotechnology information, NCBI under the accession number AF338658.1. Based on the genetic characterization of this operon, *pia* sequences show similarities with iron transporters found in both gram positive and gram negative bacteria (Brown et al, 2001). To investigate the physiological properties of iron-binding proteins of pneumococcal cell wall, *pia*A defective mutants were constructed by the method of insertional mutagenesis as described in the materials and methods. Plasmid pJDC9 contains an erythromycin-resistance gene, and functions as a suicide vector once internalized by *S. pneumoniae*. Since the plasmid cannot replicate, the presence of erythromycin selective pressure in the medium would force a crossover event and duplication on the homologous regions of the internal fragment of *pia*A.

To examine the gene structure of the *pia*A in mutant, investigators at BAC took advantage of the unique HindIII site in the plasmid pJDC9 and at the nucleotide no. 84 of *pia*A gene. The chromosomal DNA of *pia*- and its parental strain were digested with the restriction enzyme HindIII and analyzed by southern hybridization using a radiolabelled internal fragment of *pia*A gene as probe. **Figure 5** show a 2.8 kb HindIII fragment in the Rx1 chromosomal DNA. Nucleic acid analysis of piaABCD gene from *S. pneumococcus* obtained at pubmed indicate that Rx1 cell has a single copy of *pia*A gene and has another HindIII site located immediately downstream of *pia*C, this is further supported by the lack of HindIII sites in either *pia*B or *pia*C. When mutant *pia*A- chromosomal DNA was used as template, two HindIII fragments were identified with the molecular size of approximately 0.8 and 9.0 kb respectively (**Figure 5**). The point of nucleotide insertion in *pia*A⁻ was determined by PCR, nucleic acid sequencing and alignment of *pia*A in parental Rx1 strain and plasmids *pia*AF and *pia*AR. The erythromycin-resistant *S. pneumoniae* transformant, *pia*A-, was isolated. PCR primers *pia*AF and pJcryR was used to amplify gene in parental strain to amplify mutated gene in *pia*A-. Attempts using PCR failed to amplify *pia*A in *pia*A- . Collectively, these results indicate the insertion of plasmid pJDC9 at nucleotide no. 1059 (**Figure 6**) in the coding sequence of *pia*A and the duplication of internal sequence of *pia*A gene in the mutant piaA-. As expected, the inability of PCR to amplify *pia*A in mutants indicates an absence or modification of the PCR annealing regions in *pia*A- and *alb*-.

CELL-WALL IRON (III) BINDING AND G-3-P-D STUDIES

To identify cell wall iron binding proteins, Matrix-Assisted Laser Deabsorbtion Ionization Time of Flight Mass Spectrophotometer (MALDI-TOF MS) was used to analyze unseperated trypsin digests of 4 to 12 % SDS polyacrylamide gels for the determination of molecular mass and relative abundance of 50 and 37 kDa fragment (**Figure 9** and **10**).

Prior to this, reducing agents were introduced into the electrophoresis buffer for optimal protein separation. MALDI-CID MS on MH^+ 2160.03 and 2301.18 (monoisotopic) fragments were used to obtain additional sequence information for matching in NCBI genetic databases of *S. pneumoniae* conducted using pubmed databases. This information as been summarized (**Table 5 and 6).** To determine the identity of the protein from MALDI TOF MS and MALDI-CID MS, investigators determined that 50 kDa protein purified was significantly homologous to the Ef-Tu and the 37 kDa identical to G-3-P-D proteins of *S. pneumoniae.* To characterize mutant strains for cell walls ability to bind iron (III), the investigators synthesized and mounted a synthetic siderophore, ($C_6H_{12}FeN0_6$), on a 98 μm polystyrene bead to create a 50 μl iron (III) affinity column (**Figure 9**). After growing cells in low iron environment to genetically stimulate expression of cell wall iron receptors, investigators isolated and incubated cell wall extracts with iron (III) beads. The iron-binding proteins eluted from column were run in a 4 to 12% gradient gel.

The major iron (III) binding proteins purified from parental Rx1 strain was 50, and 37 kDa in size; however, other fragments were visible (unpublished data). Absence of 37 and 50 kDa and minor fragments in *pia*A- and *alb*- indicate there is an absence of binding activity, further suggesting absence, or loss in integrity of structure or function of proteins iron-binding proteins in *pia*A- and *alb*-. In a similar study, Ef-Tu, Fur, Aconitase, PPIase, Lsr2, HSP, Oxidoreductases and a 21.5, and a 15.9 kDa hypothetical protein were successfully identified in *Mycobacterium tuberculosis* using similar technique (Wong et al, 1999). Furthermore, Mass spectrophotometry has been used successfully in the identification of bacterial proteins expressed under condition of low and high iron concentrations (Wong et al, 1999). This technology is therefore a powerful tool for analyzing iron-binding proteins. Ef-Tu is a GTPase, which delivers aminoacyl-tRNA to ribosomes.

Ef-Tu has been shown to be become membrane associated when *E. coli* is starved for nutrients (Young, et al, 1991); raising the possibility that Ef-Tu may have additional regulatory functions under conditions of stress. As a G-protein, Ef-Tu can be linked to an iron-dependent holoenzyme receptor or proteins. Receptor-ligand interactions generate transducing signals for relay to the nucleus, where they alter the expression of specific genes associated with receptor-ligand complex. The property or signal relay can significantly change if property of receptor-ligand is changed. Ef-Tu homolog's in the cell wall extract of *pia*- and *alb*- stains fail to bind iron (III) beads. Based on this observation, investigators at BAC performed antimicrobial susceptibility analysis and growth promotion analysis using the iron-containing hydroxamate antibiotics, albomycin, and salmycin, and hydroxamate siderophore ferrichrome. The intent of this analysis was to determine if a relationship exists between the process of cell wall iron (III) binding and resistance to hydroxamate type antibiotics. Specifically, by additionally performing the assay with salmycin and ferrichrome, the investigator wanted to see what impact, if any, the difference in sugar moiety of albomycin and salmycin have in drug resistance at the cell wall level.

Zones of inhibition to albomycin and salmycin measured 23 mm, and 22 mm in Rx1, <1 mm in both *pia*A-, and *alb*- mutants, indicating that both mutants were completely resistant to albomycin and salmycin (**Table 4**). During the antibiotic susceptibility studies, Optochin or ethyl hydrocupreine hydrochloride, an antibiotic widely used in diagnostic laboratories to differentiate *S. pneumoniae* from *Enterococcus,* viridians and group D streptococcus, was used to ensure proper selection of pneumococcal strains. Zones of inhibition of all three strains measured 15 mm. Values represent means from three replicates, ($P = 0.05$, readings have a differential of $\pm$ 3). These results show that resistance to hydroxamate antibiotics is independent of sugar moieties. (**Table 4**). These results suggest that multiple drug resistance in microbes appears to be linked to iron (III) dependent reductase and ATP and perhaps even play a role in particulate transport and the uptake of antibiotics. Interestingly, the 37 kDa G-3-P-D identified appears similar to:

- A 34 kDa PiaA reported by Brown et al, 2001, based on Ni^{2+}-NTA purification protocols based on His_6-PiaA fusion analysis of *pia* in pneumococcal strain type 2 D39.
- 37 kDa PiuA, reported by Tai et al, 2003, based on Ni^{2+}-NTA purifications based on His_6-PiaA fusion analysis of *piu* in pneumococcal strain Rx1
- 37 kDa, PsaA reported by Sampson et al, 1994, based on immunoblot analysis of lysates from clones of recombinant plasmids containing *psa* from pneumococcal strain R36A derived from partial digests of genomic library

These observations are significant because fundamentally, polystyrene beads used in this study, unlike the material used in other studies, are inert chemically. NTA-iron-polystyrene affinity columns (BAC El Paso USA) used in this study can increase specificity and sensitivity for iron binding proteins while Ni^{2+}-NTA, His_6 and polysaccharide beads used in other studies are less stringent and lack binding specificity. In summary, BAC investigators determined that the *S. pneumoniae* 37 kDa cell wall heme-binding protein previously identified as PsaA; PiaA; and piu may be an iron-binding, G-3-P-D.

STUDIES WITH IRON-CONTAINING METABOLIC INHIBITORS AND SEDEROPHORES

Based on the observations made during the albomycin and salmycin susceptibility studies (**Table 4**), investigators studied the role of *pia*A in hydroxamate siderophore utility by conducting ferrichrome utility assays using growth as a measurable index. To achieve this, parental Rx1 and the *pia*A- and *alb*- strains were cultured in 1% THB media pre treated with chelex. Growth, as an index of ferrichrome utility, was determined spectrophotometrically at A_{600}. The result of these experiments show that *S. pneumoniae* Rx1 parental strain and **pia**A- attain absorbance of 0.2 in 1% THB while *alb*- strain grew to a maximum absorbance of 0.17 **(Figure 7A)**. After treatment with chelex, growth of *alb*- was only partially reduced to 0.1, while growth of Rx1 and *pia*A- were both significantly reduced to values lower than 0.05 **(Figure 7B).** When ferrichrome supplements were added to deferrated media, of the three strains, the parental Rx1 strain was able to utilize ferrichrome for growth to attain a final absorbance of 0.15. (**Figure 7C**) values represent means from three replicates ($p = 0.01$). The ability for ferrichrome to improve growth conditions in parental Rx1 strain suggest that albomycin and salmycin resistance is specifically linked to the utility of the iron (III)-containing region of both antibiotics and that spontaneous albomycin resistant strains have less stringent metabolic needs for iron. In a previous study, Kadner et al, 1980, showed mutations in either ferric heme uptake gene, *fhu*ABCD, of *Escherichia coli*, result in albomycin resistance.

Albomycin is a seryl tRNA antagonist (Stefanska, et al, 2000) and is known to be potent against both gram negative and gram positive bacteria (Gause et al, 1955). Substituting its sugar moiety with a ribosyl analogue will eliminate antimicrobial activity in albomycin (Paulsen et al, 1987). Enzymatic cleavage of the thiorybosylepyrimidine antibiotic group of albomycin from its iron-chelating portion, a tri-δ-N-hydroxy-δ-n-acetyl-L-ornithine peptide can be accomplished by peptidase N in *E. coli* (Braun et al, 1983). In gram-negative bacteria, the inhibitory effect of albomycin is dependent on its ability to utilize the ferric hydroxamate uptake system for transport across outer and inner membranes.

Like albomycin, salmycin are iron-hydroxamate siderophore with antibiotic properties, but differ in the composition of their sugar moieties. Albomycin has a thiorybosylepyrimidine moiety (Paulsen et al, 1987), while the sugar moiety in salmycin is made up of a didehydrohexose (Von László et al, 1995). Unlike the iron-hydroxamate antibiotics, ferrichrome is a cyclic hexapeptide containing a triglycine sequence. It lacks sugar moiety found in iron-hydroxamate antibiotics, and supports growth in bacteria. The outer three amino acids are derivatives of δ-N-hydroxyornithine, which are linked in the cyclic peptide by normal α- peptide bonds. The three hydroxyl-amino-groups are N-acetylated to give three substituted acetohydroxyamic groups per molecule. Additionally, ferrichrome display potent growth factor activity in some organisms.

The mode of action for both albomycin and salmycin is now clear. It appears the methylated and iron containing amino acid, and sugar moiety of antibiotics target microbial signal transducing, cell wall bound, G-3-P-D. The methyl, sugar, and iron components of the antibiotics act as "Trojan Horses" to attract microbe. Consequently, killing the pathogen by inactivating the apoenzyme, NAD, $^{+}$ and iron cofactor components of G-3-P-D.

O. SUMMARY OF FINDINGS

S. pneumoniae is a gram positive pathogen implicated in 50% of all neonatal infections world-wide. Increases in multiple drug resistant strains have been reported. Here, investigators at BAC show that various cell-wall proteins from Rx1 pneumococcal strains grown in deferrated THB media bind Fe^{3+}- affinity ($C_6H_{12}FeN0_6$) beads. Gradient sodium dodecylsulphte polyacrylamide gel electrophoresis and silver staining, and partial amino acid sequencing by mass spectrometry and database analysis was used to identify a major 37-kDa protein to be G-3-P-D, and show it to be significantly homologous to prominent Fe^{3+}- binding and transport proteins in gram-positive and gram-negative bacteria. Unlike parental Rx1 strains, whole cell G-3-P-D and cell-wall Fe^{3+}- binding assays performed with alb- suggest reduced activity.

Furthermore, *alb*- grown in deferrated THB fails to utilize ferrichrome for growth. Overall, investigators realized comparable results with *pia*A- implying a link exists between the impairment of iron-transport ligands and earlier observations. This insight may be used in future studies to better understand functional attributes of iron-siderophore receptors. In this study investigators at BAC have used this information to develop antimicrobial targets against cysteine containing microbial reductase. Gradient sodium dodecylsulphte polyacrylamide gel electrophoresis and silver staining, partial amino acid sequencing by mass spectrometry and database analysis was used to identify several of iron-binding proteins. Results show some to be significantly homologous to prominent ferric and heme cell-wall binding proteins in gram-positive and gram- negative bacteria.

Collectively, these results suggest that albomycin utility (ferrichrome is growth stimulating analogue of albomycin) from environmental sources is significantly reduced in *alb*$^-$ and *pia*A$^-$ suggesting multiple drug resistance in microbes is linked to iron-uptake; and a reductase dependent activity. An outcome of this information has led investigators to develop Braunmycin® Olisferrol™, which functions as a none-specific oligopeptide antibiotic **(Figure 12)** entirely from computational biology. Spontaneous albomycin resistance is common. Previously, *pia*ABC was reported (Olisa et al, 2000), and characterized as the major iron-transporter used for growth in *S .pneumoniae* (Brown et al, 2002). *alb*- strains grow rapidly in controlled media when compared to Rx1 and *pia*A- (**Figure 7A**). Furthermore, there is significant loss in growth of Rx1 and *pia*A- and limited growth of *alb*- in deferrated media **(Figure 7B**). **Figure 7C** shows that ferrichrome supplements significantly improve growth of Rx1 but not *alb*- and *pia*A- in deferrated THB. Spontaneous albomycin, *alb*- resistance in *Streptococcus pneumoniae* is common. Here, BAC investigators show that various cell wall proteins from Rx1 pneumococcal strains grown in deferrated THB media bind Fe^{3+}- affinity ($C_6H_{12}FeN0_6$) beads.

Unlike parental strains, cell wall iron-binding activity was limited in *alb*$^-$ strains. Furthermore, deferrated THB supplemented with ferrichrome failed to improve growth conditions in Alb. Overall, observations imply that there is a link between PiaABC and cell-wall expression of G-3-P-D **(Figure 8**). It would be worthy to note that iron (cofactor) - NAD^+ (coenzyme) complex jointly provide energy (ATP) needed for G-3-P-D (holoenzyme) activity (sugar metabolism), during substrate level phosphorylation. Movement of electrons creates energy (ATP) and electron gradients that facilitate energy dependent particulate (antibiotics) uptake in microbes.

Spontaneous albomycin resistance in *Streptococcus pneumoniae* is characterized by loss in cell-wall Fe^{3+}- binding protein activity of a 37- kDa G-3-P-D. Multiple drug resistant bacteria are susceptible to albomycin **(Table 4).** Albomycin is an iron containing seryl tRNA synthethase antagonist. Spontaneous albomycin resistant strains of S pneumoniae show resistance to major classes of antibiotics except cell wall inhibitor. This result suggests that one method for resistance could be the absence of energy dependent drug uptake. Interestingly, seryl tRNA is cell wall bound in bacteria. Specifically, to GTP, a major component of cysteine containing signal transducing permease and electron transport chain which is responsible for substrate level phosphorylation, and energy needed to selectively transport molecules in and out of the cell **(Part 1; Chapter 2; Section 2).** *pia*A gene is absent in multiple drug resistant clinical isolates of *S. pneumoniae*; *alb*⁻ and *pia*A⁻**,** these results suggest that multiple drug resistance in bacteria is an energy and iron-dependent process involving selective transport. Furthermore, cysteine and oxido-reductase activity can be used to characterize this permease.

P. CONCLUTION

Based on proteomic studies (unpublished data), energy generated by NAD^{+}, and iron cofactor components of G-3-P-D can be used: (1). In sugar metabolism that is initiated at the cell wall level. Examples can be found in *Mycobacterium tuberculosis*, *Streptococcus pneumoniae* Methicillin resistant *Staphylococcus aureas* (MRSA). (2). In viral and microbial cell wall attachment (Plasmodium, HIV, H5N1 virus).

In deed, some human cancer tumor cells express exceptionally high levels of transferrin molecules. Close analysis of X-Cys-X iron binding moiety suggest they contain atypical amino acids that characterize human transferrin suggesting that microbes may have contributed to this variation. **Figure 12** is a synthetic peptide structure mock up that summarize the discovered differences.

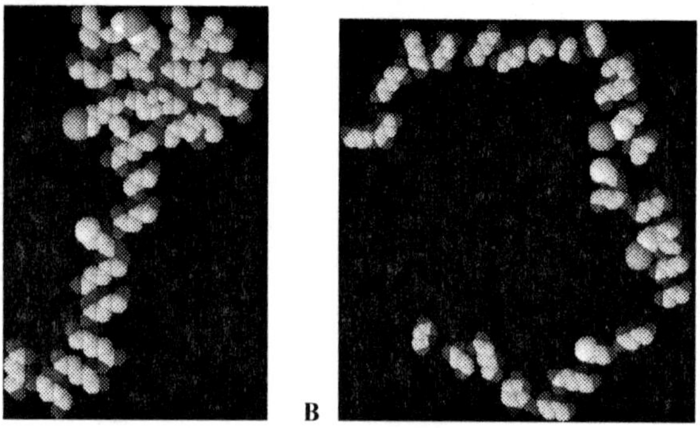

A. B

Figure 12. The molecular structure of Braunmycin ® Olisferrol ™ ($C_{119}H_{163}Fe_2N_{29}0_{71}S_4$) **A.** Braunmycin ®. **B.** Olisferrol™. Antibiotics. Synergy formula can contain one or a combination of FDA approved human interferon γ; human defensins; human lysozymes; human lactoferrin, nisin, and bacitracin peptides. Human and veterinary vaccines (synproteovax™) are engineered using computational proteomics technologies from information derived in **Figure 9; Figure 10; Table 5 and 6.**

TOTAL QUALITY MANAGEMENT AND VALIDATION FOR THE LABORATORY

OBJECTIVES

Upon completion of this section, performers will be able to:

- Establish cost-effective evaluation research for quality control in molecular diagnostics laboratories based on quasi-experimentation and computational biology
- Comprehend threats associated with internal, external and construct validity
- Interpret clinical, or public health data to determine causes and affect patterns needed to make interpretations for process evaluation in clinical and or public health laboratory

A. INTRODUCTION

The best practice for testing infectious agents cost effectively should involve using biochemistry and molecular diagnostics analytical and/or clinical methods. Regardless, these processes of evaluation research should involve quasi-experimentation. In other words, a major goal is to determine cause and effect using non-experimental platforms. The underlying principle here is that of Koch's Postulate **(Part 1; Chapter 2; Part 2)**. Samples tested may be clinical (body fluids), or environmental (food, air, water). Prior to testing, samples should be treated with biochemical's (treatment) using diagnostic and/or research platforms. The process should also involve the use of positive controls which are introduced to screen if outcome of test or assay is influenced by external validity. Simultaneously, negative controls can also be introduced to screen for influences of internal validity.

Testing in clinical and public health laboratories should be none randomized. The process should involve the use of "natural" and "unknown" samples. The performer should have "zero" control over the nature or content of the sample. For this reason, the treatment process should be regulated by government, quasi-judiciary, and/or medical non-governmental agencies like the College of American Pathologists (CAP); American Society for Clinical Pathology (ASCP); Food and Drug Administration (FDA); Environmental Protection Agency (EPA). Furthermore, these agencies should set and implement the standards. One way they can achieve this is by certifying or licensing the performers and the workplace— in this case laboratories.

B. THREATS TO EXTERNAL VALIDITY

Threats to external validity can come from interaction of performer with the testing platform. Furthermore, it puts to question the ability of performer to carry out the protocol, and can include the performer's ability to carry out measurements; or the accuracy and precision of instrumentation. In addition, during testing, the introduction of positive controls can ably assist in the detection of threats as a result of external validity. When positive controls are used as they should, outcomes can be interpreted that threats to external validity are minimal but not entirely absent.

C. THREATS TO INTERNAL VALIDITY

These can come from the quality of the reagents used, or from contamination of either reagents, or samples during testing. Threats to internal validity can be detected with negative controls. Some common negative controls include normal saline or distilled and/or deionizer water. During testing, most negative controls are expected to show neutral, or non-reactivity for expected outcome. Threats to internal validity can also arise from improper refrigeration, or storage of reagents (history of sample), or from a samples expiration (maturation of sample), or the use of improper instrumentation; and the improper selection of reagents or sample.

Generally speaking, threats to internal, external, and construct validity can be detected and minimized by performing and averaging series of tests, or by using positive and negative controls frequently during all tests. Internal validity is a serious problem in Clinical and public health laboratories because, unlike experimentation, in quasi-experimentation, there can be no randomization to minimize threats in this category. All samples have to be tested and interpreted. One way to detect threats to interval validity is to benchmark. That is, to routinely compare present data to historical data in the same category as a way to detect irregularities in trend. The premise for testing in clinical or public health laboratory is action and reaction, or cause, and effect. A single treatment to a sample could lead to a single, or multiple quantifiable observations.

Conversely, multiple treatments to a sample could result in single or multiple quantifiable observations. In either case, the quantifiable observation should be, in all cases, the expected outcome. When choosing a cost effective test; quality of test should super-seed quantity of analysis regardless if test in question involves hybridization, PCR amplification, oncology, genetics, or basic microbiology staining and biochemistry. Quality can be defined in terms of how deterministic the test is, or how precise, and accurate the treatment is in determining the expected outcome(s). Nonetheless, in some cases, qualitative tests may be introduces as a "shot-gun" approach. The use of qualitative assays should be minimized in testing for pathogens associated with infectious disease because they increase threats to construct validity.

D. CONSTRUCT VALIDITY

The main theme of construct validity is bias, and irrelevancies in interpretation. It usually presents it's self as a form of human error, and can involve outcome guessing, misinterpretation. It involves how we translate our work.

E. TOTAL QUALITY MANAGEMENT

According to Berte and Nevalainen, (2000), quality can be defined as the totality of a characteristic of an entity that bears on its ability to satisfy stated and implied needs. *Quality Controls* (QC) are therefore operational techniques and activities used to fulfill requirements of quality. When these activities are planned, and systematic, then the term *Quality Assurance* (QA) implies. *Quality Systems* (QS) would therefore involve an institutionalized form of quality assessment and is more process and resource driving. The planning and development of policies, and evaluating and assessing quality systems can be defined as *Quality Management* (QM). Often, the term *Total Quality Management* (TQM) is used when a long term strategy is in place.

Perhaps one of the first steps in implementing cost effective quality control platforms is the identification of stakeholders. Key amongst which are the medical, or laboratory directors, an appointed quality assurance chairperson, or director (Bozzo, 1991). Collectively, based on existing or needed policies and guidelines, stakeholder should institute a quality assurance plan. Furthermore, planning should be performed strategically **(Part 1; Chapter 1; Section 3, and 4).** In addition, risks and needs assessments should be performed **(Part 1; Chapter 1; Section 5-6).** In addition, assessments and evaluations should involve the use of information systems **(Part 1; Chapter 2; Section 12).**

According to Clarke, (1995), a good plan should accommodate dealing with inspections conducted by regulatory organizations like Joint Commission on Accreditation of Healthcare (JCAHO). Other investigators (Montgomery, 1995; Versalovic, and Unger, 2004), suggest that laboratories should be standardized with implemented proficiency testing programs, quality control standards from Centers for Disease Control and Prevention (CDC), and with Occupational Safety and Health Administration (OSHA) standards for infectious disease handling of: hazardous waste disposal, personal protective equipment (PPE), and monitoring, especially when handling highly infectious samples, particularly microbes associated with the Strategic National Stockpile (SNS) for vaccines like Avian Influenza (Revell, 2007).

Generally, quality control should also consider guidelines from the National Association of County and City Officials (NACCHO) on: record keeping, equipment, and instrumentation, and laboratory safety (Miller, and Wentworth, 1985). On the subject of TQM, monetary costs needed to implement QC platforms should include the following: time required to perform QC, costs of reagents and instruments, instrument maintenance costs, manpower costs for trouble shooting, and time for making assessments. Furthermore, to achieve these ends the process used can either be analytical or a clinical in approach.

The analytical approach takes into account if two or more different methods yield the same analytical answer, while clinical comparisons is used to determine if the analytical approach provided crucial datum rather than data to assist in diagnosis and treatment. Most public health laboratories are concerned with analytical comparisons; while clinical laboratories utilize both approaches. Therefore, in these cases, the goal of standard QC should be to detect 100% of all errors (systematic, and random), have 0% false rejection, in addition to be able to identify all sources of error.

Accordingly; in the preanalytical QC phase it is important to develop proper patient sampling identities, and proper methods of handling, transporting, and sorting samples. Following QC, it is also important to have proper, secure, and timely charting, and reporting systems. In this era of new public management **(Part 1; Chapter 1; Section 2)**, it would be preferably to administer, analyze, and evaluate data with electronic online information's system and proper regression analysis software. Linear and multiple regressions analysis are preferred over other statistical analysis because they are predictive, and can determine causality, and affect. Other test statistics are inappropriate because they measure correlations instead.

F. BENCHMARKING

Benchmarking in the laboratory involves comparing the laboratories mean value from mean values from other laboratories, and then applying the rules of TEa. Furthermore, this comparison can be achieved using the Standard Deviation Index or SDI. Note that some amount of error is allowable:

Total Error allowable (TEa) =

(Mean-true value) + 2S = BIAS + 2SD = **SDI** = $(X_{lab} - X_{group}) / SD_{group}$

These methods of inter-laboratory comparisons do not occur in all laboratories at the same time. During the process, data is usually collected independently by a third regulatory authority like CAP or CLIA. Furthermore, introduction of reagents, instruments and platforms upgrades tend to affect the SDI because data can vary month to month. Accordingly, commercial controls have to be introduced when benchmarking.

G. CLINICAL METHODS OF COMPARISON

For the most part, analytical methods are used when methods agree. Conversely, when methods disagree, perhaps because the newer method may be more accurate, clinical methods of comparison should be used. Here, in this type of quasi-experimentation, samples are assayed by one, or more method. Furthermore, methods can be compared to the expected outcome (diagnosis).

H. ASSESSING THE PRECISION OF TWO METHODS

According to Plaut, (1998), one way of assessing the precision of two methods is to determine the Random Error (RE). *Precision* is the reproducibility of a test or instrument; this should not be confused with *accuracy* which is measure of "how close" a measurement is to a numerical value. Since precision is affected by external, internal, and construct validity, the best practice is to determine precision at different levels using a control or standard. Furthermore, increasing the cut-off of a test will increase the specificity, and lower the sensitivity. Additionally, increasing the sensitivity will lower the specificity and vice versa. The sensitivity, and specificity of a test is a function of the population studied and the prevalence of the disease

- **SENSITIVITY** = True positive (TP)/ [(TP) + False Negative (FN)]
- **SPECIFICITY** = True Negative (TN)/ [TN)+ False Positive (FP)]
- **EFFICIENCY** = (TP)/+ (TN)/ TOTAL
- **POSITIVE PREDICTIVE VALUE (PPV)** = (TP)/ [((TP) +(FP)]
- **NEGATIVE PREDICTIVE VALUE (NPV)** = (TN) /[(TN) + (FN)

I. LINEARITY AND DATA COMPARISON METHODS

F RATIO = STANDARD DEVIATION (SD) $_{\text{lab tests}}$ / (SD) $_{\text{standard or reference}}$

The F ratio was developed by R.A Fisher to look for differences (compare variances) between standard deviation of inherent or random error. Once the F value has been determined, the performer needs to determine if that value is statistically significant using statistical tables to determine the critical value of F which is a function of the two standard deviations being compared at the desired degree of confidence.

T TEST = (MEAN $_X$ – MEAN $_Y$)* n / $\sqrt{(SD^2_X + SD^2_Y)}$

The T test looks for differences between the mean of two methods. Furthermore, it looks for random error. Once the T value has been determined, the performer needs to determine if that value is statistically significant using statistical tables. The assumption here is that the probability for two methods to have the same mean is "nil" either due to internal validity which can cause random error, or construct, and external validity which can cause systematic errors. As the value of T increases, so does the chance of error between both methods. Nonetheless, it is important to note that statistical differences do not always correlate to clinical differences. In addition, the difference may be due to the increase in accuracy of the new method. Accordingly, a new reference range will be needed to accommodate the new method.

J. PAIRED T TEST

Paired T test is a more sensitive test for linearity than the T test, and looks for differences between average differences of pairs of data, and for systematic errors. This test has two major disadvantages. First, the concentrations of samples need to be known, and methodology should contain few threats to experimental validity (a line can be straight and fail a T test). Second, these tests cannot detect all forms of error. Test pairs and observed values should have corresponding or assigned known concentrations.

K. LINEAR REGRESSION

This is one of the most common methods used in analytical and clinical comparisons because of its power to predict and estimate. It was said to have been developed by Carl Gauss. The assumptions hear is that the value of the X axis or dependent variable is without error, and that the variable or independent variables are on the Y axis. The two unknowns are the slope and the intercept. To minimize standard error between two points, calculations should take to account the points with the shortest distance. Nonetheless, it is important to note that the accuracy of a regression analysis is limited by internal, external, and construct validity. The ideal slope should be 1. 0. In addition, lines outside the range of 0.95 -1.05 should be questioned for validity. The ideal intercept should be 0.0, but this is unlikely for the reason previously stated. To this end, both the Correlation Coefficient, and Standard Error can measure the combined Random Errors from two methods. Normally, the value of (r) ranges from -1.0 to 1.0 (where r values of 1.0 means data are identical). *As the measure in comparison diverge, (r) decreases.* When (r) is less than 0.95 (increases in scatter), threats to data validity should be assessed. As (r) approaches 1.0, standard error approaches 0.0. As (r) decreases, S.E.E increases, and so does scatter. According to NCCLS standards, linearity is defined as the measure of the degree a curve approximates a straight line. Today, the best practice is the use of statistical software to determine lines of best fit, (r) value, and standard error.

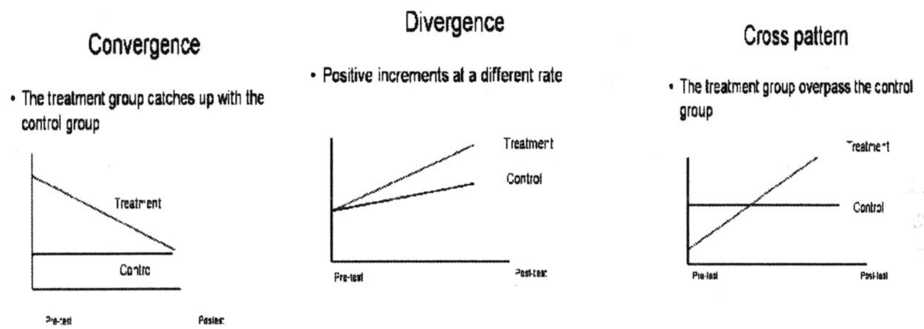

Courtesy: Sergio Pena

Figure 13. Relationships between input (treatment) and outcomes

L. REGRESSION ANALYSIS

As previously stated, regression analysis are used to determine correlations, and causation between two or more variables, usually, an X (dependent variable) and Y (independent variable). Fundamentally both are different. Perhaps the most important use of multiple regressions is in forecasting, and can be used in the determination of rates of change (like infections surge) in X, relative to Y. Multiple variables correlations can be used to determine how two variables are related while causation determines how one variable affects the other. The regression line shows how much X variable affects changes in Y variable. Furthermore, this value can be used for forecasting and in the determination of causality **(See Figure 13)**.

$$\mathbf{Y = a+bX}$$

Where **a** is the value of **Y** when **X** is 0.0, the constant or intercept; and **b** is the slope or the value of **X**. Here, there are imperfect relationships between **Y** and **X** consequently,

$$\mathbf{Y = a+bX+e}$$

Where (**e**) is the *stochastic or error estimation.* The sum of squares of error (SSE) is used to minimize the error in the prediction of **(b).** As stated earlier, the best practice in performing regression analysis is the use of software like SPSS or BiologicalAgents Index in Spreadsheets (BAC, El Paso, USA) available at *www.biologicalagents.com.* Furthermore, the goal of the least squares concept is to minimize the error in the prediction of (**b**) or (SSE) summing the squares of the errors (summing the errors of each prediction).

$$SSE = \sum (Y_{\text{initial intercept}} - Y_{\text{final intercept}})^2 = (\text{observed error} - \text{predicted error})$$

Sum of Squares of b is least when

$$b = \sum (X_{\text{intercept}} - X_{\text{mean}})(Y_{\text{intercept}} - Y_{\text{mean}}) / \sum (X_{\text{intercept}} - X_{\text{mean}})^2$$

$$a = Y_{\text{mean}} - bX_{\text{mean}}$$

M. INTERPRETING REGRESSION ANALYSIS

R (model fit) is the % of variability that dependent variable Y is affected by change in independent variable X. This % change is the amount of variance in Y that is explained by X variable. Furthermore, Beta Coefficient (B) measures how one unit change in X (dependent variable) affects changes in Y (independent variable).

N. EVALUATING DISINFECTANTS AND ANTISEPTICS

The standard way for evaluating disinfectants is through the use of the *Phenol coefficient* (PC). This is the ratio of the effect of the antimicrobial agent compared to a similar concentration of phenol:

Concentration Antimicrobial Compound / Phenol Coefficient Same Concentration of Phenol:

A compound that has a phenol coefficient greater than 1.0 is more effective than phenol. Furthermore, an agent that has a greater antimicrobial effect under lower concentrations and less toxicity is generally favored.

O. METHODS FOR DETERMINING PHENOL COEFFICIENT

Use-Dilution Method (USD): The process involves the use of small metal cylinders which are soaked in bacterial cultures of *Pseudomonas aeruginosa, Staphylococcus aureus,* and *Salmonella cholerasuis* var. *typhimurium*. Each cylinder is placed into different concentrations (dilutions) of a test disinfectant and left to incubate for 10 minutes. The cylinders are then removed, rinsed with sterile water and placed in sterile nutrient broth. In addition, the broths are incubated at 37 °C for 48 hours. If the broth is cloudy following incubation, the compound is not effective. Among the broths that are free of microbial growth, the performer should choose the one that (a) is best at controlling all three species (if possible) and (b) is the lowest effective concentration.

In-Use Method (IUM): Here, phenol coefficient and *use dilution* can give valid results when performed properly, but may be misleading since both utilize only a small number of microbes that may, or may not represent the population on any given surface. The *in use* test involves taking test swabs of surfaces and equipment before and after disinfection, which, while taking longer than the other tests, but gives a more realistic result for the given environment that is tested.

ESTIMATING INFECTION SURGE

A. INTRODUCTION

The *biological agents* ® Index [© 2002-2008] (BAC, El Paso, USA) offers a systematic approach to predicting the outcome (prevalence) of highly infectious disease outbreaks prior to initial strategic planning. The major advantage here is the ability to plan and adjust exiting plans as needed in "near real-time" at the grass roots level, in any defined environment— a planning process known as transformation. To validate the index, data on the 2003 outbreak of Severe Acute Respiratory Syndrome (SARS), a highly infectious mutant strain of the coronavirus, one of many viruses that cause the common cold, have been analyzed. Data for the investigation was acquired from the Centers for Disease Control & Prevention, CDC&P.

Using quasi-experimentation, BAC developed a non-experimental, descriptive study, using a novel mathematical algorithm **(Part 1; Chapter 2; Section 8)** for the *biological agents® Index* [© 2002-2008]. Furthermore, this algorithm was developed using an outbreak coefficient (ω) to formulate a multiple regression equation based on the *Epidemiological Transition Theory* (Orman, 1977); and the *Mass Action Principle* (Busenberg, and Chavez, 1991; Nokes, and Anderson, 1988) and outbreak coefficient **(Part 1; Chapter 2; Section 14)**. Independent variables are number of ways a pathogen is transmitted (Y_1), its infective dose in half the population (Y_2), and the regions location quotient (LQ)— an economic index (Y_3).

According to Alan Murray, in a recent paper published in the Wall Street Journal— the real problem in healthcare is the <u>lack</u> of good information on quality and outcomes, <u>not</u> quantitative financial or manpower investments. In other words, rubbish in, rubbish out. The analysis obtained by using the *biological agents ® index* [© 2002-2008] for real-time modeling and analysis is only as good as the quality of information input from the user. Therefore, to optimize on quality of output information, investigators at BAC created several realistic evaluation check-points in the systems architecture.

A multiple regression analysis of the index [$P = \omega R_0 + \omega RR + \omega I + \varepsilon$: where $\omega = [1/b\ (Y_2 / Y_1 * Y_3)]$ using SPSS (SPSS Inc. Chicago, USA) statistical platform show that 99.9% ($R^2 = 0.999$) of the dependent variable—disease prevalence (P) can be explained by the following: incidence (I), a microorganisms reproductive rate (Ro), the relative risk for infection (RR), and an outbreak coefficient (ω) when used in a multiple regression equation.

From the SPSS analysis, $R^2 = (0.999)$, represents a 9.99 % increase in prediction accuracy over existing models. Interestingly, of the three independent variables, (I) has the <u>least</u> impact in the prediction of (P) [each unit increase in (I), results to a corresponding 0.46 unit increase in (P), compared to 100 unit increase in (P) caused by (RR), and 9,133 unit increase caused by (Ro). These values were determined by β – coefficient analysis. Finally, when applied, (ω), significantly diminished the collinearity between (Ro), (RR), and (P). The BiologicalAgents Index spreadsheet (a medical device) can be used in the hyper text markup language (HTML). Consequently, it can be used in policy, and cost-benefit analysis of healthcare intervention outcomes worldwide because international organizations, like the United Nations Development Program (UNDP), Pan American Health Organization (PAHO), World Health Organization (WHO), and World Bank, and the Centers for Disease Control & Prevention (CDC& P) base the majority of their programs on health related policy and emerging technology. In the past, the evaluation, implementation, and the monitoring of the impact of these policies have been problematic for a number of reasons. First, quantifying the situation is problematic. Second, there is the problem of monitoring the implementation process for purposes or regulation and quality control. Finally, there is the problem is developing efficient and cost effective technology.

B. DERIVING THE OUTBREAK COEFFICIENT (ω)

An outbreak can be defined as a sudden eruption of a disease. Investigators at BAC derived an "outbreak coefficient" using standard existing formulas for the general reproductive rate (R_0 = ßXD), and incidence (I=ßXZ), where (ß) is the transmission coefficient (Baker, 1989; Nokes, and Anderson, 1988). As mentioned earlier, the concept of the outbreak coefficient is novel. In previous studies, basic reproductive rate of an infectious agent was used to determine the threshold result in an epidemiological model (Blaser, and Newman, 1989; Nokes, and Anderson, 1988; Baker, 1989).

Furthermore, these investigators noted that disease would persist if $R_0 > 1$. R_0 for an infectious agent can be determined in the presence of variables such as two or more pathogens. In addition, by combing the empirical and theoretical formulas from these studies, investigators were able to develop the equation for computing disease incidence and prevalence when mixing was homogeneous (Busenberg, Castillo-Chavez, 1991). This is not the first use of time real-time prediction models (Meester et al, 2002). However, here, for the first time, the use of: infective dose (Id_{50},), defined as the amount of pathogen that can cause disease in 50% of the population in question at a point in time; Location Quotient (LQ), an economic index for development, and number of ways a pathogen is transmitted within a population have collectively been used to create a real-time predictive model (Olisa, 2002; 2007).

In addition, mathematical models formulated by interaction and mixing of microbe and host are ultimately dependent on the number of ways the infectious agent is disseminated. In this case, the Id_{50} becomes a direct reflection of the innate biological characteristics that impacts the rate of infection (Nokes, and Anderson 1988). To formulate the outbreak coefficient, investigators at BAC took to account the "mass action principal", defined as the net rate at which new cases of an infection arise, This value is proportional to the density (or number) of susceptible individuals (X) times the density of infectious persons (Z) times the probability of transmission (β) from infectious to susceptible individuals (Busenberg, and Chavez, 1991; Nokes, and Anderson, 1988). When interaction is homogeneous, incidence rate (I), can be then formulated as follows:

$I = \beta XZ$..................... (1) Here $0 \leq \beta \leq 1$

$[1/T] = [1]\ [1/T]\ [1]$

Where, (β) is the *probability of transmission* or the *transmission coefficient.* It is the probability that an infectious agent will transmit disease. Incidence rate is a direct estimate of the probability, or risk, of developing a disease during a specific period in time. R_0 represents the basic reproductive rate of infection. R_0 can be described as the number of secondary cases of infection derived by one primary case, and is formulated as

$R_0 = \beta XD$...... (2)
$[1/T] = [1]\ [1/T]\ [1]$

Where (D) is the length of time the primary case is infectious to others, and (X) is the number of susceptible individuals, as before, R_0 is dependent on the typical course of infection, the social and demographic makeup of the community, and the biology of the infectious disease. For infection to persist R_0 would have to be ≥ 1. Solving the equation for (X) in equation (2), subsequently:

$X = R_0/\beta D$.................. (3)

To address individual mixing, investigators at BAC found the transmission coefficient to be directly proportional to the number of ways an infectious agent is disseminated. As one increases mixing or dissemination, the rate of transmission also increases. This statement can be expressed as:

$\beta \propto Y_2$ .... (4)

Where Y_2 is the number of ways that an infectious agent can be disseminated or contribute to spreading throughout a population (e.g., via air, food, and water). BAC investigators also considered the infective dose since it represents the probability for the infectious agent to infect and cause disease in half the exposed population. Consequently, the transmission coefficient is inversely proportional to the infective dose:

$\beta \propto 1/Y_1$.............................. (5)

Where, Y_1 is that agent's Id_{50}. As the Id_{50} decreases, transmission increases. Furthermore, it was determined that the regions location quotient, or LQ formulated as:

% employed in specialized industry's) in region /
% employed in same sector in the United States

LQ would be the most effective predictor of a regions economic development. Based on the Epidemiologic Transition Theory, LQ is negatively correlated to the transmission coefficient. That is:

$\beta \propto 1/Y_3$.................. (6)

$\beta \infty Y_2 \ / Y1{*}Y_3$ .... (7)

Subsequently,

$\omega\beta = (Y_2/ Y_1{*}Y_3)$...... (8)

$\omega= [1/\beta\ (Y_2/ Y_1{*}Y_3)]$... (9)

Where (ω) is the "outbreak coefficient" and (β), the "transmission coefficient" is equal to 1.0.

To develop a multiple regression equation, the "Relative Risk" (RR) was used as an independent variable— lower risk, means a lower probability for infectious disease outbreak to evolve to an epidemic. Mathematically, If (P) is the prevalence of a disease or infectious agent in the general population, expressed as a percentage (e.g., 0.85 = 85%). (Z) Is the population density (outbreak community) of interest or the percentage of people exposed to the agent. Furthermore, this (possibly hypothetical) outbreak shall be called the "present case." (1– Z) or (Z') is the percentage of people NOT exposed to the infectious agent in the "present case." (I_b) is the incidence of a disease or infectious agent in the general population (a state or country) being used as a basis of comparison or the percentage of people in that population. Often, historical cases of outbreaks are used for such comparisons. In addition, this outbreak, which is probably not hypothetical, shall be called the "control case." (1– I_b) or (I_b') is the percentage of people NOT exposed to the agent in the "control case". (**See Part 1; Chapter 1; Section 5**).

Table 7. Input table of the Biological Agents Index.

	Y1	Y2	Y3	ω	X"	Z	D	X1(Iβ=X"*Z	X2(P=I*D)	X3(Ro=X"*	X4=RR	ω*X1	ω*X2	ω*X3	ω*X4	X(ωX1+ωX2+ωX3+ωX4
4/1/2003	1	1	1	1.00	25	1804	0.08	45,100	3,608	2.00	1.00	45,100	3,608	2.00	1.000555	48,711
4/5/2003	1	1	1	1.00	25	2416	0.16	60,400	9,664	4.00	1.00	60,400	9,664	4.00	1.000414	70,069
4/12/2003	1	1	1	1.00	25	2960	0.25	74,000	18,500	6.25	1.00	74,000	18,500	6.25	1.000338	92,507
4/19/2003	1	1	1	1.00	25	3547	0.33	88,675	29,263	8.25	1.00	88,675	29,263	8.25	1.000282	117,947
4/28/2003	1	1	1	1.00	25	5050	0.41	126,250	51,763	10.25	1.00	126,250	51,763	10.25	1.000198	178,024
5/2/2003	1	1	1	1.00	25	6054	0.5	151,350	75,675	12.50	1.00	151,350	75,675	12.50	1.000165	227,039
5/12/2003	1	1	1	1.00	25	7447	0.58	186,175	107,982	14.50	1.00	186,175	107,982	14.50	1.000134	294,172
5/13/2003	1	1	1	1.00	25	7548	0.66	188,700	124,542	16.50	1.00	188,700	124,542	16.50	1.000133	313,260
5/20/2003	1	1	1	1.00	25	7919	0.75	197,975	148,481	18.75	1.00	197,975	148,481	18.75	1.000126	346,476
5/23/2005	1	1	1	1.00	25	8117	0.83	202,925	168,428	20.75	1.00	202,925	168,428	20.75	1.000123	371,375
5/31/2005	1	1	1	1.00	25	8360	0.91	209,000	190,190	22.75	1.00	209,000	190,190	22.75	1.00012	399,214
6/16/2005	1	1	1	1.00	25	8460	1	211,500	211,500	25.00	1.00	211,500	211,500	25.00	1.000118	423,026

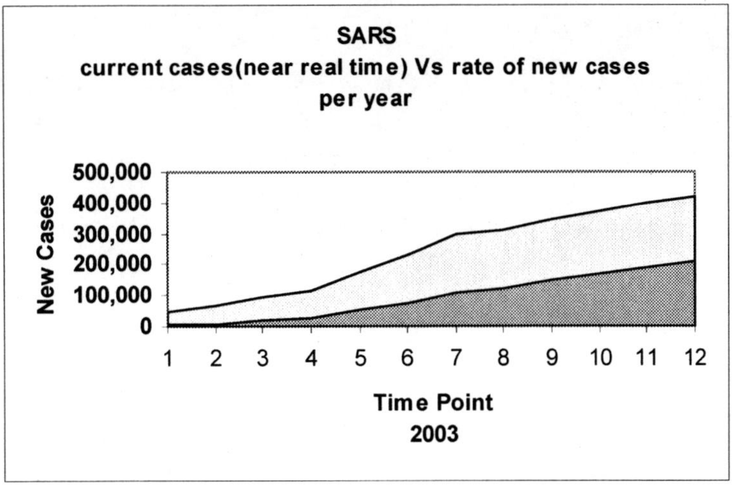

P or realistic number of cases in "Real-Time"
I, or probabilistic Rate of Spread / year at a point in time

Figure 14. Biological Agents Index output

B. STATISTICAL ANALYSIS

Table 8. SPSS output: multiple regression, collinearity, correlation, and analysis of variance output.

Correlations

		P	Ro	RR	I
Pearson Correlation	P	1.000	.991	-.824	.952
	Ro	.991	1.000	-.879	.963
	RR	-.824	-.879	1.000	-.934
	I	.952	.963	-.934	1.000
Sig. (1-tailed)	P	.	.000	.000	.000
	Ro	.000	.	.000	.000
	RR	.000	.000	.	.000
	I	.000	.000	.000	.
N	P	12	12	12	12
	Ro	12	12	12	12
	RR	12	12	12	12
	I	12	12	12	12

Model Summary

Model	R	R Square	Adjusted R Square	Std. Error of the Estimate
1	1.000[a]	.999	.999	2381.16007

a. Predictors: (Constant), I, RR, Ro

Coefficients[a]

Model		Unstandardized Coefficients		Standardized Coefficients	t	Sig.
		B	Std. Error	Beta		
1	(Constant)	*********	14510900		-12.949	.000
	Ro	9133.181	366.158	.932	24.943	.000
	RR	2E+008	14502937	.363	12.947	.000
	I	.460	.058	.394	7.901	.000

Model		95% Confidence Interval for B		Collinearity Statistics	
		Lower Bound	Upper Bound	Tolerance	VIF
1	(Constant)	-221362349.2	-154437958.5		
	Ro	8288.820	9977.542	.069	14.588
	RR	154319261.28	221206928.32	.121	8.241
	I	.325	.594	.038	26.000

a. Dependent Variable: P

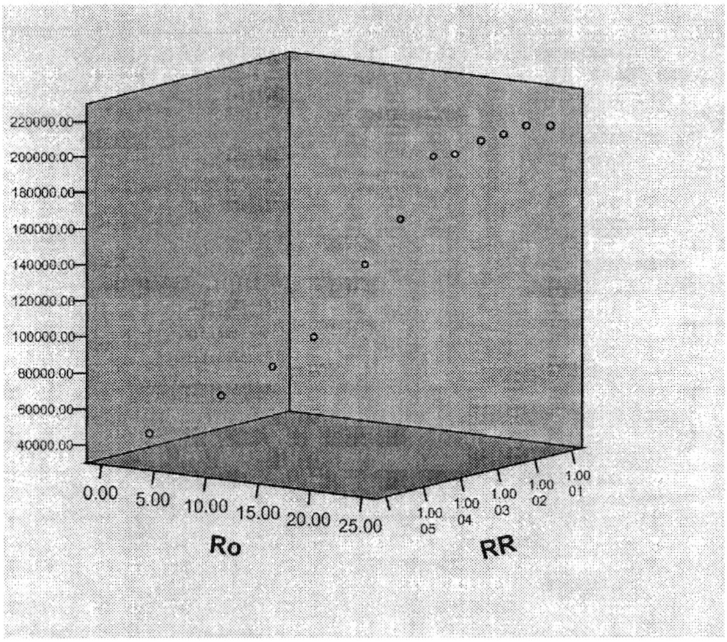

Figure 15. Relationship between prevalence, microbial reproductive rate, and the relative risk of disease.

The *biological agents* ® index [© 2002-2008] as proposed here, is by no means perfect. However, a multiple regression analysis of this model using SPSS suggests that 99.9% (R^2=0.999) of the dependent variable, or disease prevalence (P) can be explained by a microorganisms reproductive rate (Ro), the relative risk for Infection (RR), and incidence (I), when an outbreak coefficient is applied in a multiple regression equation. $P = \omega R_0 + \omega RR + \omega I + \varepsilon$: where (ω) is novel outbreak coefficient (**Table 7 and Figure 14**). In the absence of (ω), (RR), and (Ro), the model fit is < 90.3% (R^2 = 0.903). In other words, the *biological agents* ® *Index* can predict (P) with about 10 % more accuracy than existing models. **Figure 14 and 15** shows that (Ro), and (RR) are positively correlated to (P). Furthermore, based on the SPSS output, (I) has the least impact on (P). Each unit increase in (P), results to a corresponding 0. 46 unit increase in (I) as suggested by the β – coefficient analysis (**Table 8)**

Finally, the goal of this study is to use the *biological agent's* ® *Index* [© 2002-2008] to forecast the probability of developing new cases and old infectious disease. The study has little emphasis on the reliability of the independent variables in this estimation. Nonetheless, statistical analyses for collinearity of independent variables based on the VIF output of the SPSS shows that collinearity between (Ro), (RR), and (P) is significantly low and that their relationship is linear (**Figure 15**). This can be attributed to (ω) (**Table 7 and 8**). In the absence of (ω), correlation, collinearity, T ratio, β-coefficients, and R,^{2} and other relationships in the multiple regression equation appear to be compromised. In addition, this is the first report of a study where investigators incorporate (Ro), (RR), and (ω) in a regression analysis for predicting (P) (Olisa, 2002; 2003).

INFECTIOUS DISEASE SURVEILLANCE

A. INTRODUCTION

Based on the fundamentals of organizational theory **(Part 1; Chapter 1; Section 7),** biological information systems (BIS) can be used in organizing information for management of human resources, and for the assessments, and evaluation of program activities, and services. In infectious disease laboratory terms, this would be known as QA and QM.

Information systems are the hallmarks of New Public Management (NPM) **(Part 1; Chapter 1;Section 1)**. In the United States, and all over the world, there are numerous information systems in use for disease surveillance. However, a cost effective system, in other to justify its expense should be: user friendly, contain feedback mechanisms, be adaptive, and easily accessible worldwide. To best illustrate these features, part B will showcase a self explanatory systems architecture illustration of the National Electronic Evaluation System for Infectious Disease Surveillance or NEMeSIS™ (BAC, El Paso, TX, USA).

B. SYSTEM COMPONENTS OF NATIONAL ELECTRONIC EMAIL EVALUATION SYSTEM FOR INFECTIOUS DISEASE SURVIELLANCE (NEMeSIS)

BIOLOGICAL AGENTS ® INDEX

- Data Collection
- Data Analysis

↑↓ ←

World Wide Web →

AMERICAN JOURNAL OF BIOLOGICAL DEFENSE ®

- Evaluation & Assessment of Data
- Advocacy/Linkage Institution

↓↑

INTERNATIONAL MOLECULAR DIAGNOSTICS & RESEARCH LAB ®

- Analytical Platform
- Pharmaceuticals Platform
- Environmental Health and Industrial Hygiene Platform

REFERENCES

1. **Advisory Committee on Immunization Practices.** 1997. Prevention of pneumococcal disease. *Morbid Mortal Weekly* Rep. **46.No.RR-8:** 1-24.
2. **AlonsoDeVelasco, E., A.F. Verheul, and H. Snippe.** 1995. *Streptococcus pneumoniae*: virulence factors, pathogenesis, and vaccines. *Microbiol. Rev.* **59:**591-603.
3. **Baker, R.D.** 1989. Calculating the basic reproductive rate Ro when there are 2 or more pathogens. *Ann Soc Belg Med Trop.* **69.**1:99-107; discussion 144.
4. **Barksdale, L, 1990**. *Corynebacterium diphteriae* and its relatives. *Bacteriol Rev.* **34:**378-422.
5. **Barksdale, L, and A.M. Jr. Pappenheimer.** 1954. Phage-host relationships in non toxigenic and toxigenetic diphtheria bacilli. *J. Bacteriol.* **56:**220-232.
6. **Berte, L.M., and D.E. Nevalainen.** 2000. Quality systems for the laboratory. *American Society for Clinical Pathologists.* 1-20.
7. **Berry, A.M., J. Yother, D.E. Briles, D. Hanson, and J.C. Paton.** 1989. Reduced virulence of defined pneumolysin-negative mutant of *Streptococcus pneumoniae*. *Infect. Immun.* **57:**2037-2042.
8. **Bhatti, Z, and C.S. Berenson** 2007. Adult systemic cat scratch disease associated with therapy for hepatitis C. *BMC Infect Dis* **7:**8.
9. **Boulnois, G.J.** 1992. Pneumococcal proteins and the pathogenesis of disease caused by Streptococcus *pneumoniae*. *J. Gen Microbiol.* **138:**249-259.
10. **Bradford, M.** 1976. A rapid and sensitive method for the quantification of microgram quantities of proteins utilizing the principles of protein-dye binging. *Anal Biochem.* **72:** 248-254.
11. **Braun, V., C. Bos, M. Braun, and H Killmann.** 2000. Outer membrane channels and active transporters for the uptake of antibiotics. *J. Infect. Dis.* **182:** S12-S16. Review.
12. **Braun, V.** 1988. Pumping iron through cell membranes. *Science.* **282:**2202-2203.
13. **Braun, V., K. Hanke, and W. Koster.** 1983. Iron transport and storage in microorganisms, plants, and animals. *J. Bacteriol.* **156:**308-315.
14. **Braun, V., R. Goss, W. Koster, and L. Zimmermann.** 1983. Plasmid and chromosomal mutants in three iron (III)-aerobacin transport system of *Escherichia coli*. Use of streptonigrin for selection. *Mol. Gen Genet.* **192:**131-139.
15. **Brown, J.S., A.D. Ogunnlyl, M.C. Woodrow, D.W. Holden, and J.C. Paton.** 2001. Immunization with components of two iron uptake ABC transporters protects mice against systemic *Streptococcus pneumoniae* infection. *Infect Immun.* **69:**6702-6706.
16. **Brown, J.S., S.M. Gilland, and D.W. Holden.** 2001. A *Streptococcus pneumoniae* pathogenicity island encoding an ABC transporter involved in iron uptake and virulence. *Mol. Microbiol.* **40:**572-585.
17. **Bozzo, P.** *Implementing quality assurance.* 1991. Chicago, IL, USA: American Society for Clinical Pathology Press. 159-165.
18. **Busenberg, S. and C. Castillo Chavez.** 1991. A general solution of the problem of mixing sub-populations, and its application to risk-and age-structured epidemic models for the spread of AIDS. *IMA J. of Mathematics Applied in Med. and Biol.* **8:**1-29.
19. **Chen, J.-D, and D.A Morrison.** 1987. Cloning of *Streptococcus pneumoniae* DNA fragments in *Escherichia coli* requires vectors protected by strong transcriptional terminators. *Gene.* **55:**179-187.
20. **Clark, G.** 1995. *Systemic quality management.* Chicago, ILL, USA: American Society for Clinical Pathologists. 110-179.
21. **Cornelissen, C.C, and P.F. Sparling.** 1994. Iron piracy: acquisition of transferrin bound iron by bacterial pathogens. *Mol. Microbiol.* **14:**843-850.
22. **Doige, C.A, and G.F. Ames.** 1993. ATP-dependent transport systems in bacteria and humans: relevance to cystic fibrosis and multi-drug resistance. *Annu Rev Microbiol.* **47:** 291-319.
23. **Dutton, C.J., Haxell, M.A. McArthur, H.A, and Wax, R.G.** 2002. *Peptide antibiotics: Discovery, modes of action, and applications.* Ney York, New York, USA: Marcel and Dekker, USA. pp. 1-287.
24. **Dyer, D.W., W.R. Mckenna, J.P. Woods, and P.F. Sparling.** 1987. Isolation by streptonigrin enrichment and characterization of a transferrin-specific iron uptake mutant of *Neisseria meningididis*. *Microb Pathog.* **3:** 351-363.

25. **Ferguson, A.D., V. Braun. H.-P, Fiedler, J.W. Coulton, K. Diederichs, and W. Welte.** 2000. Crystal structure of the antibiotic albomycin in complex with the outer membrane transporter FhuA. *Protein. Sci.* **9:**956-963.
26. **Ferreiros, C., M.T. Criado, and J.A. Gomez.** 1999. The neisserial 37kDa ferric binding protein (FbpA). *Comp Biochem Physiol.* **123:**1-7.
27. **Fisher, E., B. Strehlow, D. Hartz, and V. Braun.** 1990. Soluble and membrane-bound ferisiderophore reductase of *Escherichia coli. Arch Microbiol.* **153:**329-336.
28. **Fleming, A.** 1922. On a remarkable bacteriolytic element found in tissues and secretions. *Proc Roy Soc Ser* **93:**306-17.
29. **Gause, G.F.** 1955. Recent studies on albomycin, a new antibiotic. *Brit. Med. J.* **12:**1177-1179.
30. **Genco, C.A., C.-Y. Chen, R.J. Arko, D.R. Kapczynski, and S.A. Morse.** 1991. Isolation and characterization of a mutant of *Neisseria gonorrhoeae* that is defective in the uptake of iron from transferrin and hemoglobin and is avirulent in mouse subcutaneous chambers. *J. Gen Microbiol.* **137:**1313-1321.
31. **Hakanson, A., H. Roche, S. Mirza, L.S. McDaniel, A.B. Walter, and D.E. Briles.** 2001. Characterization of binding to human lactoferrin to pneumococcal surface protein A. *Infect. Immun.* **69:**3372-3381.
32. **Guerinot, M.L.** 1994. Microbial iron transport. *Annu Rev Microbiol.* **48:**743-772.
33. **Hammerschmidt, S., G. Bethe, P.H. Remane, P, and G.S. Chhatwal.** 1999. Identification of pneumococcal surface protein A as a lactoferrin binding protein of *Streptococcus pneumoniae. Infect. Immun.* **67:**1683-1687.
34. **Henderson, D.P, and S.M. Payne.** 1983. *Vibrio cholerae* iron transport systems: role of heme and siderophore iron-transport in virulence and identification of a gene associated with multiple iron transport systems. *Infect Immun.* **62:**5120-5125.
35. **Holmes, R.K., and L.M. Russell.** 1983. *Role of iron in regulating the synthesis of bacterial toxins. P. 359-362. In D. Schlessinger (ed), Microbiology-1983.* Washington DC, USA: American Society for Microbiology press.
36. **Janulczyk, R., Pallon, J, and L. Bjorck.** 1999. Identification and characterization of a *Streptococcus pneumoniae* ABC transporter with multiple specificity for metal cations. *Mol Microbiol.* **34:**596-606.
37. **Kadner, F., K. Heller, J.W. Coulton, and V. Braun.**1980. Genetic control of hydroxamate mediated iron-uptake in *Escherichia coli. J. Bacteriol.* **143:**256-264.
38. **Hancock, R.E, and T.J. Falla.** 1997. *Cationic peptides. In* Biotechnology of antibiotics, (2nd ed.) Ney York, New York, USA: Marcel Dekker, Inc. 1997. 471-488.
39. **Hanson, J.N**. *Nisin ad Related Antimicrobial Peptides. In Biotechnology of Antibiotics*, (2nd ed.). Ney York, NY, USA: Marcel Dekker, Inc. pp.437-461.
40. **Holder, A.A.** 1996. *Preventing merozoite invasion of erythrocytes. In* Malaria vaccine development: A Multi immune response approach. Washington DC, USA: American Society for Microbiology Press. pp. 77-105.
41. **Isaacs, A, and Lindenmann, J.** 1957. Virus interference in the interferon *Proc. Roy. Soc. Lond. B Biol.* Sci. **147:**258-267.
42. **Johnson, B., Anker H, Meleney F.** 1945. Bacitracin: a new antibiotic produced by a member of the *B. subtilus* group. *Science* **102.**2650:376–377.
43. **Knüsel, F, and W. Zimmermann.**1975. *Sideromycins. In* Cochran. J.W. and Hahn, F.E. (ed). Antibiotics III. Mechanisms of action of antimicrobial and antitumor agents. Heidelberg, Germany: Springer Verlag, pp. 653-667.
44. **Kim, C., Gajendran, N, Mittrücker, H, Weiwad, M, Song Y, Hurwitz R, Wilmanns, M, Fischer, G, Kaufmann, S.** 2005. Human alpha-defensins neutralize anthrax lethal toxin and protect against its fatal consequences. *Proc Natl Acad Sci U S A.* **102.**13: 4830-5.
45. **Leboffe, M.J, and B.Pierce.** *A photographic atlas for the microbiology laboratory.* (1st ed.) Englewood, CO, USA: Morton Publishing Company, USA. 1996. 1-30.
46. **Lin, R, J., Liao, C, L, Lin, E, Lin, YL.** 2004. Blocking of the alpha interferon-induced Jak-Stat signaling pathway by Japanese encephalitis virus infection. *J. Virol.* **78.**17:9285-94.
47. **McDaniel, L.S., J. Yother, M. Vijayakumen, L. McGarry, W.R. Gould, and D.E. Briles.** 1987. Use of insertion inactivation to facilitate studies of biological properties of pneumococcal surface protein A (PspA), *J. Exp. Med.* **165.**381-394.

48. **Macleod, C.M., R.G. Hodges, M. Heidelberger, and W.G. Berhard**.1945. Prevention of pneumococcal pneumoniae by immunization with specific capsular polysaccharides. *J.Exp Med.* **82:** 445-465.
49. **Meester R., J. de Koning, M.C. de Jong, O. Diekmann.** 2002. Modeling and real-time prediction of classical swine fever epidemics. *Biometrics.* **58.**1:178-84.
50. **Minks, M.A** et al. 1979. Structural requirements of double-stranded RNA for the activation of 2', 5'-oligo (A) polymerase and protein kinases of interferon-treated HeLa Cells. *The Journal of Biological Chemistry* **254.**20:10180-10183
51. **Miller, M.J, and B. Wenthworth.** 1985. Method for quality control in diagnostic microbiology. *American Public Health Association.* 63-323.
52. **Miller, J.E, and C.E. Samuel**. 1992. Proteolytic cleavage of the reoviruses sigma 3 protein results in enhanced double-stranded RNA-binding activity: identification of a repeated basic amino acid motif within the C-terminal binding region. *Journal of Virology* **66.**9:5347-5356.
53. **Moiseeva, O., F.A. Mallette, U.K, Mukhopadhyay, A. Moores, G. Ferbeyre.** 2006. DNA damage signaling and p53-dependent senescence after prolonged beta-interferon stimulation. *Mol. Biol. Cell* **17.**4:1583-92.
54. **Montgomery, L.** 1995. *Health and safety guidelines for the laboratory.* Chicago, Ill, USA: American Society for Clinical Pathology. pp.69-206.
55. **Murray, A**. *Health-care fixes should focus on quality.* Retrieved May 23, 2006. Wall Street Journal. *https://www.wsj.com.*
56. **Munoz, R., E. Garcia, and A.G. De La Campa**.1996. Quinine specifically inhibits the proteolipid of the $F_oF_1H_+$-ATPase of *Streptococcus pneumoniae. J. Bacteriol* **178:**2455-2458.
57. **Nunoshiba, T., F.Obata, C. Boss, S. Oikawa, T. Mori, S. Kawanishi, and K. Yamamoto.** 1999. Role of iron and superoxide for generation of hydroxyle radical, oxidative DNA lesions, and mutagenesis in *Escherichia coli. J. Biol Chem.* **274:**34832-34837
58. **National Association of County and City Health Officials**. 2004. *The strategic national stockpile*: a reference for local planners.
59. **Nagano, Y, and Y. Kojima**. 1958. Inhibition de l'infection vaccinale par un facteur liquide dans le tissu infecté par le virus homologue" C.R. Seances *Soc. Biol.***152:**1627-1629.
60. **Watanabe, Y.** 2004. Fifty years of interference. *Nature Immunology* **5:**12:1193.
61. **Nagano, Y, and Y. Kojima**. 1954. Boudoir immunizing du virus vaccinale inactive par des rayon's ultraviolet's C.R. seances *Soc. Biol.* **148:**1700-1702.
62. **Nokes D.P, and R.M. Anderson.** 1988. The use of mathematical models in the epidemiological study of infectious diseases and in the design of mass immunization programmes. *Epidemiol Infect.* **101.**1:1-20. Review.
63. **Novak, R., J.S. Braun, E. Charpenter, and E. Tuomanen**. 1998. Penecillin tolerance genes of *Streptococcus pneumoniae*: the ABC-type manganese permease complex Psa, *Mol. Microbiol.* **29:**1285-1296.
64. **Olisa, N.R,** 2006. Molecular Microbiology: Diagnostic Principles and Practice. *LabMedicine*: 36:11. Review.
65. **Olisa, N.R.** 2004. *Purified Cys moiety for iron reductase and methods for obtaining and using same* United States Patent and Trademark Official Gazette. US 2004/0214998 A1.
66. **Olisa, N.R.** 2003. *Purified Cys moiety for iron reductase and methods for obtaining and using same* United States Library of Congress. TXu 1-100-385.
67. **Olisa, NR,** 2003. *Online algorithm for use in biological defense***.** United States Library of Congress. TxU 1-101-217.
68. **Olisa, N.R.** 2002. *Modeling and real-time prediction of Salmonelliosis.* United States Library of Congress. TxU 1-068-657.
69. **Olisa, N.R., J.K. Lee, and S.S. Tai**. 2000. *Identification of pneumococcal iron acquisition gene locus.* Abstrt. B-22, p.45. In Abstracts of the 100th General Meeting of the American Society for Microbiology, Washington DC.
70. **Paton, J.C**. 1996. The contribution of pneumolysin to the pathogenecicity of *Streptococcus pneumoniae. Trends in Microbiol.* **4:**103- 106.

71. **Paton, J.C., P.W. Andrew, G.J. Boulnois, and T.J. Mitchell**. 1993. Molecular analysis of the pathogenicity of *Streptococcus pneumoniae*: the role of pneumococcal proteins. *Annu Rev Microbiol.* **47:**89-115.
72. **Paton, J.C., R.A. Lock, and D. Hansman**.1983. Effect of immunization with pneumolysin on survival time of mice challenged with *Streptococcus pneumoniae*. *Infect Immun.* **40:**548-552.
73. **Payne, S.M**. 1993. Iron acquisition in microbial pathogenesis. *Trends in Microbiol.* **1:**66-69.
74. **Omran A.R.** 1977. Epidemiologic transition in the United States: the health factor in population change. *Popul Bull.* **32:**2:1-42.
75. **Paulsen, H., M. Brieden, and G. Benz**. 1987. Synthese des sauerstofanalogs der des-ferriforn von δ_1 –albomycine. Liebigs. *Ann. Chem.* 565-575.
76. **Peschel, A**. 2002. How do bacteria resist human antimicrobial peptides. *Trends in Microbiology.* Review. 1-6.
77. **Plaut, D.S.** 1998. *Quality control, method validation, and linearity. Workshops for laboratory professionals.* Chicago, Ill, USA: American Society for Clinical Pathology Press. pp.1-118.
78. **Philpott M**., 2003. Defensins and acne. *Mol Immunol* **40.**7: 457-62.
79. **Ratledge, C, and L.G. Dover**. 2000. Iron metabolism in pathogenic bacteria. *Annu Rev Microbial.* **54:**881-941.
80. **Ratledge, C.** 1999. *Iron metabolism.* pp. 260-281. *In* Ratledge, C. and J. Dale (ed). Mycobacteria: molecular biology and virulence. Oxford, UK: Blackwell Science.
81. **Reeves, S.A., A.G. Torres and S.M. Payne**. 2002. TonB is required for intracellular growth and virulence of *Shigella dysentariae. Infect Immun* **68:** 6329-6336.
82. **Revell, P.A**. 2007. Avian Influenza A (H5N1): Pandemic potential and role of the clinical microbiology laboratory. *LabMedicine.* 740-744.
83. **Rohrbach, M.R., V. Braun, and W. Koster**. 1995. Ferrichrome transport in *Escherichia coli* K-12: altered substrate specificity of mutated periplasmic FhuB. *J. Bacteriol* **177:**7186-7193.
84. **Rubins, J.B, and E.N. Janoff**. 1998. Pneumolysin: a multifunctional pneumococcal virulence factor, *J Lan Clin Med.* **131:** 21027.
85. **Sambrook, J., E.F. Fritsch, and T. Maniatas.** 1989. *Molecular cloning: a laboratory manua*l. 2nd ed. Cold Spring Harbor, N.Y, USA: Cold Spring Harbor Laboratory.
86. **Sanger, F., S. Nicklen, and A. Coulson**. 1997. DNA sequencing with chain-terminating inhibitors. *Proc Natl Acad Sci.* **74:**5463-5476.
87. **Schmitt, M.P**. 1997. Utilization of host iron sources by *Corynebacterium diphtheriae:* Identification of a gene whose product is homogeneous to eukaryotic heme oxygenases is required for acquisition of iron from heme and hemoglobin. *J. Bacteriol.* **179:**838-845.
88. **Schwyne, B, and J.B. Neilands**. 1987. Universal chemical assay for the detection and determination of siderophores. *Anal Biochem.* **160**:47-56.
89. **Sen, G. C.** 2003. Viruses and Interferons. *Annual Review Microbiology v.***55:**255-281.
90. **Schryvers, A.B, and I. Stojiljkovic**. 1999. Iron acquisition systems in Pathogenic Neisseria. *Mol. Microbiol.* **32:**1117-1123.
91. **Schultz-Hauser, G., W. Koster, H. Schwarz, and V. Braun**. 1992. Iron (III) hydroxamate transport in Escherichia coli K-12: FhuB mediated membrane association of the FhuC protein and negative complementation of FhuC mutants. *J. Bacteriol.* **174:**2305-2311.
92. **Sebulsky, M.T., D. Hohnstein, M.D. Hunter, and D.F. Heinrichs**. 2000. Identification and characterization of membrane permease involved in iron-hydroxamate transport in *Staphylococcus aureus J. Bacteriol.* **182:**4394-4400.
93. **Shoemaker, N.B, and W.R. Guild**. 1994. Destruction of low efficiency markers is a slow process occurring at a heteroduplex stage of transmission. *J. Bacteriol.* **128:**283-290.
94. **Silhavy, T.J., N.L. Berman, and L.W. Enquest**. 1984. Experiments with gene fusions. Cold Spring Harbor N.Y USA: Cold Spring Harbor Laboratory.
95. **Spitzer, S.G, and M. Hotaling**.2002. Clinical molecular diagnostics, In workshops for laboratory professionals. Washington DC, USA: *American Society for Clinical Pathologists.*
96. **Tai, S.S., T.R. Wang, and C. Lee.** 1997. Characterization of heme binding activity of Streptococcus *pneumoniae. Infect. Immun.* **65:**1083-1087.
97. **Tai, S.S., C.Lee, and R.E. Winter.** 1993. Heme utilization is related to virulence in *Streptococcus pneumoniae. Infect. Immun.* **61:**5401-5405.

98. **Tai, S.S., A.E. Kraft, P. Nootheti, and R.K. Holmes**.1990. Coordinate regulation of siderophore and diphtheria toxin production by iron in *Corynebacterium diphtheriae Microb Pathog.* **9**:267-273.
99. **Takaoka, A., Hayakawa, S., Yanai, H**. 2003. Integration of Interferon –alpha/beta signaling to p53 responses in tumor suppression and antiviral defense. *Nature* **424.**6948: 516-23.
100. **Tam, R. and Jr. H.M. Saier.** 1993. Structural, functional, and evolutionary relationships among extracellular solute-binding receptors of bacteria. Microbiol Rev. **57:** 20-346.
101. **Tardat, B, and D. Touati**. 1993. Iron and oxygen regulation of *Escherichia coli* MnSoD expression: competition between the global regulator Fur and ArcA for binding DNA. *Mol Microbiol.* **9:**53-63.
102. **Thomas, C.E., B. Olsen, and C. Elkins**. 1998. Cloning and characterization of *tdh*A, a locus encoding a TonB-dependent heme receptor from *Haemophilus ducreyi. Infect Immun* **66:**4254-4262.
103. **Torres, A.G, and S.M.Payne.** 1997. Haem iron-transport system in enterohaemorrhagic *Escherichia coli O157:H7. Mol Microbiol.* **23:**825-833.
104. **Verslalovic, J., and E.R. Unger**. 2004. *External quality assessments and proficiency testing in diagnostic molecular microbiology. In* Molecular Microbiology: Diagnostic principles and practice. Washington DC, USA: *American Society for Microbiology Press.* pp. 691-702.
105. **Viswanathan, V.K., P.H. Edelstein, C.D. Pope, and N.P. Cian-ciotto**. 2000. The *Legionella pneumoniae ira*AB locus is required for iron assimilation, intracellular infection, and virulence. *Infect Immun.* **68:**1069-1079.
106. **Wooldridge, K.G., and P.H. Williams.** 1993. Iron uptake mechanisms in pathogenic bacteria. FEMS. Microbiol. Rev. **12:**325-348.
107. **Yeowell, H.N., and J.R. White**. 1982. Iron requirement in the bactericidal mechanism of Streptonigrin. *Antimicrob Agents'. Chemother.* **22:**961-968.
108. **Yother, J., L.S. McDonald, and D.E. Briles**. 1986. Transformation of encapsulated *Streptococcus pneumoniae. J. Bacteriol* **168:**1463-1465.
109. **Zhu, W., A. Wilks, and I. Stojiljkovic**. 2000. Degradation of heme in gram negative bacteria: the product of hemeO gene of Neisseria is heme oxygenases. *J Bacteriol* **182:**6783-6790.

BiologicalAgents INDEX (Third Edition): Quality Management of Infectious Disease Intervention Programs
Author: Nze Robert Olisa

Chapter 4

PROGRAM EVALUATION OF INFECTIOUS DISEASE INTERVENTIONS

INTRODUCTION

A good way to discuss the problem of planning in rural communities would be to take an example from studies along the US-Mexico border. Recent reports have shown that there is an overwhelming need for infectious disease intervention (Price-Smith, 2001). Based on impact theory, urban development can be achieved in rural environments by initiating economic development programs at the grass roots level through policy statements and appropriations in congress; the consequent output can lead to new industry based businesses. Furthermore, the outcome increases regional GDP and LQ. Accordingly, based on past studies in South America on impacts of epidemiological transition, perhaps urban development can be used as an intervention for declines in various infectious disease indices (Larroca, 2000).

As earlier mentioned, metaphorically, *urban* is used to describe progress and affluence. The term *urban* development symbolizes an urban make over and is frequently used to label projects needed to develop inner cities or slums. Evidently, according to recent studies, the systematic approach to quantify and evaluate impact of urban development measures on infectious disease intervention outcomes for health care policy, cost-effective analysis, and the performance of quasi-judicial reviews have been problematic (Rossi et al, 2004; Bingham and Felbinger, 2002). Currently, most policies surrounding urban development and its relationships to infectious disease are confronted by "wicked problems" and analysis is performed using branched evaluation techniques (Blanco, 1994; Lindblom, 1958).

One limitation of this inadequacy is that executive branch agencies and institutions may not be able to effectively justify the need for urban development as a line item in respective budgets for accountability purposes to congress, quasi-judiciary branches of government; and article III courts for the purpose of judicial reviews or appropriations.

Numerous investigators of epidemiologic transition have measured and quantified the impact of economic development and industrialization on infectious disease using gross domestic product (GDP) of defined locations and corresponding infectious disease prevalence to measure the size of the problem and impact (Serow et al, 1998; Hackenberg, 1988; Omran, 1977). In addition recent studies show that a complex range of socio-economic and biological factors are associated with epidemiologic transition. (Serow et al, 1998; Rogers, and Hackenberg, 1987; Omran, 1977).

At present, in the US, numerous executive branch agencies have been tasked with rural urban development, healthcare, and security along the US-Mexico border. Some of these agencies include Departments of Labor, Health and Human Services, Homeland Security, and Defense. All these agencies face "wicked problems." Furthermore, other non-governmental agencies like the Pan American Health Organization are unable to effectively evaluate impact of urban development projects on infectious disease health care interventions along the US-Mexico border for the same reason as the US agencies. In addition, public health advocacy groups and academics in the field are yet to determine whether the costs of industrialization are less than the benefits they present to infectious disease eradication in comparison to existing intervention programs like education, disease surveillance, testing, and treatment. Perhaps investigators may have to think out of the box to best evaluate trends against the current status quo. To address some of these problems, the performer should use data on LQ or GDP and existing indices on infectious disease outcomes and prevalence of various infectious diseases to comparatively determine cost effectiveness of using urban development as an infectious disease intervention.

According to recent reports (Price-Smith, 2002), and the United Nations Industrial Development Organization (UNIDO), the standard indices for Economic Development are the GDP or GNP. Numerous investigators have quantified infectious disease impacts using relative risk of infection, organism reproductive rate, and disease incidence (Rogers and Hackenberg, 1987; Omran, 1977). Furthermore, past studies have shown that a major problem in the evaluation of socio-economic programs is the over or sub-estimation of program outcomes in self selected samples. However, this problem can be overcome by basing the measurement of economic development using a ratio to avoid over-or-under reporting of infectious disease due to false positive diagnoses on both the clinical and laboratory levels (Patton et al, 1993). In the United States, there is enough transparency on data quantifying the extent of urban development and demographic information. Consequently, the determination of impacts associated with urban development can be justified and used for accountability and the determination of accuracy of impact studies, specifically with respect to infectious disease. Consequently, issues of "non-programs" or incomplete intervention and unstandardized information will not be an issue. This is not the case in many other parts of the developing world.

According to a United Nations Industrial Development Organization (UNIDO), and a World Health Organization 1980 and 1979 report, there are reported successes in disease eradication worldwide. Furthermore, these successes have been based on political commitment and socioeconomic development as a function of political processes (Iatridis, 1990). In past reports, investigators show that countries with high Gross National Product (GNP) have health care policy frameworks which result in better health care for their nationals (Roger and Hackenberg, 1987; Price-Smith, 2002). Interestingly, some policies, like the Cuban healthcare system, thrive in political ideology but have a low GNP compared to other South American countries like Brazil and Mexico where globalization has resulted in urban restructuring and sustainable economies and environments (Batley 1997).

Furthermore, Cuba's health care system has produced awe-inspiring high rankings on world health indicators despite its economic shortcomings. If these estimates are factual, then indeed these attributes may have implications for the US health care system because it suggests that equitable distribution of health care services in the US may not be dependent on human resources and technology, but in better service and delivery system and urban planning. Unlike other similar studies where investigators use multiple attribute matching to compare impact of socioeconomic factors on disease in four Latin American countries (Albala, 1997), the authors of the Cuba health care policy adopt neither this nor any similar technique. Furthermore, in past studies, investigators who study the impact of US policies on US-Mexico border issues have noted cause-and-effect relationships, like uncontrollable migratory forces, and policies that lead to ballooning socio-economic trends like escalations in teen birth rate which subsequently lead to increases in health cost (Andreas 1994).

Consequently, the scope and impact of Cuba's health policies in the absence of assessments to internal validity may have been underestimated. The experimental design appears to be a quasi-experimental, cross-sectional study of Cuba's health care system. This in itself creates numerous biases. Combined with the absence of any form of benchmarking, the study design introduces threats to instrumentation, history, maturation, attrition, and testing scores. In respect to external validity, the author does not address increases in disease trends, but rather focuses on primary health care policies and local self governance or health management. Consequentially, this over generalization of the relaronship of health care at one time point, in a single population, without defining the different grades of health care, i.e. health promotion preventative medicine efforts, potentially threatens the validity of the report. Furthermore, the Cuban health delivery system appears to weigh in more heavily on primary care and less on preventative medicine. This single attribute has the tendency to have system level effects (Price-Smith, 2002, pp. 14).

On closer examination on the Cuba health report, and to be critical, the author does not address the impact of government fiscal policy on healthcare or the fact that fiscal administrative data for Cuba are not accessible to scholars worldwide for verification, nor does the author state that primary statistical data on health care for Cuba in comparison to other Latin America countries are few. In addition, the impact of Cuba's program on other governmental programs like school enrollment is not clear. Cuba regional or international correlation studies were not performed or referenced to eliminate the perception of generalization. Finally, based on the Cuba health study, it appears that the issue of construct validity may present itself as a major problem in this proposal; however, unlike the Cuba study, impact studies in the US show convincing data on GDP and disease prevalence. These indices, unlike those used in the Cuba study, can be used to measure cost effectiveness of urban development programs, and other strategic outcomes.

Finally, the objective of reviewing health policies in Cuba and the US is to illustrate to the performer how study relationship between successes and failures of Urban Development programs (policies) and infectious disease outcomes in different parts of the world can be used as benchmarks. In the process, the performer can investigate policy evaluation frame work for urban development at the grassroots level and the role this framework plays in the efficiency of implementing infectious disease and healthcare programs implementation and outcomes (Iatridis, 1990). and to outline assumptions made to program design and conceptualization.

A. CONCLUSION

In conclusion, several approaches and steps can be adopted to determine urban development policy impact. First, the performer can use impact models **(Part 1; Chapter 1; Section 4)** to better define target samples or communities. Second, a more systematic approach can be utilized to perform retrospective, longitudinal time series, and cohort studies to reduce threats to internal validity. Third, the performer can select better measures for programs, means, outputs, and outcome to reduce threats to construct validity. Fourth, the performer can introduce benchmark studies to reduce generalization and other threats to external validity and to provide better realization of the social health problems and other necessary health impacts of urban development actions that need to be taken into consideration. Later in the next chapter, several synopses will be discussed to better illustrate these options.

SOCIAL AND ECONOMIC DEVELOPMENT PROGRAM EVALUATION

A. INTRODUCTION

According to S.O Biobaku (1972), it appears that most rural economic development programs move at paces that leave the targeted rural population behind. Furthermore, he states that as a matter of urgency, there is currently the need to infuse information and biological technologies in rural areas to help facilitate economic development. One way of achieving this would be to introduce a combined system that increases wages and incentives for labor, local and international investors, farmers, and industrialists. Perhaps the single most important change needed in developing economies is an overhaul of the taxation system. In more industrialized countries, like the US, greater investments should be made in the retention of nurses since they form the core of the healthcare sector. Nurses are best suited for performing needs assessments during crisis. These policies, if properly planned and implemented could save hundreds and thousands of dollars.

Other important infrastructure needed include the following: improved health facilities, better water supply, and electricity supply, more feeder roads, better storage facilities, and improved marketing and credit organizations. To achieve these goals, the following steps are recommended for evaluating economic developing projects:

- Examine feasibility and rational of sated outcome
- Examine program inputs and outputs
- Examine programs fiscal policies

Clearly, the world is in an age of rural economic development. But the paradigm needs to shift from seeing and quantifying the progress or lack of rural economic development in terms of Gross Domestic Product (GDP) or Gross National Product (GNP), but rather to quantify development relative to Location Quotient (LQ) or the measure of manufacturing, administrative and other forms of industry. Furthermore, developed countries and international agencies can implement processes that lead to this change. Perhaps, the former US President, John F. Kennedy, best illustrated the importance of the outcomes of poor development strategies when he said: "if the free society cannot help the poor man, it can never save the few that are rich" – 1961 inaugural address.

According to Harold Wilson, in the book War of Poverty (1953), "the international community should attack poverty aggressively. Furthermore, he stated "Britain should 'go it alone' if needed." The significance of this statement is that at the time, Britain was the world's super power and had hundreds of colonies. Interestingly, today this role can be attributed to the United States. Justifiably, the call by most reformers of the day is for the US to seize the initiative for change. As for Britain, her time is over now.

Interestingly, the performance of the United Nations (U.N) has been worse than that of Britain. Furthermore, as far back as the sixties, the Jackson Capacity reports are full of examples of duplication of efforts, extravagance, and UN misallocation of resources. Based on this track record, the administrative incompetence on the part of the UN has served mainly to create economic development illusions. The UN has achieved this by using emphasis on rate of growth in GDP, on the volume of savings and investments on export trade, and in other major economic parameters to blur the key economic activity indicators like number of manufacturing industries and efficiency of public administrative sectors. In addition, GDP has been preferred by the UN because it is easily quantifiable. However, economic development is about more than increasing the rate of savings and investments; it is about creating savings and investments and the growth rate of the GDP.

In developing economies, economic development has to include the following: manufacturing economics, social and administrative reforms, tax reforms, changes in the attitude of people and not utopian promises by governments and international agencies. Confounding this problem, at the present time, local governments look up to state or central governments, while these central or state governments look up to federal governments. Furthermore, federal governments in developing countries often reach out to international institutions for financial support and technology transfer. In the long term, this practice needs to be discouraged. One way of achieving self reliance in developing economies would be for federal governments to decentralize, consequently, local and state governments will formulate policies which focus on development needs. Developing economies should strengthen fiscal policies and taxation laws and devise other processes and practices that can regulate local and state governments. A major shortcoming of this system is that foreign experts and advisors are viewed as not yielding knowledge and expertise to their local counterparts. Economic development has to start from the grass roots level and move upwards. International institutions should not create illusions that communicate the presence of correlations between expansion of administrative services and economic development. Furthermore, the tendency for most developing countries to equate solely agriculture, particularly food production, with economic development at the expense of public administrative reform and modern industry has changed. Finally, to achieve economic development, the idea that economic development should be emphasized first and industry later should be questioned and discouraged at the very least.

Also, economic welfare has commonly been associated with economic development. In actuality economic welfare is a part of social welfare and is more concerned with social equity. The fact is that most international institutions are more concerned with promoting social equity than with promoting economic development. Interestingly, one can argue that a major way to provide social equity would be to first provide economic development. Furthermore, until this sentiment is negotiated, developing countries will continue to fall short because their economies will continue to have welfare programs that carry the illusion of economic development programs.

B. IDEAL OBJECTIVES OF ECONOMIC DEVELOPMENT PROGRAMMES

In order to avoid the failure of the past, the ideal program genuinely intended for economic development should discourage capital investments in government, quasi-governments, or international institutions, but rather, invest heavily in the private sector. Unlike developed economies, in emerging economies, oversight of the private sector should be in the hands of non-governmental organizations or (NGOs) and not in federal governments for the simple reason that most governments in emerging economies lack adequate fiscal policies in taxation, transportation, and infrastructure needed to support economic growth. One way the NGOs can achieve regulation is by packaging resources like capital and finance deals and the use of incentives and coercion. For example, rather than solely involving, say, the health department or ministry in interventions, the economic development or communications ministry along with private sector mass communication can be invited to participate and compete for resources as condition for funds distribution. Additionally, performance measures should be designed such that they can be unattainable except with the collaborative involvement of all stakeholders. On a cautionary note, management practices and managers alike would have to rely heavily on economic principles governing the outcomes and applications of *Game Theories* **(Part 1; Chapter 1; Section 11).** The practice of staffing academic over industrialists should be discouraged since scholars, with a few exceptions, tend to bring to favor concept over feasibility. Furthermore, it should be mentioned that in most developing economies, the rural sector should be equated to the non-mechanized agricultural sector and can be characterized as quasi-educated. With this in mind, the ideal objective of economic development programs should include the creation of the following:

- Strong and reliant nation
- Dynamic economy
- Social equity
- Democracy

According to Robert Gardner, "one of the paradoxes of developing countries, Africa in particular, is that their societies, although predominantly agricultural, are becoming acutely lacking in food." Today we know the reason for this, and indeed the greater problem of the lack of economic development is poor public administration. *The first step* in implementing any program should be the *proper estimation* of the magnitude of the problem. Once the inputs and outputs needed have been determined, the right fiscal policies should be put in place to implement them. In so many cases, governments in developing economies tend to develop policies to no end.

With the desired outcome in mind, policy makers should first estimate what can be termed consequential. Accordingly, existing indices have to be revised while new ones need to be created. This is important with respect to management of the economic trilogy (land, labor, capital). Once this has been achieved with economic parity, the overall planning strategy can then be adapted for the ideal objectives. Some of the biggest problems that can be expected include the following:

- Lack of policy co-ordination
- Duplication of research
- Unnecessary research

Overcoming these problems would require a strong equity based system. It would be essential to minimize if not to eliminate entirely the powers of abuse and corruption at all levels of government. The first step to achieve this is democratization. A second step would be to provide incentives for increased productivity and inputs like land labor and capital to reduce the over-extension of local ministries of government. Subsequently, economic development can be measured as a steady flow of resources from industry to other sectors like health, administration, education etc. Third, and perhaps most importantly, once the democratic system is in place, the government's role to legislate policy in support of needed economic development frameworks has to be instituted. One way to raise this need would be to mobilize linkage institutions like the mass media or Political Action Committees (PACs). Subsequently, this method of promoting *laissez faire*, or increasing limited transportation and accessibility to rural areas can help facilitate economic development at the grass roots level.

C. ROLE OF FISCAL POLICY IN RURAL ECONOMIC DEVELOPMENT

According to V.P Diejomaoh, rural development can be defined as "a process of increasing the level of per capita income and standard of living of the rural sector." Rural can be seen from both a special (population density) and occupational (agricultural), context. A good policy for economic development should include the following:

- Reformation of taxation to provide revenue for government and incentives to local industry
- Improvement of roads, bridges, electricity, water, and communication
- Heavy engagement in Non-Governmental Organizations (NGOs) and the private-sector
- Discouragement of government or quasi-governments from roles other than regulation of NGOs
- Promotion of NGOs in the regulation of the private sector
- Availability of maximum material resources and finance for the project
- Maintenance of reasonable economic and price stability despite inflationary pressures
- Promotion of social equity.

According to A.O Phillips the impact of these policies, once I place, would include program input and output extension, stabilization, increased government revenue through taxation, and better management of *inter alia* (problem of rational special inter-population distribution and the balancing of urban development). However, on a cautionary note, urbanization should not be equated to industrialization. It is noteworthy that a major consequence of this single problem of *inter alia* has been the major cause of inter ethnic and tribal wars, as well as incidences of ethnic cleansing in recent times. Additionally, policy priorities should include the following: needs assessments, adequate data collection in the targeted areas, provision for the public's education, and social equity. Furthermore, regional consideration should be made for the decentralization of power from federal, and state, to local governments. In summary, good economic policies, backed with didactic and feasible outputs, should improve overall economic performance.

Finally, economic policies should closely examine structural and functional attributes of rural industries like social and economic backgrounds of industrialists, size of the area in question, capital requirements, and obstacles, which could be managerial, technical, financial, or commercial. Additionally, the government's role in providing transportation, rural electricity and water supply, information, finances, and regulations, should be defined. On a cautionary note, to avoid pitfalls of the past, international institutions and NGOs that manage or implement economic development programs should first direct resources to governments that already have provided these infrastructures because economic development will be near impossible without them. Perhaps, the first strategy for rural industrialization should be to mobilize governments to provide and effectively sustain good transportation, electricity, water, and communication in rural areas.

According to Austin Ramney, politics involve the allocation of values and struggles among persecuted people who try to realize different goals and opposing interest. Others like David Easton describe politics as an activity with deals and authoritative decision making and implementation. Harold Lasswell and Abraham Kalan defined politics as a process for shaping and sharing power in society. In turn, power can be defined as ability and means to shape individual behavior so people do what is required of them. In other words, politics is used to decide who gets what, when, and how of the total wealth in the society.

The main task of politics is to oversee formal policy making, informal policy procedures, selection of officials, and the relationship of stakeholders to the community and to themselves. In democratic societies, the society decides who gets what and takes steps to implement decisions. According to J.R. Pennock and David G. Smith, politics refer to all the forces, institutions, and organizational forms in the society that are recognized as having the most inclusive and recognizable authority needed for that society to maintain order. Yet others, like Dan Nimmo and Thomas D. Ungs, see politics in terms of crisis resolution and conflict representation that involves the articulation and aggregation of interests, the definition of goals, and the socialization and mobilization of individuals into positions of decision making and / or implementation. The process can also involve the adjudication of disputes within politically relevant systems in a specific situation.

SANITATION AND HEALTH PROMOTION PROGRAM EVALUATION

A. INTRODUCTION

According to theories in economic transition, the outcome of proliferation of infectious disease in underdeveloped communities is related to activities, or lack of activities in areas such as war, agriculture, and manufacturing, in addition to economic development (manufacturing). In other words, deprive a community of rest, high standards of living, and or food, and you will most likely inflict or increase the prevalence of infectious disease.

Furthermore, outcome (infectious disease) and activities, like health promotion, mentioned are related (linearly and exponentially) to traditional activities and services to eradicate infectious disease; also see **Part 1; Chapter 2; Section 7-13**. Furthermore, while the implementation of primary healthcare provision has been very effective, its impact has been slow to develop. To remedy this problem, fiscal policies, embedded in macroeconomics, and applications with foundations in game theories, and New Public Management can be used to boost community outreach towards embracing information technology, and biotechnology, while attempting to reduce infectious disease and increase food supply. On the subject of war, in recent times few democracies have been known to go to war with the other. In part, perhaps, this is because economic development as a political variable can be, and has been one of the most cost-effective interventions; since its successful implementation has been shown to also reduce the occurrence of infectious disease, wars, and hunger.

B. HEALTHCARE POLICY EVALUATION PROCESS

According to Patton and Sawicki, (1993, pp. 2-7), systematic procedures or policy analysis methods can be used to tackle current policy problems. The methods they use could involve quick analysis or planning or systematically searched kind of analysis or policy analysis. Furthermore, several skill sets are associated with planning and policy analysis. According to Patton and Sawicki (1993, pp. 8-23), the performer should adopt methods associated with policy analysis and planning by recognizing specific basic methods and applications like the following competency of using the methods in design and analysis and the communication of results as key steps. Furthermore, key practical principles for being policy analysts require the following attributes from the performer:

- Learning to focus quickly on central decision criterion of problem
- Thinking about type of policy actions that can be taken
- Avoiding the use of tools because a particular method of analysis is favored
- Learning to deal with uncertainty
- Quantifying variables numerically and emphatically
- Making an analysis simple and transparent
- Checking the facts
- Learning to advocate the position of others
- Presenting the client with analysis and not decisions
- Pushing the boundaries of analysis beyond the policy envelope
- Avoiding to make absolute decisions, but rather to make rational and complete analyses.

C. EVALUATING ACTIVITIES AND SERVICES (OUTPUT EVALUATIONS)

A program output consists of activities and services needed to implement a program. Currently, as discussed in **Part 1; Chapter 1; Section 4**, most policies surrounding urban development and its relationships to infectious disease are confronted by "wicked problems." Consequently, analysis can be performed using branched evaluation techniques (Blanco, 1994; Lindblom, 1958). Performers may have to think out of the box to investigate trends against the current status quo. Furthermore, the fundamental question of whether a program works as intended can be answered by the use of the cost benefit or cost effective analysis (Bingham and Felbinger, 2002, pp. 179). Additionally, Rossi et al, (2004, pp. 331-336) presents a technical approach for comparisons of cost and benefits associated with social programs. For instance, the authors suggest the performer answer the following questions:

- Is there a lack of need for efficiency analysis if efficacy of program is very minimal or very high
- Is there a need for an efficacy program when a program is effective in a imperfect way
- Is there a need for technical procedures to require methodological sophistication that are unfamiliar to project staff

Different types of controversies may arise from placing economic values on input or output measures, while expressing results of evaluation studies on efficacy may selectively take different costs and outcomes into account.

D. EVALUATING IMPACT AND OUTCOMES (PROGRAM EVALUATION)

According to Bingham and Felbinger (2002, pp. 5-7), impact evaluations refer to impact, outcome, or summative evaluations that are interested in quantifying what is happening. These are of two types: one that revolves around assessing an output, and another that measures effectiveness. Both focus on measuring outcomes. Meta evaluations are often used to evaluate impact studies and are similar to literature reviews and are considered as qualitative exercises (Bingham and Felbinger, 2002, pp. 8). Here, the criteria needed to perform impact and outcomes evaluation include the following:

- Describe the context (what is the problem?)
- Describe the goal of the evaluation (what is being tested?)
- Describe the research/evaluation design (what does it do?)
- Determine what threats to internal validity can be remedied
- Determine the matching procedure
- Establish the control group
- Decide what can be done to ensure the groups are equivalent

In situations like this, the major threat(s) will be those to selection and outcome. Both are interrelated. Threats to selection will lead to threats to outcome. To avoid or minimize threats to outcome, selections of economic and infectious disease indices in the intervention groups, regardless of geography, should conform to acceptable standards. One way to achieve this is by the use of indices (ratios) to define the selection group.

Furthermore, to rule out threats to internal validity (instrumentation, history, maturation, attrition; testing scores, and regression towards mean) the programs measurements should be retrospective (Bingham and Felbinger, 2004). In addition, indices can be used to address social demographic impact, and epidemiological impacts and bias (Orman, 1977). For example, at present, evaluation, implementation, and the monitoring of the impact of health delivery policies associated with tuberculosis intervention are problematic due in part to estimation of the benefit of outcomes (Krieger et al, 2003). Previous studies show that effective TB intervention measures—such as monitoring, control, and health delivery—are correlated to cost (Clarke et al, 2006; Currie et al, 2005; Dasgupta and Menzies, 2005).

According to Bingham and Felbinger (2002, pp. 10-21), once data is collected, they should be utilized after internal and external factors are validated using one of the following methods: reflexive designs; one-group pretest and posttest designs, simple time series design, quasi-experimental designs, pretest-posttest comparison group design, experimental design, pretest and post test control group designs. Consequently, when identifying goals and objectives the performer should correct data collected for the occurrence of either type one or type two errors.

E. EXPERIMENTAL AND NON EXPERIMENTAL APPROACH TO PROGRAM EVALUATION

Before choosing between experimental or non-experimental designs, the following questions should be asked:

- What needs to be evaluated?
- What are the administrative objectives?
- What are the administrative standards?
- What monitoring services are needed?
- What should the functions of the monitoring services be?

According to Bingham and Felbinger (2002, pp. 1-3), process evaluation uses scientific methods for gathering empirical data to test hypotheses. Evaluators should look for broad based goals and for clearly stated measurable objectives by which the goals can be reached. In addition, evaluations should involve fundamental goals and objectives of the program and a process that involves assessing program activities (Bingham and Felbinger, 2002, pp. 4-5). Summary questions include the following:

- What statistical techniques did the researcher use to ensure comparability?
- Was the researcher able to rule out self-selection bias? What about other threats, such as maturation, mortality, history, etc.?
- What can the performer do to improve the evaluation design?
- What can the performer say about issues of external and construct validity?

The recommendatation forwarded in the third edition of *Biological Agents Index* is intended to help the performer use rational models when developing needs assessments. To achieve this goal, the proposal is for the performers to use non experimental designs, preferably quasi-experimentation, when evaluating infectious disease programs, specifically, post-test-only comparison groups where selection is done through a non-random process (Bingham and Felbinger, 2002, pp. 123). The major threat(s) to validity would be those to selection and outcome. As stated earlier, threats to selection will lead to threats outcome. To avoid or minimize threats to outcome, selections of economic and infectious disease indices in the intervention groups, regardless of geography, should conform to internationally acceptable standards. These indices (ratios) for GDP (LQ should be used if available) will be used to define the selection group. Furthermore, to rule out threats to instrumentation, history, maturation, attrition, testing scores, and regression towards mean, the program measurements should be retrospective (Bingham and Felbinger, 2004). In addition, indices used should address social demographic impact, and epidemiological impact (Orman, 1977), and bias.

In addition, it is recommended that the performer use multiple attributes matching to compare impact of economic development on infectious disease in the experimental group. Finally, it is recommended that the performer use mathematical models and the multiple linear regression equation where the dependent variable is infectious disease prevalence (outcome), and independent variables are relative risk for infection (multiplied by number of ways microbe is spread), inverse of gross domestic product and microbial infective dose), microbial reproductive rate (multiplied by number of ways microbe is spread, and inverse of gross domestic product and microbial infective dose), as well as infectious diseases incidence (multiplied by number of ways microbe is spread, and inverse of gross domestic product and microbial infective dose) .

To accomplish group comparability, the performer can benchmark outcome data, which is collected prior to the Average Monthly (periodic) Changes in number of new infectious disease cases per month (period) over a year relative to GDP. Furthermore, comparability can be ensured using the regression model, R-square statistic, regression coefficient, intercept, and autocorrelations as described by Bingham and Felbinger (2002, pp. 132). To rule out self-selection bias and other threats such as maturation, mortality, and history, performers should sample community GDPs and collect Average Monthly (periodic) changes in new cases of infectious disease in these communities randomly. This is typical of quasi-experimental designs (Bingham and Felbinger 2002, pp. 123). However, other forms of bias, like threats to maturation, can be reduced significantly by conducting the study retrospectively and making several observations at different time points (time series) (Bingham and Felbinger, 2002, pp. 123). Before data collection, urban communities can be selected based on histories of economic development programs and location. To reduce threats to external validity, performers can use large sample sizes and perform a cohort study of the experimental group. Where possible, the non-arbitrary zero point can be used to estimate interaction of selection and treatment, setting and treatment, as well as to history and treatment (Patton and Sawicki, 1993, pp. 131).

Also, as previously mentioned **(Part 1; Chapter 1; Section 11)**, efficacy analyses can be conducted prospectively (*ex ante* efficiency analysis) during the planning and design phase of an imitative or retrospectively (*ex post* efficiency analysis). *Ex ante* efficiency analysis is important for programs that are difficult to abandon due to extensive commitment needs in funding and time (Patton and Sawicki, 1993, pp. 257-259). *Ex post* efficiency analysis, on the other hand, is useful after a program has been in place for a time and has been demonstrated to be efficient by an impact evaluation. *Ex* *post* efficiency analysis rests in dubious assumptions and should be limited to utility, the program has to have independent or separable funding (cost can be separated from those of other activities). Second, the program should be ahead of its developmental stage and should have certain effects. Third, the programs impact and magnitude should be known or can be easily estimated. Fourth, benefits can easily translate into monetary terms. And finally, decision makers should consider using alternative programs as backup (Rossi et al, 2004 pp. 336, 361-362).

F. EXPERIMENTAL DESIGNS

According to Bingham and Felbinger, pretest and posttest is the classic experimental design and consists of two comparable groups: one experimental (or intervention group) and another control. These two groups should not be used interchangeably. True control groups should be formed randomly (Bingham and Felbinger, 2002, pp. 58-60). Randomization can be accomplished by flipping a coin, throwing names into a hat, or using a table of random numbers, etc. The after treatment, data on measures of cognitive development from the experimental design and subjects in the comparison group can be taken for analysis (Rossi, 2004, pp. 241-249). The nature of gains of treatment, and durability and the social significance of the data can then be assessed and explained (Bingham and Felbinger, 2002, pp. 61-71; Rossi, 2004, pp. 235).

SOLOMON FOUR GROUP DESIGN: The Solomon four-group design two group pretest and post test design is used to confound or confuse training effects when testing a sample with a treatment by using interaction between pre-testing and training (Bingham and Felbinger, 2002, pp. 79). Solomon's four-group design shows whether groups are sensitized by the pretest and quantifies the sensitization when it exists. This analysis contains additional sets of comparisons that are not measured initially, resulting in comparisons of policy (Bingham and Felbinger, 2002, pp. 79). The Solomon four-group design is rarely needed for evaluating infectious disease programs but is appropriate in cases when pretest is used and when the effects of this pretest are substantial, for example, in educational (socio-economic) programs. Alternatively, Posttest-only control group design is a variation of the pretest posttest design. It differs in that it omits the pretested group. Here, individuals are randomly assigned to both control and experimental groups (Bingham and Felbinger, 2002, pp. 95).

G. QUASI-EXPERIMENTAL DESIGNS

Quasi-Experimental designs employ comparison groups just to do experiments. These include pretest-posttest comparisons, group design, the regression-discontinuity design, the disrupted-time-series comparison group design, and the posttest-only comparison group design (Bingham and Felbinger, 2002, pp. 107). Furthermore, when nonrandomized designed are preferred, selection and other sources of bias can be estimated by constructing social groups by matching and using statistical controls and using multivariate statistical techniques and selection modeling to determine outcomes(Rossi et al, 2004, pp. 276-287; Patton and Sawicki, 1993, pp. 378-384). When developed correctly, quasi-experimental designs can be used to estimate program effects. These advantages rely on the practicality and situation where randomized protocols are not feasible.

COMPARISON / NON-COMPARISON GROUP DESIGN: According to Bingham and Felbinger, pretest-posttest comparison group design or nonequivalent group design, is similar to pretest-posttest design except that variables or comparisons are not randomly assigned. Furthermore, the validity of this quasi-experimental design depends on the extent to which the comparison group resembles the experimental group. There are greater risks for bias in this design. (Bingham, and Felbinger, 2002, pp. 109; Rossi et al, 2004, pp. 295-297).

The quasi experimental design has little strength because, first, the control and experimental groups are alike, and second, there are few threats to internal validity. Another major disadvantage is that there are limits to random assignment (Bingham and Felbinger, 2002, pp. 120; Patton and Sawicki, 1993, pp. 378-384). In addition, interrupted time series group comparison test examines how and whether interruption (of treatment or program) affects a social process and whether observed effects are different from processes observed in an untreated group or among different types of treatment (Bingham and Felbinger,. 2002, pp. 123; Patton and Sawicki, 1993, pp. 378-384). Posttest-only comparison group is similar to the posttest, only control group but differs in that the latter uses a randomly assigned control group (Bingham and Felbinger, 2002, pp. 137).

Posttest-Only comparison group is used when evaluation is proposed after the fact. The subjects of reflexive designs are not so easily defined. These designs are concerned with the evaluation and use of the target group (Bingham and Felbinger, 2002, pp. 150; Rossi et al, 2004, pp.290). The most commonly used form of the reflexive design is the One-group-pretest-posttest design (comparison of before and after data) – this evaluation process can be described as unpowerful and prone to internal validity problems (Bingham and Felbinger, 2002, pp. 153; Rossi et al, 2004, pp. 291). Furthermore, this design is traditionally used as the last resort test. Secondarily, the time series design is often referred to as the single interrupted time series design. It is useful when pre-program and post program measures are available on a number of occasions before and after the implementation of the program (Bingham and Felbinger, 2002, pp. 169).

REFERENCES

1. **Adedibu, A.A.** 1983. Solid waste management in Nigeria, problem and prospect. Paper presented at national conference on development and management, NISER, Ibadan.
2. **Albala, C. Vio F., Yanez, M**. 1997. "Epidemiological transition in Latin America: a comparison of four countries. *Rev Med Chil.* June. **125:**6:719-27.
3. **Batley R.** 1997. "Social agency versus global determinism in Latin American urban development". *Third World Plan Rev. November.* **19:**4:333-346.
4. **Barnett, D.J., Balicer, R.D., Lucey, D.R., Everly, G.S., Omer, S.B., Steinhoff, M.C., and Grotto, I.** 2005. A systematic analytic approach to pandemic influenza preparedness planning PLoS *Med.* December. **2:**12:359.
5. **Bingham, Richard, D., and Claire L. Felbinger**. 2002. Evaluation in Practice: A Methodological Approach. (2nd Ed.). .*Chatham House Publishers.* New York.
6. **Blanco, Hilda.** 1994. "How to Think about Social Problems: American Pragmatism and the idea of planning". *Greenwood press.* London
7. **Chaulk C.P., Friedman M., and Dunning R**. 2000. "Modeling the epidemiology and economics of directly observed therapy in Baltimore." *Int J Tuberc Lung Dis,* **4:**3:201-207.
8. **Diejomoah V.P.** 1970. Tax and revenue allocation policies. *The Journal of Business and Social Studies.* **3.**1:137
9. **Easton, D.** 1953 **the** *political system: An inquiry into the state of political science.* New York, NY USA: Random house.
10. **Gardner, R, and K.G. Heider.** 1969. *Gardens of war: life and death in the New Guinea stone age: Harvard-Peabody New Guinea expedition.* New York, Random House
11. **Heikkila, Eric J**. 2000. "Economics of Planning". *American Planning Association, Center for Urban Policy Research.*
12. **Herman, K, and M.S. Bisesi**. 1980. Handbook on environmental health and safety. Principles and practices. Volume 2. London, UK: Paragon Press.
13. **Iatridis D.S.** 1990. Cuba's health care policy: prevention and active community participation. *Soc Work.* January. **35:**1:29-35
14. **Kelman, S.** 1981. "Cost-Benefit analysis and ethical critique. *Across Board.* **18**.7.74-82
15. **Larroca N, H.** 2000. "Man, health, development and economics". *World Hosp Health Serv.* **36:**3:19-22; 36-7.
16. **Lasswell, H.D., N. Constantin, L. N. Leites, R. Fadner** 1968. *Language of Politics: Studies in quantitative semantics.* Cambridge, MA, USA: MIT Press.
17. **Lasswell, H.D, and A. Kaplan.** 1950. *Power and society: A framework for political inquiry.* New Haven, CT, USA: Yale University Press.
18. **Lindblom, Charles E.** 1958. "The Science of Muddling Through". *Administration Review.* **19:**79-88.
19. **Nimmo, D.D. and T.D. Ungs** 1969 **American** *political patterns: Conflict and consensus.* London, UK: Little, Brown
20. **Omran, A.R**. 1977. "Epidemiologic transition in the United States: the health Factor in population change. *Popul Bull.* May. **32:**2:1-42.
21. **Patton, Carl V., David S. Sawicki**. 1993. *Basic Methods of Policy Analysis and Planning,* (2nd Ed.). Prentice Hall, USA.
22. **Pennock, J.R.** 1960. Hobbe's confusing "clarity": the case of liberty. *American Political Science Review.* **54:** 428-436.
23. **Phillips. A.O.** 1968. Nigeria's experience with income tax exemption. Exemption *the Nigerian Journal of Economic and Social Studies.* **10.**11:33
24. **Price-Smith, Andrew T. 2002.** The Health of Nations: Infectious Disease, Environmental Change, and Their Effects on National Security and Development *BMJ.* 324:683.
25. **Ramney, A.** ed. 1968 Analysis *of legislative bodies.* Utah, USA: Legislative bodies
26. **Rogers, R.G., and Hackenberg R**. 1987. Extending epidemiologic transition theory: a new stage. *Soc Biol. Fall-Winter.* **34:**3-4: 234-43
27. **Roemer, M.I.** 1980. Health development and political policy: the lesson of Cuba. *J Health Polit Policy Law.* **4:**4:570-578.

28. **Richard, G, Hackenberg, R, and Hackenberg, R.** 1988. The Epidemiologic Transition Theory. *Social Biology*. **34:**3-4.
29. **Rossi, H. Peter., Mark W. Lipsey., and Howard E. Freeman**. 2004. Evaluation: A Systematic Approach. (7th Ed), Thousand Oaks, CA, USA: Sage Publications.
30. **Serow W.J, Cowart, M.E, Camezon**. 1998. Epidemiologic Transition Theory and Aging: Hispanic Populations of North America and the Caribbean. *Journal Health and Human Services Administration*. **20:**3:333-47.
31. **Smith, D.G.** 1971 the *emerging pattern of federalism: the case of public health*. In Public Health Administration Chicago USA: Aldine Atherton pp. 131
32. **United Nations Industrial Development Organization UNIDO**.Industry in developing countries: some recent trends. 1980. *Dev Dig*. **18:**1:1-16.
33. Wilson, **H.** 1953 *the War on world poverty: An* ***appeal*** *to the* ***conscience*** *of* ***mankind***. London, UK: Gollancz, pp. 232.
34. **Zavala De Cosio, M.E.** 1992. The Demographic Transition in Latin America and Europe. *Notas Poblacion*. **20:**11-32.

PART III: CASE STUDIES

Chapter 5

SYNOPSIS ONE:

EVALUATING IMPACTS OF SOCIO-ECONOMIC DEVELOPMENT ON NEW AND OLD CASES OF TB IN EL PASO

A. INTRODUCTION

Tuberculosis ranks as one of the most infectious diseases in the world. Its mortality has often been used as a marker for the spread of other highly infectious diseases. Here, the Epidemiologic Transition Theory is used to hypothesize the framework (Rogers and Hackenberg, 1987; Serow, Cowart, and Camezon, 1998), for a descriptive research deign, to study economic, sociologic, demographic, and biologic antecedents associated with tuberculosis eradication (Armstrong, Conn, and Pinner, 1999). In practice, the policies for preventing and tracking disease in the Americas are developed by the Pan American Health Organization (PAHO) in collaboration with the World Health Organization (WHO) and the Centers for Disease Control and Prevention (CDCP) (Albala, Vio, and Yanez, 1997; Albala, Vio, and Yanez, 1997). In border regions, PAHO play an increased role in coordinating disease tracking efforts between the US and Mexico. This study uses published reports, available at *www.cdc.gov* and *www.census.gov* to comparatively study regional impact of physical, demographic, social, and economic development on tuberculosis in El Paso, Texas.

In comparison to Texas, and the US in general, the median earnings of both males and females and the number of graduate and bachelor degree earners are numerically lower in El Paso. In addition, most industries located in El Paso are mainly self sustaining but some may need to import goods and services for support. It is not surprising that the mortality rate of tuberculosis per 100,000 in 2004 in El Paso is greater than that of the rest of Texas, and double the national rate. Results are consistent with the Epidemiological Transition Theory model and suggest that relatively high incidence of tuberculosis in El Paso may be negatively correlated to low and median location quotients (LQ).

The General Theory of Epidemiologic Transition was first theorizes in 1977. The theory argues that the periodic changes in health status and disease in different populations can be attributed to demographic and socioeconomic policies and conditions, and that disease cases result in population change. Furthermore, in emerging economies, general social and economic development projects can be expected to influence outcomes mortality (Omran 1977). In a more recent report, Rogers and Hackenberg (1987) suggest that mortality due to infectious disease had been partially and significantly reduced by economic development in the western hemisphere. However, the authors noted that this trend is reversed in developing economies.

Traditionally, world governments develop socioeconomic policy and have the mandate to implement multinational policy for disease eradication. These multinational governmental platforms include the PAHO, WHO, World Bank, and others. It is not surprising that most of the data used in epidemiological transition studies come from PAHO. According to the previous director, the PAHO is a regional / international public health agency that works to improve health and living standards in the US and the Americas (Alleyene, 2002). At present, PAHO and other nonprofit agencies are involved in several US public health initiatives, ranging from Hurricane Katrina disaster to US-Mexico border infectious disease surveillance (Neff, 2004; Kuiken, 2005; Giesecke, 1996; Elias et al, 1990), and the implementation of a community network of laboratories for testing human disease in collaboration with the world health organization (Meijer et al, 2005; Van Man et al, 1998).

Furthermore, by mandate, the PAHO has a regional influence in the Americas and serves as the World Health Organization representative in the US (Organizational Chart). In North America, the PAHO have been chartered by the United Nations to function as a linkage institution between the US, Canada, and Mexico on domestic and international border public-health-related issues (Aziz, and Wright, 2005; Garrette, 1997; Weinberg et al, 2003). In addition, PAHO, along with WHO has been tasked to assist in the assessment of the economic impacts of policy and disease in the Americas (Fairchild, 2004; Mukherjea 2003; Adams, and John Paul II; Stehr, 2005; Nelson et al, 2005). Organizationally, the PAHO is headed by an executive committee that is composed of nine member states of the organization. A council or general elections is responsible for electing committee members for three terms during conferences.

The committees usually meet twice yearly. During this time, two standing sub-committees—one for women, health, and development, and the other for planning and programming—jointly develop policy and economic strategies for the organization. From previous publications, it is evident that most of the clients in the PAHO surveillance programs come from Canada, the US, central Caribbean, and South America countries, and the UN (Garrette, 1997; Fox et al, 2005; Guzman, 2005). In addition to the surveillance of AIDS and other communicable diseases, PAHO coordinate family medicine and other non-communicable disease policies in collaboration with the UN (Nicoll et al, 2005; Scorgie, 2002; Ojeda, 2003).

At present, according to published reports, the PAHO functions to integrate biomedical technology as it affects public health and to initiate public health interventions in the region (Alleyene, 2002). In general, public health situations and national disasters determine these initiatives. Resources are donated by member nations, and funds trickle down to corporations and academics for various programs (Alleyene, 2002). The Centers for Disease Control and Prevention is an agency of the Department of Health. Its main task is disease control and prevention through disease surveillance, immunization, diagnostic laboratory regulation, and health education. Over the years, they publish a weekly morbidity and mortally report for the nation in collaboration with the US census bureau.

In previous Epidemiologic Transition Theory studies, the independent variables were identified as economic development and demographics and were measured by the gross domestic product (GDP), an index, and national census data (Brass, 1980), while the dependent variable was infectious disease mortality. These epidemiologic changes were measured by disease incidence or the rate of disease per year and life expectancy (Ruzicka, 1983; Zavala, 1992). In these studies, the GDP data was acquired from the US census bureau while the mortality data was acquired from the CDC&P. There was general consensus about the causes and the independent variables used. Prior to this landmark study (Omran, 1977), there had been speculations, mainly by skeptics, that the Epidemiologic Transition Theory lacked credibility. At present, based on findings in numerous studies, the theory is generally accepted. However, a few investigators (Gaylin, and Kates 1997) have published reports that suggest the theory provide only partial explanation for socioeconomic transition.

In other reports, interval measurements were taken to provide the index used to measure GNP and to define disease based on both clinical and laboratory diagnosis. A non-experimental research design (longitudinal) was carried out to determine causality. In the methodology, data on GDP, important disease trends were obtained and predictions of independent and dependent variables made from official information of local and international organizations like PAHO, WHO, World Bank, US Census Bureau, and CDC&P (Alba, Vio, and Yanz, 1997; Murray, and Lopez, 1997). In health policy inclusion and mortality studies, surveys were conducted to quantify socioeconomic differentials and indices (Brass, 1980; and Fairchild, 2004).

In a previous report, Rogers and Hackenberg (1987), suggest that economic development in the western hemisphere had partially phased out mortality caused by infectious disease but has had little effect on mortality due to non-infectious disease. This trend is reversed in developing economies. Finally, using data from published report, in various hospital and border surveillance studies (Nelson et al, 2005; Simon, 2002) researchers have increased the efficiency of the PAHO over the years. Furthermore, the Epidemiologic Transition Theory appears to account for socioeconomic transition in both developed and underdeveloped economies. However, clearly, more data is needed in this area to ensure its continued competence.

In the past, the task, in the El Paso, Texas region, of implementing socio economic development programs have fallen on governmental and nongovernmental organizations like Upper Rio Grande at Work, Accion of Texas, US Small Business administration, City of El Paso Economic Development Department, and the El Paso Regional Development corporation. Collectively, these organizations identify and support new or existing business in El Paso by providing loans, business plan counseling, or by ably assisting small, median, or large businesses to gain access to land, labor, or capital in the region. The Upper Rio Grande at Work program is specifically focused on finding and placing individuals in positions of productive employment and, when possible, training and providing skill sets.

Figure 15 and **Tables 9** and **10** detail a comparison of selected economic and biological matrices that are characteristic to El Paso, Texas, and the US on the basis of regional educational, employment, tuberculosis mortality, and income. Data was used to comparatively quantify sociological and demographical impacts of education on the incidence of tuberculosis. The percentage of educational level of attainment was compared to the number of old and new cases of tuberculosis from 2000 to 2004 in El Paso, Texas, and the US. On the surface, the data shows that when compared to other parts of Texas and the US there are twice as many cases of new and old cases of tuberculosis in El Paso than in the US as whole.

Table 9. Comparison of El Paso, TX and US on the basis of: Regional Educational, Tuberculosis Mortality, and Income

	% Educational Attainment bachelors degree	graduate degree	**TB Cases** 2000-2004 per 100,000	**Median Earning (full-time, 2000)** male	**$USD** female
El Paso, TX, MSA	11	6	10	26,882	20,722
TX	16	8	8	34,925	26,168
US	16	9	5	37,057	27,194

Source United States Census Bureau. www.census.gov

Furthermore, increase in new cases (incidence) of tuberculosis negatively correlates with decrease in the attainment of bachelor and graduate level degrees. Furthermore, comparisons show El Paso has a lower median income in both males and females when compared to Texas and the US. This trend suggests that decreases in median income may positively correlate to decreases in the incidence of new and old cases of tuberculosis.

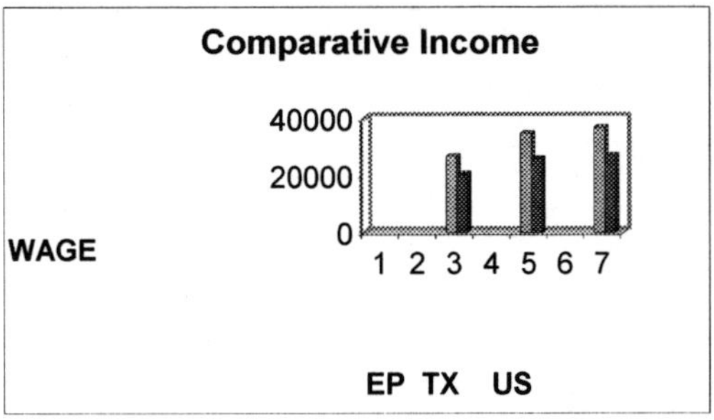

Figure 16. Regional Comparison of Income and Wages (2000)

Table 10. Comparison of Percentage Employed in Industries in El Paso, Texas, and the US

	El Paso	Texas	USA
Agriculture			
Forestry	0.6	2.7	1.9
Fishing			
Hunting			
Minning			
Construction	5.4	8.1	6.8
Manufacturing	14.5	11.8	14.1
Wholesale	3.8	3.9	3.6
Retail	11.9	12	11.7
Transportation			
Warehousing	6.8	5.8	5.2
Utilities			
information	3.4	3.1	3.1
finance			
insurance			
real estate	4.7	6.8	6.9
rental			
Scientific	7.3	9.5	9.3
health	23	19.3	19.9
Arts			
entertainment			
recreation	8.1	7.3	7.9
accomodation			
food			
Public Administratioı	6	4.5	4.8
Tuberculosis cases per 100,000	10	8	5

LQ = **%** employment in select industry sector in El Paso / **%** employment in same sector in the US

Further analysis of location quotients (LQ) show that the LQ in El Paso (**Table 11**) of almost all its industries is low compared to median. Furthermore, industries like construction, manufacturing, wholesale, rental, transportation, warehousing, utilities, information, health, and public administration in El Paso appear to be self sustaining and show little or no export activity. Other sectors, like agriculture, forestry, fishing, hunting, mining, scientific, finance, insurance, real estate, and rental require the importation of goods and service.

Table 11. Location Quotient of El Paso

Agriculture Forestry Fishing Hunting Minning	0.3
Construction	0.8
Manufacturing	1.0
Wholesale	1.1
Retail	1.0
Transportation Warehousing Utilities	1.3
information	1.1
finance insurance real estate rental	0.7
Scientific	0.8
health	1.2
Arts entertainment recreation accomodation food	1.0
Public Administratioı	1.3

B. CONCLUSION

Based on the findings in this synopsis, after comparing social, economic, demographic, and physical attributes of the El Paso economy with those of Texas and the US, it appears that overall industry in El Paso is self sustaining and not showing great signs of growth. Furthermore, the mortality (number of new and old cases) of tuberculosis per 100,000 collected between 2000 and 2004 in El Paso **(Table 9)** is double the national rate. Based on these trends, perhaps localization and urbanization of economies of scale has contributed to this outlook in El Paso. Should this be the case? Furthermore, can changes in government fiscal policy or other socio economic policies reverse this trend?

SYNOPSIS TWO

EVALUATING IMPACTS OF USING PERFORMANCE MEASURES IN PLANNING AND BUDGETING OF TB INTERVENTIONS IN EL PASO.

A. INTRODUCTION

Worldwide, tuberculosis (TB) is the leading cause of death among infectious diseases (Centers for Disease Control & Prevention, 2006). Once the leading cause of death in the United States, TB is caused by the bacterium known as *Mycobacterium tuberculosis.* Guidelines for TB program evaluation for state and local governments were established in 2005 and are currently in use. The guidelines include a set of recommended performance measures for use in program evaluation and are published by the Division of Tuberculosis Elimination, National Centers for HIV, STD, and TB Prevention at the Centers for Disease Control and Prevention (CDC&P). The guidelines are generic and recommend that health planners perform needs assessments before designing, planning and implementing recommended performance measures. CDC&P TB intervention guidelines are in use by El Paso Health District but are intended for all state and local health departments in the US. Specific details of the guidelines used in the past include the following:

- Increase the percentage of patients identified with TB who are placed on Direct Observed Therapy (DOT) within 1 month of diagnosis from 85% to 90% by January 2006
- Increase the percentage of TB patients who utilize case management services from 60% to 70% by Fall 2006
- Increase the number of referrals to the local health department made by community health centers from 100 to 150 by Fall 2006
- Increase percentage of community members who understand how TB is transmitted from 20% to 40%
- Increase the number of Spanish speaking patients; increase the clinical standards met by 100%
- Increase patient education and forms in Spanish by 100%

- Increase Spanish speaking staff by 80%; and have 90% of Spanish speaking patients report that they were treated respectfully.

Based on the classic definition of performance budgeting, of the 11 Health Districts including the Texas Department of Justice, only El Paso and Dallas have true performance budgets as defined by Mikesell (2003, pp. 191-194; 206-217). In this study, the effectiveness of TB interventions in the El Paso City-County Health & Environmental District and 10 other Texas Health Districts including Houston City and the Texas Department of Justice is analyzed. Data on performance measures used for TB interventions (new cases) and the per capita cost for these interventions in the El Paso City-County Health & Environmental District were collected. To better understand the findings, data collected for El Paso County were benchmarked using similar data from Houston, Dallas, Travis, Bexar, Cameron, Harris, Hidalgo, Tarrant, and Nueces health districts, and the Texas Department of Criminal Justice (TDCJ).

Results from benchmarking show that use of performance measures in combination with increased per capita expenditures (**Table 12, and 13**) may have been responsible for the desirable TB intervention outcomes in El Paso (0.16 Average Monthly New Cases from Jan to December 2005). Other health districts like Dallas (0.6); Cameron (0.5), Hidalgo (0.37), Houston (5.3), Travis (0.42), Tarrant (0.33), and Bexar (0.22)— which either have clear intended outcomes (TB reduction), poorly defined problems and needs or budgets that do not segregate the funding by program— show higher increases for average number of new TB cases than El Paso (**Table 12 and 13**). In addition, evidence of the use or lack of use of performance measures or TB intervention expenditures was not available for Harris, Nueces, and TDCJ. Collectively, based on data on benchmarking, these results suggest that the use performance measures and increases in per capita TB expenditures may be responsible for the lower average numbers of new TB cases recorded in the El Paso Health District in contrast to other Texas health districts. However, further studies need to be conducted to better determine the characteristics of these relationships.

B. BACKGROUND INFORMATION ON TB

TB is the leading cause of death among infectious diseases worldwide CDC&P the leading cause of death in the United States. TB is caused by bacterium known as *Mycobacterium tuberculosis.* According to the Centers for Disease Control & Prevention (CDC&P), the bacterium attacks the lungs and other parts of the body (CDC&P). It is an airborne disease and spreads through coughs, sneezes, or conversation when people speak in tiny (microscopic) drops of moisture. There are two stages of TB: infection or inactive TB: and disease or active TB (CDC&P). An infected individual can carry the inactive bacteria without spreading it to others (CDC&P). Conversely, an individual with active TB disease can spread the bacteria. Treatments for TB were discovered in the 1940s. At present, TB can easily be treated with medication known as isoniazid (INH) alone or in combination with Rifampin and Pyrazinamide, a common practice used to reduce the threat of multiple drug resistance in the TB germ. Historically, the disease started to disappear until the mid- 1980s. Since the mid 1980s, more than 25,000 Americans have

developed TB on a yearly basis. Eventually, 10 million have contracted the germ and may never develop the disease (CDC&P). Some academics have attributed this increase to the emergence of HIV, which weakens the immune system of individuals that would ordinarily harbor inactive TB. Interestingly, it is not easy to become infected with TB because the healthy person's immune system can fight the germ. TB is not spread by contact, through clothing, bedding, or dishes. The risk of contact by someone coughing in restaurants is low (CDC&P). For infection, extended exposure in the form of associations between family members, co workers, and friends is required. People with TB infection can be asymptomatic. About 9 out of 10 Americans infected with TB will develop the disease (CDC&P). Furthermore, pediatric TB is a special concern because children have weaker immune systems.

Without treatment, TB disease can be fatal. Clinical symptoms include a persistent cough, chest pain, coughing up blood or phlegm, weakness, fatigue, weight loss, fever, chills, and night sweats (CDC&P). The only way to determine TB infection is to have a tuberculin skin test. During this test, the healthcare provider injects a small amount of tuberculin, or testing fluid, just under the skin or forearm. After about two to three days, the body reacts in the form of a swelling localized around the injection site. The size of reaction determines a positive or negative result. A positive skin test usually warrants further tests on sputum and chest X rays (CDC&P).

The CDC&P recommend that everyone have a tuberculin skin test at least once. Additionally, individuals should be tested if they have TB symptoms, have had close contact with people with TB disease recently or in the past, are HIV positive; have conditions that lower immunity, are from a countries which TB disease is common, work or live where TB disease is common, are IV drug users, or are persons that abuse substances, or are required to be tested at school or at work (CDC&P). Finally, the spread of TB can be controlled by early detection; prompt treatment; effective disease surveillance; sleeping in rooms with adequate ventilation; covering the mouth with tissue when coughing, sneezing or laughing; and by notifying people when testing positive to TB.

Tuberculosis (TB) is recognized as a leading public health problem by the federal governments of both Mexico and the United States (Schneider et al, 2004). At present, there are federal TB intervention guidelines in the US to eradicate the threat. These guidelines have been developed as a road map for conducting evaluation. The TB intervention guidelines describe the activities, and explain when and how they should occur, and who is responsible for completing them. In addition, the guidelines document the process for all stakeholders. In most cases TB programs are managed and implemented by both state and local government health departments in the US.

C. INTERVENTION INPUTS AND OUTPUTS

According to Webb, Holcombe, and Pearson (2003), activities associated with TB interventions consist of testing (objective or activity), treatment (objective or activity), surveillance (objective or activity), and education (objective or activity). These are TB intervention program objectives and activities. There is a cost (input) value associated with each of the basic strategic activities. TB intervention in general is governed by federal and local laws/statutes. Consequently, El Paso City-County Health & Environmental District TB program managers comply with federal guidelines on how they should implement the TB intervention program. According to the guidelines proposed by the National Centers for HIV, STD, and TB, Centers for Disease Control and Prevention, key interventions include TB screening and laboratory testing, public education and awareness, treatment of active or latent TB, and directly observed therapy services (DOT). DOT is the practice where health administrators directly observe patients to make sure the medication is taken. This practice is necessary in the case of TB because patients frequently discard obtained medication.

Published reports indicate that planning and implementing disease intervention programs require that planners modify either or both the environmental and behavioral factors to achieve a desirable reduction in disease prevalence (outcome). Behavioral factors include smoking, which increases risk for TB and the use of condoms, which reduces the risk for HIV and, subsequently the risk of contracting TB, since HIV can increase the risk for developing clinical TB. Other behavioral factors of concern include failure to complete TB medication doses, failure to attend scheduled check up and evaluations; alcohol consumption by patients on medication; and improper diet that could lead to reduced immunity. Environmental modifications include implementation of indoor Environmental Protection Agency (EPA) standards for air ventilation at risk locations and homes and general environmental sanitation standards in high risk communities.

In a recent study, investigators tried to determine whether improvements in TB program activities correlated with incidence (occurrence of new) TB cases (Lobato et al. 2006). Results from this study showed that there are observable improvements in performance measures when program funding increases (Lobato et al, 2006). These results suggest that expanded TB program activities like DOT, and therapy resulted in significant reductions of national TB cases (Lobato et al, 2006).

Currently, in the US, tuberculosis control is coordinated by the National Centers for HIV, STD, and TB Prevention at the Centers for Disease Control and Prevention (CDC&P). This government agency has developed guidelines for TB program evaluation for state and local governments. The guidelines used by the El Paso City Health District were established in 2005 and are currently in use. The guidelines in the past include a set of recommended performance measures for use in program evaluation. These include:

- Increasing the percentage of patients identified with TB who are placed on DOT within one month of diagnosis from 85% to 90% by January 2006

- Increasing the percentage of TB patients who utilize case management services from 60% to 70%
- Increasing number of referrals to the local health department made by community health centers from 100 to 150
- Increasing percentage of community members who understand how TB is transmitted from 20% to 40 %

- Increasing the number of Spanish speaking patients; increase the clinical standards met by 100%
- Increasing patient education and forms in Spanish by 100%
- Increasing Spanish speaking staff by 80%
- Having 90% of Spanish speaking patient's report they were treated respectfully by 90%

In conclusion, current reports indicate that the use of CitiStat an electronic accountability and evaluation tool in performance management is commonplace in some cities (Behn, 2004). However, measurement tools used to evaluate TB intervention performance measures require benchmarking (Carroll & Malefoasi, 2004), and the rigorous review of reports and inputs from public health and academic institutions (Dye et al, 2005; Pio et al, 1997). In addition, the role of the community in any TB intervention cannot be overemphasized (Maher, 2003; van Rensburg et al, 2006). More research is needed to improve efficiencies in performance management technologies and more literature published to better educate users.

D. OBSERVED OUTCOMES

In this study, logic matrices were used to collected data on TB intervention planning in 11 health districts with the highest reported new cases of TB. Eleven health districts studied showed different levels of per capita funding inputs: El Paso ($1,080.29), Dallas, ($20.88), Houston, ($1,154.28), Cameron, ($1,179.42), and Hildigo ($22.64). Furthermore, El Paso, Dallas, and Houston document inputs that are physical or structural in nature like testing facilities or air monitoring systems. Interestingly, only El Paso Health District (**Table 13**) documents inputs like outreach and education or training. However, none of the health districts studies shows records in its budgets for partnerships with non government organizations mentioned as recommended by the CDC&P (**Tables 12,13,14,15,16,17, and 18**).

Furthermore, a review of the budgets shows that all the counties have expenditures for human resources in the health sector; however, direct funding for TB interventions recommended by the CDC was found only in El Paso, Dallas, and Houston budgets. Interestingly, funds for TB related programs were either not available or line itemed in the other counties studied, suggesting that TB intervention funding may have come from the general health budget. This may mean that intervention programs are not segregated in the health department budget. On the subject of outputs, results from this study show that El Paso and Houston have outputs that meet CDC definitions but fall short of containing traditional performance measures (**Table 12**). In addition, other counties studied fall seriously short on output measures based on the same definition (**Table 12**).

According to Mikesell (2003, pp. 192), a good performance budget's productivity section should present cost per activity unit. Furthermore, the effectiveness section should show a unit's performance against a criteria and how it intends to accomplish set objectives. Based on these criteria, results from this study show that the El Paso County Health District has a good performance budget and that the budget for Dallas Health District is fair **(Table 12).** However, for other counties, in 2006, there is no evidence that true performance budgeting was done. The results also show that in addition to CDC&P suggested measures, El Paso County Health District has introduced a system to measure continued quality assurance. Based on performance measures proposed in this study (Averages in Monthly New Cases of TB (AMNC), El Paso County Health District's current measures have been very effective.

Furthermore, collectively, preliminary results in this study suggest that the use of new performance budgets in El Paso combined with high per capita expenditures on TB intervention programs may be responsible for the low cases of new TB in comparison with other Texas health districts. Further analysis of the data (**Tables 12,13,14,15,16,17, and 18**) show that only Dallas out of the 10 other health districts studied adopted the use of true performance measures (Mikesell, 2003). Other health districts surveyed with no performance measures and high numbers of Average Monthly New TB cases include the following: Dallas (0.6), Houston (5.3), Travis (0.42), Tarrant (0.33), and Bexar (0.22). Per capita TB expenditures for Harris (0.11), Nueces (0.38), and TDCJ (unknown) are unknown at this time.

Table 12. Per capita TB intervention cost, new cases of TB (outcome) per month and average monthly growth rate of new cases: 11 Texas Health Districts including: City of Houston and the Texas Department of Criminal Justice 2005

	bEl Paso New Cases	TB Cases per 100,000	dDallas New Cases	TB Cases per 100,000	eHouston New Cases	TB Cases per 100,000	Harris New Cases	TB Cases per 100,000	fCameron New Cases	TB Cases per 100,000	gHidalgo New Cases	TB Cases per 100,000	hTravis New Cases	TB Cases per 100,000	Nueces New Cases	TB Cases per 100,000	Tarrant New Cases	TB Cases per 100,000	iTDCJ New Cases	TB Cases per 10,000	Bexar New Cases	TB Cases per 100,000
*Population	679,622		2,305,454		23,218		3,400,578		335,227		569,463		812,280		313,645		1,446,219				1,392,931	
Jan	0	0	11	0.47713	6	25.842	5	0.147034	1	0.298305	2	0.35120807	1	0.1231103	0	0	1	0.06914582	2	unknown	3	0.215373195
Feb	0	0	9	0.39038	17	73.2191	0	0	0	0	2	0.35120807	4	0.492441	2	0.6376636	5	0.3457291	0	unknown	1	0.071791065
Mar	0	0	16	0.69401	18	77.5261	3	0.08822	0	0	0	0	_		1	0.3188318	4	0.27658328	1	unknown	0	0
Apr	1	0.147141	6	0.26025	17	73.2191	3	0.08822	0	0	0	0	3	0.3693308	0	0	4	0.27658328	0	unknown	2	0.14358213
May	5	0.735703	19	0.82413	17	73.2191	6	0.176441	4	1.193221	5	0.87802017	5	0.6155513	2	0.6376636	11	0.76060403	1	unknown	4	0.28716426
Jun	4	0.588562	17	0.73738	25	107.675	4	0.117627	3	0.894916	7	1.22922824	7	0.8617718	3	0.9564954	9	0.62231239	4	unknown	5	0.358955325
Jul	0	0	29	1.25789	26	111.982	3	0.08822	2	0.596611	2	0.35120807	2	0.2462205	0	0	4	0.27658328	4	unknown	1	0.071791065
Aug	0	0	7	0.30363	10	43.07	2	0.058814	0	0	0	0	4	0.492441	1	0.3188318	3	0.20743746	3	unknown	3	0.215373195
Sep	_		_		_		_		_		_		_		_		_		_	unknown	_	
Oct	0	0	10	0.43375	15	64.605	3	0.08822	1	0.298305	0	0	3	0.3693308	1	0.3188318	4	0.27658328	1	unknown	5	0.358955325
Nov	_		_			0	_		_		_		_		_		_		_	unknown	_	
Dec	1	0.147141	15	0.65063	16	68.9121	9	0.264661	6	1.789832	3	0.5268121	2	0.2462205	2	0.6376636	4	0.27658328	1	unknown	7	0.502537455
Average Number of Monthly New Cases		0.161855		0.60292		65.388		0.111746		0.507119		0.36876847		0.4240464		0.3825982		0.33881452		_		0.222552302

Sources

*US Census Bureau http://factfinder.census.gov/servlet/GCTTable?_bm=y&-geo_id=04000US48&-_box_head_nbr=GCT-PH1&-ds_name=DEC_2000_SF1_U&-redoLog=false&-mt_name=DEC_2000_SF1_U_GCTPH1_ST2&-format=ST-2

bEl Paso City-County Health and Environmental District El Paso County online records not used. Rather for uniformity, state records have been used.El Paso County online records not used. Rather for uniformity, state records have been used.

cTexas Department of Health Services http://www.dshs.state.tx.us/idcu/disease/tb/statistics/default.asphttp://www.dshs.state.tx.us/idcu/disease/tb/statistics/default.asphttp://www.dshs.state.tx.us/idcu/disease/tb/statistics/default.asp

d Dallas County Local Government http://www.dallascounty.org/department/budget/documents/Volumel2ndQtrFY06.pdfhttp://www.dallascounty.org/department/budget/documents/Volumel2ndQtrFY06.pdf

eHoustoun City Government http://www.houstontx.gov/budget/05budadopt/V_HHS.pdfhttp://www.houstontx.gov/budget/05budadopt/V_HHS.pdfhttp://www.houstontx.gov/budget/05budadopt/V_HHS.pdfhttp://www.houstontx.gov/budget/05budadopt/V_HHS.pdf

fCameroun County Government http://www.co.cameron.tx.us/auditor1/forms/AnnualFinancialReport2005.pdfhttp://www.co.cameron.tx.us/auditor1/forms/AnnualFinancialReport2005.pdfhttp://www.co.cameron.tx.us/auditor1/forms/AnnualFinancialReport2005.pdf

gHidalgo County Government http://www.co.hidalgo.tx.us/auditor/2005FinancialReport/report.htmhttp://www.co.hidalgo.tx.us/auditor/2005FinancialReport/report.htmhttp://www.co.hidalgo.tx.us/auditor/2005FinancialReport/report.htm

hTravis County Government http://www.co.travis.tx.us/planning_budget/FY05/documents/FY05%20Adopted%20Budget%20HHS%20Program%20Area.pdf

iTexas Department of Criminal Justice

Table 13. Logic matrix with performance measures for TB intervention in El Paso County

	Program Function: TB Intervention			**FY 05**					
	Strategic Goals	**Policy Priorities**	**Problem, Need, Situation**	**Service or Activity**	**Benchmarks**	**Outcomes**		**Measurement Reporting Tools**	**Evaluation Process**
					Output Goal	**Achievement Outcome Goals**	**End Results**		
County	1		2	3	4	6	7	8	9
	Policy		Planning		Intervention	Impact		Accountability	
El Paso	Control Spread of TB	El Paso County Residents HIV patients Cases of [b]MDRTB	Incomplete Therapy	Therapy	90% on [a]DOT 92% complete treatment therapy for 61% test positive	Reduce TB Prevalence	Increase Quality of Life	Online Reporting To State Health Department	Evaluation Committee
			False positive results	Testing	screen 92% test positive for [b]MDRTB evaluate 81% TB test positives with HIV				
			Low Budget Low Budget	Surveillance Outreach and Education	none contact 90% test positives				

Table 14. Logic Matrix with performance measures for TB intervention in Dallas County

	Program Function: TB Intervention			FY 06					
	Strategic Goals	Policy Priorities	Problem, Need, Situation	Service or Activity	Benchmarks	Outcomes		Measurement Reporting Tools	Evaluation Process
					Output Goal	Achievement Outcome Goals	End Results		
County	1		2	3	4	6	7	8	9
	Policy		Planning		Intervention	Impact		Accountability	
Dallas	Reduce Incidence of TB	Dallas County Prison Inmates	Incomplete Therapy	Direct Observed Therapy X Ray Services	none none	Reduce TB Prevalence	Increase Quality of Life	Online Reporting To State Health Department	Evaluation Committee
			False positive results	Laboratory Testing	none				
			Low Budget Low Budget	none none	none none				

[a] Guidelines are set by Department of Health and Human Services

Table 15. Logic matrix with performance measures for TB intervention in Houston City Health District

County	Strategic Goals	Policy Priorities	Problem, Need, Situation	Service or Activity	Benchmarks	Outcomes		Measurement Reporting Tools	Evaluation Process
	Program Function: TB Intervention		FY 05						
					Output Goal	Achievement Outcome Goals	End Results		
	1		2	3	4	6	7	8	9
	Policy		Planning		Intervention	Impact		Accountability	
Houston	Reduce Incidence of TB	Houston County Grouping Health Performance Measure (no single measure for TB)	Incomplete Therapy	Direct Observed Therapy Air Monitoring Systems	none none	Reduce TB Prevalence	Increase Quality of Life	Online Reporting To State Health Department	Evaluation Committee
			False positive results	Laboratory Testing	none				
			Low Budget Low Budget	none none	none none				

[a] Guidelines are set by Department of Health and Human Services

Table 16. Logic matrix with performance measures for TB intervention in Cameron Health District.

	[a]**Program Function:** TB Intervention			**FY 05**					
	Strategic Goals	**Policy Priorities**	**Problem, Need, Situation**	**Service or Activity**	**Benchmarks**	**Outcomes**		**Measurement Reporting Tools**	**Evaluation Process**
					Output Goal	**Achievement Outcome Goals**	**End Results**		
County	1		2	3	4	6	7	8	9
	Policy		Planning		Intervention	Impact		Accountability	
Cameron	prevent transmission of infection and disease	Cameron County	mobile phones communications insurance	none identified	none identified	Reduce TB Prevalence	Increase Quality of Life	Online Reporting To State Health Department	Evaluation Committee

[a] Guidelines are set by Department of Health and Human Services

Table 17. Logic matrix with performance measures for TB intervention in Hidalgo County.

	Program Function: TB Intervention[a]			FY 05					
	Strategic Goals	Policy Priorities	Problem, Need, Situation	Service or Activity	Benchmarks	Outcomes		Measurement Reporting Tools	Evaluation Process
					Output Goal	Achievement Outcome Goals	End Results		
County	1		2	3	4	6	7	8	9
	Policy		Planning		Intervention	Impact		Accountability	
Hidalgo	prevent transmission of infection and disease	Hidalgo County	none identified	none identified	none identified	Reduce TB Prevalence	Increase Quality of Life	Online Reporting To State Health Department	Evaluation Committee

[a] Guidelines are set by Department of Health and Human Services

Table 18. Logic matrix with performance measures for TB intervention in Travis County.

	[a]Program Function: TB Intervention		FY 05							
	Strategic Goals	**Policy Priorities**	**Problem, Need Situation**	**Service or Activity**	**Benchmarks**	**Outcomes**		**Measurement Reporting Tools**	**Evaluation Process**
					Output Goal	**Achievement Outcome Goals**	**End Results**		
County	1		2	3	4	6	7	8	9
	Policy		Planning		Intervention	Impact		Accountability	
Travis	prevent transmission of infection and disease	Travis County	none identified	none identified	none identified	Reduce TB Prevalence	Increase Quality of Life	Online Reporting To State Health Department	Evaluation Committee

[a] Guidelines are set by Department of Health and Human Services

Table 19. Comparative analysis of impact of performance measures on Average Monthly Growth Rate.

TB Intervention Budget Description (Mikesell, 2003 pp. 191-192)	**El Paso**	**Dallas**	**Houston**	**Harris**	**Cameron**	**Hidalgo**	**Travis**	**Nueces**	**Tarrant**	**TDCJ**	**Bexar**
1. Budget Organized in Terms of Activities	yes	yes	yes	no	no	no	no	unknown	unknown	unknown	unknown
2. Activities Measures	yes	yes	no	no	no	no	no	unknown	unknown	unknown	unknown
3. Cost Associated with Activities	yes	yes	yes	no	yes	yes	no	unknown	unknown	unknown	unknown
4. Efficiency Associated with Activities	yes	no	no	no	no	no	no	unknown	unknown	unknown	unknown
5. Actual Cost of Activity or Accomplishments	yes	no	no	no	no	no	no	unknown	unknown	unknown	unknown
6. Activities Associated with End Results	no	no	no	no	no	no	no	unknown	unknown	unknown	unknown
Average No. Monthly New Cases (per 100,000)	0.16	0.6	5.3	0.11	0.51	0.37	0.42	0.38		0.33	0.22

Table 20. Impact of performance measures on Average Monthly Growth Rate of new TB cases

	Texas County		Average No. Monthly TB Cases (per 100,000)	FY05 PerCapita (USD)
1	El Paso	Use of Peformance Measures	0.16	$ 1,080.00
2	Dallas	Use of Peformance Measures	0.6	$ 20.88
3	Houston	No Performance Measures Used	5.3	$ 1,154.00
4	Harris	unknown	0.11	unknown
5	Cameron	No Performance Measures Used	0.5	$ 1,179.00
6	Hidalgo	trace of performance	0.37	$ 22.64
7	Travis	No Performance Measures Used	0.42	unknown
8	Nueces	unknown	0.38	unknown
9	Tarrant	No Performance Measures Used	0.33	unknown
10	TDCJ	unknown	unknown	unknown
11	Bexar	No Performance Measures Used	0.22	unknown

E. EVALUATION OF PROGRAM ACTIVITIES AND SERVICES

New performance budgeting and the logic model are frequently used by managers in strategic planning. As the name suggests, the logic model includes the policies, goals, and objectives that lead to specified inputs, outputs, and outcomes needed to evaluate program performance. **Figure 20** conceptualizes a flow chart with all the activities, and services that would be needed for quality management and assessment of infectious disease programs. The organizational chart is based on the logic model used and proposed by the US Department of Housing and has been modified to reflect policy goals and policy priorities needed for infectious disease interventions like TB.

In the El Paso City-County Health and Environmental District's TB program policy, the TB program utilizes continuous quality improvement (CQI) to evaluate and improve all aspects of performance. Its objectives are to increase the efficiency and effectiveness in the delivery of treatment and prevention services within the community; to balance the increasing demands of quality, access, and cost; to ensure continued compliance with accepted standards, rules, guidelines, and regulations; and to incorporate, implement and perform ongoing monitoring of quality improvement activities within the TB program and provider network. The performance measures utilized by the El Paso City-County Health and Environmental District TB program are DOT in 90% of patients, complete treatment in 92% of patients; therapy in 61% of test positive patients; testing 92% of test positive patients for Multiple Drug Resistant TB; evaluating 81% of test positives with HIV; and 90% outreach and education in 90% test positives.

Measures are collected monthly and evaluated on an ongoing basis to identify significant variances and trends, to determine causes of the variances, and to develop action plans to improve the process, to correct problems, or improve outcomes. The outcomes for TB intervention program for FY05 in the El Paso City-County Health District may be attributable to several factors. The department's process aligns with **Figure 12.** The main objective of the El Paso City-County Health District is quality improvement for all programs. Based on internal policy, quality improvement and assessments are adopted and used to improve the system on a continuous basis. In addition, the health district is divided into several departments that carry out TB intervention programs **(Figure 12, and 20).** These departments include health promotion, preventative medicine, and a public health laboratory.

Furthermore, the health district of El Paso collaborates with Thomason Hospital and El Paso Chambers of Commerce to organize and finance social outreach programs that target infectious disease like HIV. These interventions positively impact TB interventions indirectly since the prevalence of HIV and TB are intricately linked. In addition, the Health District departments are divided into environmental health and health promotion units which strictly adhere to internally developed performance measures. Compared to Houston, Travis, Bexar, Cameron, Harris, Hidalgo, Texas Department Criminal of Justice (TDCJ), Tarrant, and Nueces health districts (**Tables 12,13,14,15,16,17, and 18**). It appears that only El Paso Health District and Dallas Health District show documented use of strategic planning(**Table 12 and 13**). Further studies have to be performed to determine contrasts in outcome of new TB cases in the Dallas Health district compared to that of El Paso. In addition to increasing per capita funding and expenditures on TB interventions, it is recommended that Texas counties without performance measures introduce them and measure performance in the activities referenced in **Figure 19** and **20**, specifically in surveillance, outreach, treatment, and laboratory diagnostics; they should further adopt current Centers for Disease Control and Prevention performance measures for states and local governments. Finally, for evaluation and assessment of programs, benchmarks of intervention outcome should be quantified as a measure of Average Monthly New Cases of TB.

F. EVALUATION OF PROGRAM OUTCOMES

A logic model developed by the Department of Housing and Urban Development can be used comparatively to analyze performance measures associated with TB intervention adopted by the El Paso County Health District and other health districts. A logic model is a graphic depiction of a program. The model describes relationships between inputs or resources, activities, objectives, outputs, and outcomes (CDC&P, 2006) see (**Tables 12,13,14,15,16,17, and 18**). Objectives used in the matrix are statements that refer to goals intended for the targeted population. In the case of TB intervention programs, program objectives are set at the national and state levels. However, in addition to these, some counties like El Paso created their own continuous quality assessment objectives and measures in addition to federal and state objectives. Objectives are designed to be specific, measurable, achievable, relevant, and time-bound (CDC&P, 2006).

According to the CDC&P, activities in the logic model should describe what the program is doing to accomplish objectives; these procedures can include hiring and training new staff, developing and revising policies, providing targeted TB testing to specific high-risk groups, identifying persons with latent TB infection or active TB disease, administering DOT, educating patients or community members, providing laboratory and diagnostic services, surveillance, managing clinic operations, and providing technical assistance. With respect to program outputs, according to the CDC&P guidelines, these should include immediate TB education materials, services, and capacities that are a direct product of programs activities and processes and can include a strategic plan for the program, TB tests conducted, provider's education about TB, and education sessions presented to community groups. Outputs are developed to show that the program is being implemented as planned; but outputs are not necessarily indicators of effectiveness. In other words the output should show that work is performed by staff but not necessarily that changes have taken place or resulted due to these actions (CDC&P, 2006).

Furthermore, policies and protocols at the El Paso City-County Health & Environmental District should be reviewed. Specifically, policies, services, and activities associated with TB intervention functions (goals, objectives, outputs, and performance measures) should be evaluated. To begin, the performer can assess first whether performance measures are used by county health districts and whether they are good measures, and, second, performer can propose performance measures for TB intervention programs suitable for the El Paso City-County Health & Environmental District based on the best practice. The performer's assessment can consist of a non-experimental, descriptive review of current TB intervention performance measures. Furthermore, the performer should determine whether the El Paso, Houston, Travis, Bexar, Cameron, Harris, Hidalgo, Tarrant, and Nueces and the Texas Department of Criminal Justice (TDCJ) health districts have established sound performance measures. The performer should determine if they are just measures of output or if the measures are real performance measures as defined by Mikesell (2003, 191-194 and 206-217). Finally, a logic model, as laid out in **Table 12, and 14** can be used for the review.

In Texas State, the Texas Department of Health collects, confirms, and reports all cases of TB. Subsequently, to increase data accuracy, this evaluation should be collected data on all new TB cases from the Texas Department of Health. To help in the analysis, data on health district population, TB new cases, and actual cost of intervention should be collected and incorporated in (**Tables 12,13,14,15,16,17, and 18**).

In addition, for recommendations of an impact model, conceptualization flow charts should be used to illustrate best practices for TB intervention in the United States **(Figure 19 and 20).** Furthermore, data on performance measures used for TB intervention outcomes, actual FY05 intervention cost, per capita cost, and population size in the El Paso City-County Health & Environmental District can also be collected (**Table 12**). To benchmark this information—based on performance measures for TB intervention in 10 Texas health districts including Houston City and the Texas TJD Health District with relatively high rates of TB used in this synopsis (**Tables 12,13,14,15,16,17, and 18**)—TB outcomes should be measured as the number of new cases per 100, 000 (**Table 19 and 20**). To achieve this, it is recommended for the performer to use a non-experimental design, specifically, post-test only comparison groups where selection is not random (Bingham and Felbinger, 2002, pp 123).

The performer can use multiple attributes matching to compare impact of economic development on infectious disease in the experimental group (El Paso County) with similar measurements for Houston, Dallas, San Antonio, Hidalgo, Travis, and Cameron Counties without using control groups (Bingham and Felbinger, 2002, pp. 123). Furthermore, the mathematical model planned for use can consist of a multiple linear regression equation were the dependent variable is infectious disease prevalence (outcome), independent variables consist of relative risk for infection, microbial reproductive rate, infectious diseases incidence, and an economics index like Location Quotient as described by Olisa (2002, and 2003). In addition, ratios can be used in measurements (indices). The non-arbitrary zero point can be used to estimate interaction of selection and treatment, setting and treatment; and history and treatment (Patton and Sawicki, 1993, pp. 131).

Finally, benchmarks can be used to analyze the achievements and other end results for TB interventions in the El Paso City-County Health & Environmental District. In addition, recommendations for best practices for measurement reporting tools and evaluation processes should be evaluated and assessed. In this synopsis, data on new TB cases between January 2005 and December 2005 and per capita costs of TB intervention outcomes in El

Paso City-County Health & Environmental District and 9 Texas health districts and the TJD Health District were collected from the Centers for Disease Control and Prevention (CDC& P), and from the state and local government databases. In addition, data for this evaluation were collected from El Paso County Health Department and 10 Texas health districts, including Houston City and the TJD Health District. Furthermore, when evaluating, the performer should determine relationships between performance outputs and end results, and the implications of collected data on average new and old cases of disease for each year.

SYNOPSIS THREE

EVALUATING THE IMPACT OF HOSPITAL AND HEALTHCARE FINANCE APPROPRIATIONS ON NURSE RETENTION IN EL PASO

A. INTRODUCTION

In more industrialized countries like the US, more investments should be made in the retention of nurses since they form the core of the healthcare sector. Second, Nurses are best suited for performing needs assessments during crisis (**Part 1; Chapter 1; Section 6**). If properly planned and implemented, their input could save hundreds and thousands of dollars. Furthermore, nurse retention should be promoted because nurses, when placed and trained correctly, can provide the needed feedback mechanism for program evaluation.

In most developing countries, nurses and mid-wives as a skill set in the healthcare sector, supersede other skill sets in healthcare categories at the rural level. Consequently, to impact the programs target and to achieve the strategic outcome and goals of an infectious disease intervention program, activities planned should include the training and empowerment of nurses and mid-wives. While other approaches can be effective, recruiting and training nurses and mid-wife can be one of the most effective approaches. However, certain problems, and needs are anticipated. To better understand best practices for retaining nurses, this synopsis examines factors impacting nurse retention in Texas, specifically, government appropriations to see they can be used as an incentive.

B. FACTORS IMPACTING NURSE RETENTION IN TEXAS

According to the Center for Budget and Policy Priorities, the FY 2007 budget reduces national expenditures by $187 billion over five years by cutting non defense expenditures, and utilizing $156 billion over the first ten years for health related appropriations. These reductions have caused researchers in healthcare to raise the question: "would future national budgets be balanced at the expense of healthcare?" as a result, the decrease in nursing retention in the United States is causing concern among healthcare professionals. The budgetary question in nursing retention is not new. In general, it can be assumed that hospitals and healthcare facilities struggle to employ and recruit new nurses with little or no recruiting budget. Consequentially, several health institutions like the American Health Association (AHA), have called on Congress to increase the FY 07 budget to accommodate nursing funding. Meanwhile, based on numerous reports obtainable from National Council of States Board of Nursing, the nursing shortage continues to be a national crisis. However, statistically, there is evidence that the magnitude of the crisis is unevenly distributed nationally. Interestingly, the impact of state appropriations in healthcare and hospitals has not been fully studied. Here, this synopsis uses annual growth rate computations and multiple regression analysis to quantify the relationship (causality, and correlation) between Texas state healthcare and hospital appropriations, and nursing retention.

B. USING A NON EXPERIMENTAL EVALUATION APPROACH

A non-experimental descriptive approach and literature reviews have been used to collect data on health and hospital per capita budgetary appropriations in Texas State between the year 1994 and 2003 from the US Census Bureau. The numbers of active registered and licensed nurses were collected for the same period from the National Council of States Board or Nursing (Nurse Licensure and NCLEX® Examination Statistics). To analyze the potential impact of the health and hospital appropriations in Texas in nursing retention, the average annual growth rate of health, hospital and nursing retention was calculated using a standard formula (**Table 20**). A multiple regression analysis was performed using SPSS (SPSS Inc. Chicago, USA), to determine correlations and causality relationships that may exist. Furthermore, for this analysis, data on actively registered nurses is used as the dependent variable, and health, and hospital appropriations were used as independent variables to determine the extent to which each independent variable is related to the outcome of the dependent variable. Finally, results were used to predict the trends in annual growth rate of nursing registration for the future. Previously, similar studies were conducted using techniques reported by Ament, (1998). During these studies data on employment benefits were collected using questionnaires.

C. EVALUATING OUTCOME DATA

Between 1994 and 2003, the average annual growth rate of the per capita Texas expenditure for hospitals was determined to be 3.55% (**Table 20**). Conversely, over the same period, the average annual growth rate for the state per capita expenditures in health was -0.16% (**Table 21**). These results suggest the growth rates in both hospital and healthcare expenditures are polar.

Table 21. Average annual growth rate of the per capita Texas expenditure for hospitals

(THOUSANDS OF DOLLARS) USD

	1994	1995	1996	1997	1998	1999	2000	2001	2002	2003	* Average Annual Growth Rate
State Hospital Per/Capita Budget	93.67	99.25	99.3	100.91	116.66	130.46	141.36	141.9	149.08	128.18	3.55%
State Health Per/ Capita Budget	64.33	66.69	61.69	68.51	73.39	73.5	77.12	80.76	83.72	63.42	-0.16%
Active Registered & Licensed Nurses	142,578	150,587	150,587	157,307	160,224	163,608	163,946	167,170	167,173	173,695	2.22%

Source

National Council of States Board of Nursing http://www.ncsbn.org/testing/psychometrics_nclexlicensure_examstats.asp
US Census Bureau http://www.census.gov/govs/www/state.html

Average Annual Growth Rate = **[(Y/X)^(1/N)]-1**
where Y = value for last year; X value for the first year

To characterize the observed polarity and to determine its relationship to nursing retention, a multiple regression analysis using health and hospital per capita expenditures as independent variables was used to determine the relationships to the annual growth rate of active registered and licensed nurses over the same period. Earlier, the average annual growth rate of active registered nursed in the state of Texas between 1994 and 2003 was determined to be 2.22 % **(Table 21).** Based on previous findings (Donley et al, 2006; Spetz, 2006), it appears that this observed trend in the annual growth rate of active registered nurses in Texas for the year studied can qualify as the nominal benchmark for low nursing retention.

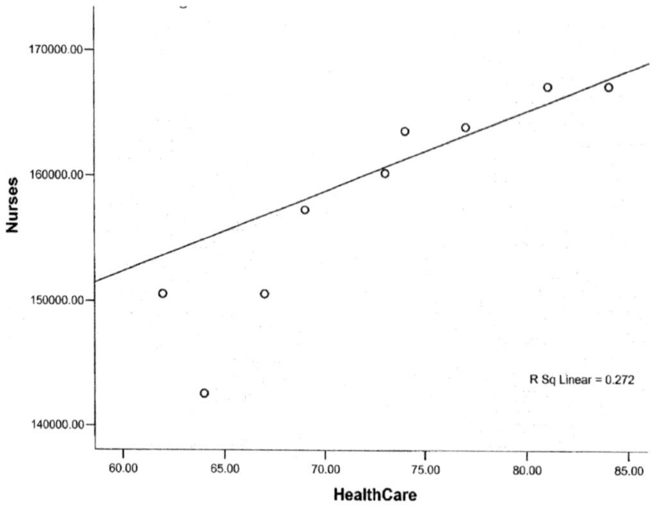

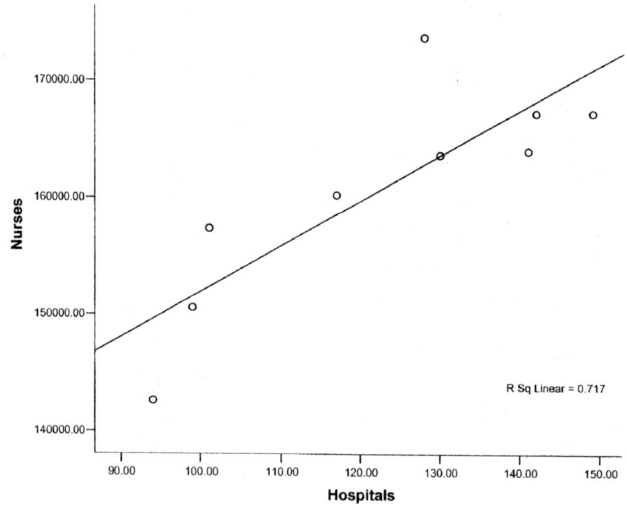

Figure 11 SPSS output showing significant correlations between (a) healthcare and (b) hospital per capita expenditure and nurse retention ($p=0.001$; $p>0.005$ respectively). Furthermore, 81% of the variability in nursing retention in Texas between 1994 and 2003 can be explained by the state appropriations in healthcare and hospitals combined. However, independently, healthcare can explain 27.2 % and hospital appropriations can explain 71.7% of the variability in nursing retention.

Previously, in *Challenges for Nursing in the 21st Century*, investigators discuss and analyze various factors that contribute to the current shortages facing the nursing profession (Donley, 2006). The author cites a lack of personal satisfaction as being the major cause for the decrease in retention, along with the negative impact of changing delivery systems brought about by insurance policies and programs, and increasing complexity of the healthcare delivery system. The author also cites the negative impact of low budgets on nursing retention (Donley et al, 2006). To remedy the problem, the author advocates thinking out of the box as a way to correct current views and visions that prevent or inhibit our capability of putting ideas into practice.

Finally, the author recommends that nurses and physicians should act together collaboratively to restore altruism within the system. At present, nurses' employment benefits represent as much as 29% of compensation provided by employees. These benefits may be increased as one way of recruiting and retaining nurses (Spetz et al, 2006). In addition, the author shows that registered nurses were more likely to enroll in non-salaried programs like retirement savings than any other profession (only 5% of registered nurses were uninsured in 2003). Furthermore, good staffing ratios and overtime work policies were more helpful in nursing retention than incrementally improving other benefits; vacation, sick leave, and unpaid time off were also found to be very important to registered nurses, as were "career ladder" programs that upgrade the education of the nurses (Spetz et al, 2006).

According to Moore et al, (1995), a reason for the positive impact of employment benefits appears to be the nurses' expectation for adequate incomes during retirement, as well as their current pension, benefit, and saving plans. In an independent study performed by Huges, et al, (1993), the benefits associated with nursing were investigated. Evaluations of the outcomes for this study show that positive outcomes are associated with nursing externships, especially when financial remunerations were offered. Perhaps one way to accommodate budgetary constraints with the goal of improving nursing retention would be to utilize Max Weber's theories in bureaucracy and formal organization to efficiently manage scarce resources and improve staff relations and working conditions with the aim of increasing retention (Liebler et al, 2004). According to Weber, this can be achieved through a charismatic approach to improving the quality of life.

Alternatively, the Deming approach emphasizes quality improvements through quality management as a human relations approach (Liebler et al, 2004). In both cases, budgetary constraints— excluding training costs— are low, or not an issue. On the subject of improving quality, several studies have detailed ways to achieve this. In study performed by the US Institute of Medicine titled *Crossing the Quality Chasm: A New Health System for the 21st Century*, researchers acknowledge that the US health care delivery system does not provide consistent high quality care to all people and that the current system was highly complex and was characterized by "more to know, and more to do, more to manage, more to watch, and more people involved". As evidence, the investigators state that Americans generally are not living longer and that organizational problems are apparent, particularly in chronic cases. Hospitals act without the benefit of complete information.

The authors then suggest six strategies to reinvent the system, which they summarize as safety, efficiency, patient focus, quick response, equitability, and cost benefit. The authors base these strategies on seven rules:

- Provision of care based continuous relationships
- Customized care based on patients needs and values
- Patient empowerment, knowledge sharing,
- Evidence based decision making
- Safety system prioritization
- Transparency, anticipated needs
- Limited waste, and increased cooperation

To implement these strategies, the authors suggest that congress and the executive get involved to change the work environment by applying evidence to health care delivery, using information technology, aligning payment policies with quality improvements, and preparing the work force. They conclude that the time for change is now.

In a recent study, it was found that most physicians do not use quality improvements in their places of work (Audet et al, 2005). According to Brooks et al, (1996), health system reform and quality are related to issues of efficacy, effectiveness, and efficiency, as well as economic issues. Furthermore, to improve performance, guidelines for improvement should be transparent and accurate (Davidoff et al, 2005). To further support this claim, Sperroff et al, (2004), suggests the use of the plan-do-study-act (PDSA) strategy, and notes that this strategy should follow policy projects.

In a separate study, suggestions were made that implementations be tracked by the Joint Commission on Accreditation of Health Care Organizations (JAHCO) using both qualitative and quantitative approaches (Williams et al, 2005). In *To Err is Human: Building a Safer Health System*, researchers at the National Institute of Medicine show that 44,000 to 98,000 people die in US hospitals each year as a result of preventable mistakes by healthcare professionals and medical errors. Furthermore, the cost in medicine of these errors runs between 17 and 29 billion dollars per year. They add that the factors and varieties of the error are attributable to decentralization and fragmentation of the system or "non system" and that the error types range from diagnostic to treatment and preventative. According to Deber, (1994), a relationship exists between physician patient decision making, the problem solving ability of the physician, and the patient's desire to participate.

In reference to this observation, Braddock et al, (1999), concludes that incomplete decision making by physicians can be perpetuated by uninformed decision making due to lack of patient participation. Furthermore, the authors suggest the trait can be reversed by increasing the patient's role in decision-making. Combined, these results appear to imply that, increasingly, patients should be involved in decision making as a way to improve healthcare quality and minimize hospital operational costs. In the article *Shared decision making, is not always a positive patient experience*, published in *Medscape* by Reuters Health Information, the publication point out the negative effects and impact of the practice of physician patient information sharing practices. Furthermore, they state that proponents suggest it makes for a satisfying relationship between both parties.

The publication concludes that only 38 % of decisions used in the study actually stimulated physician-patient engagement and that trust, power, and communication were responsible for the subjective experience encountered.

In reference to the role of improved communication, reports show that information technology improves care (Simpson, R.L. 2005). According to Halter et al, (2006), there appears to be a link between sophistication of technology and greater use of distance learning. Furthermore, this relationship is similar to the increased use of online programs as a way to increase technology proficiency. An independent study conducted by Oberprieler et al (2005), explored the efficiency of using quantification strategies as opposed to non-quantification strategies for information technologies (IT) training and integration. Findings from this study show positive correlations between this scheme and the integration of IT in undergraduate courses of health science students. Finally, recent studies performed by Desjardins et al, (2005), show that use of information and communication technologies is essential for competency for all health care professionals. In addition, to advance healthcare into the millennium, the healthcare professional must be proficient in the use of informatics. To achieve best results, healthcare institutions must incorporate IT learning as early as possibly into the educational curriculum.

D. CONCLUSIONS

In conclusion, these findings show that the correlations between hospital and healthcare per capita expenditure and nursing retention are significant ($p=0.001$; $p>0.005$ respectively). Furthermore, 81% of the variability in nursing retention in Texas between 1994 and 2003 can be explained by the state appropriations in healthcare and hospitals combined **(Table 21 and Figure 17**). However, independently, healthcare can explain 27.2 % and hospital appropriations can explain 71.7% of the variability in nursing retention. These findings suggest that an annual average growth rate of 2.22% of nursing retention in Texas between the years 1993 and 2003 may be unable to sustain required nursing manpower in the future. Furthermore, the findings of this synopsis, and those presented in earlier reports and analysis of the fiscal year 2007 US presidential budget presented by the Center on Budget and Policy Priorities, suggest that in its current form, the fiscal year 2007 budget may not go as far to increase appropriations for healthcare and hospitals in Texas to an extent that would significantly increase the average annual growth rate of actively registered nurses in Texas. Collectively, these findings suggest that average annual growth rate of nursing retention in Texas, and perhaps in the country at large, will continue to grow at an inadequate pace.

SYNOPSIS FOUR

PLANNING FOR PANDEMIC FLU IN EL PASO

A. INTRODUCTION

At present, "avian flu" is being commonly used to refer to infection from a particular subtype of influenza, a virus H5N1 which cause severe illness in humans who are infected. Currently, this strain is transmitted by contact with infected birds and has been transmitted from one person to another only in a few cases. H5N1 flu is therefore not pandemic now and is not currently capable of causing a pandemic. Only if H5N1 mutates into a form that can be readily transmitted from one person to another could it cause a pandemic.

As early as 2004, the United States government developed old assumptions for pandemic influenza planning, and these include the following:

- Pandemics can occur at any time
- Influenza pandemics have a 3% annual risk of occurrence and occurred at intervals from 10 to 40 years over the past few centuries
- Susceptibility to the pandemic influenza virus will be universal
- Efficient and sustained person-to-person transmission signals an imminent pandemic
- Clinical disease attack rate will likely be 30% or higher in the overall population during the pandemic
- Illness rates will be highest among school-aged children (about 40%) and decline with age
- Among working adults, an average of 20% will become ill during a community outbreak some persons will become infected but not develop clinically significant symptoms.
- Asymptomatic or minimally symptomatic individuals can transmit infection and develop immunity to subsequent infection

PROBLEM WITH ASSUMPTIONS

While these assumptions appear academic, the fundamental problem is that planning is ineffective when the outcome cannot be quantified. Previously, none of the previous assumptions quantified outcome. This is important since the next influenza pandemic will spread rapidly throughout the world. Modeling estimates suggest up to 180 days is needed to penetrate all sites on the globe. The pandemic will occur in waves lasting from 6 to 8 weeks in a specific community over a period of 12 to 24 months usually in 2-3 waves. Local organizations and governments may not be able to rely on the state or federal assistance to support local response efforts, except in the development of vaccine and in the dispersal of antiviral. An effective vaccine for the new virus will not be available for 3 to 8 months after the pandemic begins, and there will not be enough vaccine for everyone initially. Antiviral for treatment will be in short supply and may not be effective.

At present in the US, the following assumptions can be made: there is enough antiviral for 2% of our population now. By December 2006, the government will have enough for 6%, and by September 2007, the government will have enough for 25%. The production capacity is increasing, and these goals may be reached sooner than these dates. Insufficient medication and vaccine supplies will place a greater importance on non-pharmaceutical strategies, such as social distancing, hand washing, and respiratory etiquette. A new virus may not follow the usual seasonal pattern of influenza and may occur at any time of year. Of those who become ill with influenza, up to 50% may seek outpatient medical care. In a severe pandemic, absenteeism attributable to illness, the need to care for ill family members and fear of infection may reach 40% during the peak weeks of a community outbreak, with lower rates of absenteeism during the weeks before and after the peak. Rates may be higher in health care facilities. Rates of absenteeism will depend on the severity of the pandemic. Certain social distancing measures (closing schools, quarantining household contacts of infected individuals, "snow days") are likely to increase rates of absenteeism. The typical incubation period (interval between infection and onset of symptoms) for seasonal influenza is approximately two days. On average, infected persons will transmit infection to approximately two-three other people. Multiple waves (periods during which community outbreaks occur across the country) of illness could occur with each wave lasting two to three two months.

Historically, the largest waves of influenza outbreaks have occurred in the fall and winter, but the seasonality of a pandemic cannot be predicted with certainty. Persons who become ill may shed virus and can transmit infection for up to one day before the onset of illness. Viral shedding and the risk of transmission will be greatest during the first two days of illness. Children usually shed the greatest amount of virus and therefore are likely to pose the greatest risk for transmission. Risk groups for severe and fatal infection cannot be predicted with certainty but are likely to include infants, the elderly, pregnant women, and persons with chronic medical conditions. In the 1918 pandemic, 15-35 year olds died at a rate 20 times higher than in past. Reduction of workforces due to the direct and indirect effects of flu on employees and their families will occur; estimates range from 20% to 60%, from both illness and fear. It is reasonable to assume as many as 40% of regular employees will not be available for routine work during the peak of a pandemic; there would likely be significant disruption and impact on our community's critical infrastructure, essential services, healthcare, education, and social services.

In addition, the number of ill persons requiring outpatient care and hospitalization may overwhelm the local healthcare system; mortality rates for influenza will likely be between 0.1% (1968) and 0.5% (1918). Hospitals and clinics may have to modify their normal operational structure and standards of care to respond to very high patient volumes and keep patients isolated. Alternative care sites may need to be identified to triage and care for ill persons; shortages in certain supplies such as gloves, masks, IV fluids, and other critical items may develop due to interruptions in supply lines and production capacity; demand for hospital beds and ventilators could increase by as much as 10-fold above normal. Most hospitals are near 90-95% of capacity under routine operating conditions. Some exceed their surge capacity during a routine influenza season. Emergency Medical Services (EMS) and Urgent Care Medical Services will face extremely high demands. Nursing and other medical staff (RT, etc.) shortages will be amplified by the fact that such personnel work in multiple facilities.

B. SOLVING THE PROBLEM

The word pandemic has horrific implications. Between the period of 1918 and 1919, 50 million people died from flu viruses worldwide due to lack of efficient vaccines, poor surge, inadequate health care systems and facilities, and erratic regional planning (Bartlett, 2006). By definition, bird flu (avian flu) or H5N1 is a highly infectious mutant strain of influenza virus. Currently, the fear is that the bird flu pandemic may occur at any time, initiating an impact in terms of morbidity, mortality, and economic cost (Gust, Hampson, and Lavanchy, 2001). The challenges are enormous, including travel bans, school closings, cancellation of public events, and other widespread economic and social disruptions. So far, there are no vaccines to protect humans from the virus (Winterfeld, 2006). However, new immune boosting therapeutics based on proteomics show promise. In the absence of a vaccine, plans for responding to the pandemic are based principally on surveillance programs (Gust, Hampson, and Lavanchy, 2001). In response, in 2005, the White House drafted a national strategy for combating the bird flu / pandemic influenza.

C. US GUIDELINES AND REGULATIONS

HISTORICAL OVERVIEW

Guidelines and procedures for implementing the national strategy on bird flu for states and local governments were developed by the office of the Secretary of Health and Human Services (HHS), specifically, the Office of the Assistant Secretary for Public Health Emergency Preparedness (ASPHEP), and the Incident Management Team (IMT) within the Secretary's Operation Center (SOC). Subsequently, in addition to 500 million dollars already appropriated, state and local governments are scheduled to receive an additional 100 million dollars through the Department of HHS to strengthen preparedness efforts. This figure represents a mere portion of 350 million dollars in emergency appropriation package by Congress before 2006 (Gosnell, 2006; Winterfed, 2006). In addition, an extra 250 million dollars was allocated in August 2006.

According to procedures dictated by the National Strategic Plan laid out by the White House, predicting the outcome of the pandemic in terms of disease prevalence is the first step in any strategic planning process. Earlier, using models and experiences from the 1918 influenza pandemic and 2002 Severe Acute Respiratory Syndrome (SARS) outbreak, plans and procedure developed by the Department of Health and Human Services have mandated that local and state health department planners determine outcomes of bird flu pandemic by making the following assumptions about the pandemic:

- Relative risk (impact) of infection is universal
- Viral infection rate will be 30% in the population
- Illness rate will be highest among school-aged children (about 40%) and decline with age
- An average of 20% of working adults will become ill during a community outbreak
- Of those who become ill with bird flu, 50% will seek outpatient medical care
- The number of hospitalizations and deaths will depend on the virulence of the pandemic virus
- Because of the virulence of the bird flu virus that causes the next pandemic cannot be predicted

ESTABLISHMENT OF A COORDINATION COMMITTEE

According to HHS guidelines, the first step for state and local government's emergency managers is to establish a coordinating committee to oversee preparedness planning and ensure integration with other emergency planning efforts and ensure necessary resources are available everywhere they are needed in a short time (Winterfed, 2006). The membership of the coordinating committee should represent a range of disciplines and expertise in the public and private sectors. The committee should draft a plan that:

- Outlines human resource roles and responsibilities
- Adds to current preparedness and response plans
- Covers legal issues associated with hospital staffing, patient care, and quarantine
- Is periodically reviewed and updated
- Consolidates and advances community-based task forces that support healthcare
- Identifies the authority responsible for state-level declaration of a public health emergency and for officially activating the pandemic influenza response plan
- Identifies an overall coordinator to work with hospitals and communicating with medical and mental health personnel during a pandemic

- Identifies the jurisdiction's controlling authority over intrastate and interstate modes of transportation, which might be curtailed during a pandemic
- Identifies state and local law enforcement personnel who will assist in maintaining public order and enforcing control measures during a pandemic
- Develops and reinforces relationships with local health authorities in adjoining jurisdictions
- Makes planning decisions on acquisition and distribution of antiviral drugs and vaccines in accordance with HHS recommendations
- Ensures that plans take into account tribal populations where applicable
- Conducts state- level "table top" exercises to test response capabilities
- Encourages local jurisdictions to conduct exercises and drills

LEGAL PREPAREDNESS

Legal preparedness should be preformed to ensure laws and procedures for closing businesses or schools and suspending public meetings during a declared state of emergency; available medical volunteer licensure and liability and compensation laws for in-state, out-of-state, and returning retired and non-medical volunteers; quarantine laws and their application in a public health emergency; workers compensation laws as they apply to healthcare workers and workers who provide essential services; and reimbursement for workers placed in isolation or quarantine.

ESTABLISHMENT OF EMERGENCY SUPPORT FUNCTIONS

According to HHS, the full set of emergency support functions should include the following:

- Transportation
- Communications
- Public works and engineering
- Firefighting; emergency management
- Mass care, housing, human services
- Resource support
- Public health and medical services
- Urban search and rescue
- Oil and hazardous materials response
- Agriculture and natural resources
- Energy; public safety and security
- Long-term community recovery and mitigation
- and external affairs

To enable these functions, according to the department of health and human services, hospital staff should include the following:

- Administration/senior management
- Legal counsel/risk management
- Infection control/hospital epidemiology
- Hospital disaster/emergency coordinator
- Engineering/physical plant/industrial hygiene/institutional safety
- Nursing administration; medical staff
- Intensive-care unit
- Emergency department
- Laboratory services
- Respiratory therapy
- Nutrition and food
- Services; pharmacy
- Environmental services
- Public relations
- Security
- Materials management
- Education/training/staff development
- Occupational health
- Diagnostic imaging
- Information technology
- Adjunct staff members
- Infectious diseases
- Mental health
- Union representatives
- Human resources
- Social work
- Director of house staff/fellowship and other training programs
- Critical care medicine
- Pathology

In addition, on the level of state and local health administration, the following departments should be mobilized:

- Communicable disease division
- Laboratory services
- Medical examiners
- Community partners
- Emergency medical technicians
- Local law enforcement
- Funeral service personnel
- Community service agencies; and federally qualified health centers (FQHC)

EL PASO LOCAL GOVERNMENT GUIDELINES AND ORDINANCES

Furthermore, medical planners should conduct individual interviews with Fire Department representatives; and County Health Department administrators. Based on the outcomes of such interviews, in this synopsis, it appears that the City and County of El Paso have a bird flu emergency plan which complies with national guidelines and procedures, and in accordance with El Paso City Ordinances # 009036 (1987), Horizon City Ordinance # 060 (1995), Town of Clint City Ordinance # 88 (1995), City of Vinton Ordinance # 095-919 (1995), Commissioners Court Order # 006 (1987), Joint Resolution between the City of El Paso and County of El Paso (1987), and Inter-Local Agreements & Contracts. In the event of an emergency, the plan is coordinated from a situation room at the Emergency Operational Support Center located down town at the basement of El Paso City Hall.

D. PUTTING IT ALL TOGETHER

During a pandemic outbreak of bird flu, the emergency manager should have the capacity to direct and coordinate local county agencies involved in containing the outbreak. These agencies include county and public health epidemiology, laboratory departments, and the private sector (hospitals, pharmaceutical companies, etc.) **See (Tables 12,13,14,15,16,17, and 18)**.

In addition, under the plan, individuals have the responsibility to report incidence of disease in a timely manner. Subsequently, according to HHS, non-hospital healthcare facilities should create a planning team and develop a written plan, establish a decision-making and coordinating structure that can be tested during the inter-pandemic period and will be activated during an influenza pandemic, and determine how to conduct surveillance for pandemic influenza in healthcare personnel and for residential facilities. Furthermore, in the population served, planners should develop policies and procedures for managing pandemic influenza in patients and staff:

- Educate and train healthcare personnel on pandemic influenza and the healthcare facility's response plan
- Determine how the facility will communicate and coordinate with healthcare partners and public health authorities during a pandemic
- Determine how the facility will communicate with patients and help educate the public regarding prevention and control measures
- Develop a plan for procuring the supplies like personal protective equipment needed to manage influenza patients
- Determine how the facility will participate in the community plan for distributing either vaccine or antiviral drugs, including possibly serving as a point of distribution and providing staff for alternative community points of distribution

Finally, according to HHS, healthcare facilities should improve communication with medical care providers and health care organizations:

- Monitor local hospital resources like adult and pediatric hospital beds, intensive care unit beds, emergency department beds, medical supplies, respirators and other equipment, mortuary capacity
- Address emergency healthcare staffing needs and other medical surge capacity issues
- Encourage coordination among state and federal healthcare facilities, such as Veterans Administration hospitals, Indian Health Service facilities, and Department of Defense hospitals

HHS and other independent investigators recommend that planners conduct contingency planning with private sector groups that support hospital functions to ensure continuity of operations during the pandemic (Gosnell, 2006). These groups may include medical supply companies:

- Medical gas companies
- Companies that supply food and clean linens, and internet service providers
- Public utilities to ensure continued service during the pandemic
- Local law enforcement agencies who can help maintain order if a hospital is overwhelmed by a large volume of patients
- Identify alternative care sites for patient care and sites for quarantine
- Identify community-based organizations that can provide psychological and social Support to healthcare workers, public health field workers, and other emergency responders

E. PROGRAM EVALUATION

According to the National Strategic Plan, HHS will be tasked to evaluate current policies from data on efficiency gathered by state and local governments and from private and public professionals at national and regional conferences and workshops. Specifically, the information will be collected through the National Response Coordination Center (NRCC); the Interagency Incident Management Group (IIMG), and the Joint Information Center (JIC), medical response assets internal to HHS like the U.S. Public Health Service Commissioned Corps, and Department of Homeland Security's National Disaster Medical System (NDMS).

In addition, for purposes of accountability, HHS designated federal responsibilities include advancing international preparedness, surveillance, response and containment activities. Programs should support the establishment of countermeasure stockpiles and production capacity by facilitating:

- Developing vaccines, antiviral, diagnostics and personal protective equipment
- Supporting domestic needs and encouraging the development of production capacity around the world
- Advancing the science necessary to produce effective vaccines, therapeutics, and diagnostics
- Stockpiling and coordinating the distribution of necessary countermeasures, in concert with states and other entities
- Ensuring that federal departments and agencies, including federal health care systems, have developed and exercised preparedness and response plans that take into account the potential impact of a pandemic on the federal workforce, and are configured to support state, local and private sector efforts as appropriate
- Facilitating state and local planning through funding and guidance; providing guidance to the private sector and public on preparedness and response planning, in conjunction with states and communities.

Accordingly, state and local responsibilities designated include ensuring measures are taken to limit the spread of an outbreak within and beyond the community's borders:

- Establishing credible preparedness and response plans that are exercised on a regular basis
- Integrating non-health entities in the planning for a pandemic, including law enforcement, utilities, city services and political leadership; establishing state and community-based stockpiles and distribution systems to support a comprehensive pandemic response
- Identifying key spokespersons for the community, ensuring that they are educated in risk communication, and have coordinated crisis communications plans; and providing public education campaigns on pandemic influenza and public and private interventions

An analysis of the National Strategic Plan on the bird flu pandemic appears to show ambiguity in the first step of the plan. Consequentially, accountability for outcomes associated with the National Strategic Plan rests disproportionately on the federal government. This lack of near "real-time" capability may lead to some problems being under-determined.

Nevertheless, the political dimensions in the plan appear to be clear. The levels affecting the core of the policies are distinct, as is the plans implications and impact on individual citizens and employees. In conclusion, the National Strategic Plan for the bird flu pandemic appears to be concise and comprehensive. The process for evaluation and accountability are clear and distinct. Furthermore, the plan takes into account all levels of the government, private businesses, individual and family roles. According to Gosnell, (2006), in its present form, accountability to the outcome of the National Strategic Plan on the bird flu lies heavily on the federal government, specifically, on the Department of Health and Human Services, in part, because local and states governments have not been empowered in a key decision making process, namely in the prediction and determination of pandemic outcome at the grass roots level.

Consequently, adopted performance measures (goals, activities, and functions) may be inadequate and ineffective in the advent of an outbreak. To correct these deficiencies a systematic approach needs to be adopted to better predict pandemics outcome in "near real time" to avoid pending policy or administration gaps as well as tensions between policy and administrative decisions. Finally, planners at the local level should be empowered and better equipped to predict possible outcomes of pandemics in their communities. Perhaps the private sector could intervene and develop technologies to bridge the divide.

USING MATHEMATICAL MODELS

On the subject of pandemic flu planning, regardless of threat, and institution, the best practice would be for the medical planners to plan strategically and adopt performance-based methods. These processes would include the following: identifying stake holders early in the process, meet, and brain-storm with stakeholders to establish roles and develop, plan to mobilize target population and stakeholders. In addition, the plan has to be feasible medically, economically (budget), and logistically.

Furthermore, the plan should contain existing benchmarks (if any), develop inputs (activities) based on evaluation of these benchmarks, and in the absence of existing benchmarks, the performer should generate the best estimate of anticipated outcome. *The first step in strategic planning is to quantify the problem, situation, and needs.* Subsequently, the performer can design or implement feasible activities or inputs that would facilitate the outcome or decrease the outcome based on the programs goals. Furthermore, the plan should conform to federal, state, and local government guidelines before institutional considerations are made. A great tool for accomplishing this is with use of a logic matrix **(Part 1; Chapter 1; Section 4)**. Furthermore, some key questions needs to be asked by the planner. These questions should include the following:

- How do you determine work force needs for dealing with a possible bird flu outbreak?
- How do you develop policy and procedures to address bird flu outbreak?
- How do you determine facilities needed to handle bird flu outbreak?
- How do you evaluate your plans for the bird flu outbreak?
- What is your process for accountability?

Previously, investigators determined that the inherent variability of the bird flu virus makes the prediction of disease outcome difficult but not impossible, with the use of mathematical models. Furthermore, these models can be used to quantify key parameters and outcomes even when relationships are nonlinear and incomprehensible (McConnell, 2006; Smith, 2006). At present, there are at least two widely used systematic analytical approaches to the predicting the outcome of infectious disease: the *Haddon Matrix*, developed in the1960s, which provides a multidimensional non-linear approach to understanding the contributing factors to injury, before, during, and after the event (Barnett et al, 2005); and the Biological Agents Index (BAC,. El Paso, Texas), which is based on the Epidemiologic Transition Theory (Oman, 1977), and Mass Action Principle (Nokes and Anderson, 1988). This mathematical model uses an outbreak coefficient in a multiple regression equation where the dependent variable is infectious disease prevalence, and independent variables are relative risk for infection, microbial reproductive rate, and infectious diseases incidence. The index is available online at *www.biologicalagents.com*

Finally, socio economic problems and needs should be identified as well as the situation or other obstacles that may limit the plan. Furthermore, a good plan should detail job descriptions, staff well trained personnel, contain clear roles and responsibilities for all players as well as contingency plans, and base activities on *best practices* and not theoretical or research methods. In the absence of existing benchmarks, the performer should estimate outcome using Software like: FluSurge2.0 Excel Spreadsheets by CDC or BiologicalAgents INDEX Excel Spreadsheets (BAC, USA, El Paso, Texas). A comparison of both can be found in **Figure 18.**

Contingencies should also include planning in phases: 0, and levels 1, 2, and 3, specifically, performers should plan for: laboratory surveillance activity (level one), and a complete response plan with working budget (level one), the capability to institute preventive measures like environmental and industrial sanitation (phase one), and the capability to sustain and deploy accurate manpower and equipment (phase two).

Comparison of Input & Output of Currently Available Software for Estimating Flu Surge		
	FluSurge 2.0	BioINDEX2.0
	(CDC)	(BAC, USA, El Paso, TX)
INPUT		
Age	X	
Population (SIZE)	X	
Hospital Manpower	X	
Disease Duration	X	X
Microbial Attack Rate	X	
Microbial Infective Dose		X
# of ways Microbial is Spread		X
Location GDP or LQ		X
Population (DENSITY)		X
# Public Health & Clinical Laboratory Confirmed Cases		X
OUTPUT		
Disease Prevalence (Real-Time)		X
Disease Prevalence (Surge Estimate)		X
Microbial Attack Rate		X
Daily Hospital Admissions (Real Time)	X	
Daily Hospital Admissions (Surge Estimate)	X	
APPLICATION LIMITATIONS	Influenza	H5N1;HIV;Malaria;Multiple Drug Resistant Microbes;
		most highly infectious Disease with no known cure
SCIENTIFIC PRINCIPLE BEHIND ALGORITHM	Unknown	Epidemiologic Transition Theory;
		Microbial Mass Action Principle

Figure 18. Comparison of FluSurge2.0 and BiologicalAgent Index in Spreadsheets (BioINDEX2.0)

PRACTICE

TASK ONE

DEVELOP PROGRAM ACTIVITIES AND SERVICES

TASK

*Based on synopsis one through five, develop a comprehensive program to reduce new and old cases of TB and or avian flu in your community. Download the BiologicalAgents INDEX at **www.biologicalagents.com** (see mockup in **figure 20**). Google or Wikipedia needed information.*

A. Logon to www.BiologicalAgents.com/BiologicalAgents **Index 3RD Ed. Revised/BioIndex3.0**

- User id: biologicalagent
- Password: free

B. STEP ONE: POPULATE THE BIOLOGICAL AGENTS INDEX EXCEL SPREADSHEETS

- What is the population size of your target population?
- What is the population density of your target population?
- What is the location quotient or GDP for El Paso?
- What is the number of new and old cases of TB/Influenza in your target population?
- How many ways can TB/ influenza spread?
- What is the Infective dose of TB/ influenza?
- How many new and old cases of TB/ influenza can you expect to plan for?
- What is the attack rate of this infection?

C. STEP TWO

Based on the estimated new and old cases of disease, in the short term, determine program outputs and select manpower. Conceptual and impact models can be used to achieve this (**see Figures 19 and 20**).

- What are the intervention outputs needed to manage the healthcare surge (See **Figure 23-26**)?

- How would you plan to sustain and implement these interventions? See **Figure 19, 20, 21,** and **22.** Review **Part 1; Chapter 1; Section 1-10.**
- How would you select and organize manpower (see **Figure 20, and 22**. Review **Part 1; Chapter 1, Section 7**)

Target	Program	Means	Output	Outcome
Community	Intervention	Policy Change/ Finance	Activities/ Services	Increase in (LQ) Eradication of Infectious Disease Decrease in Infectious Disease

Figure 19. Impact model for use in selection of experimental group

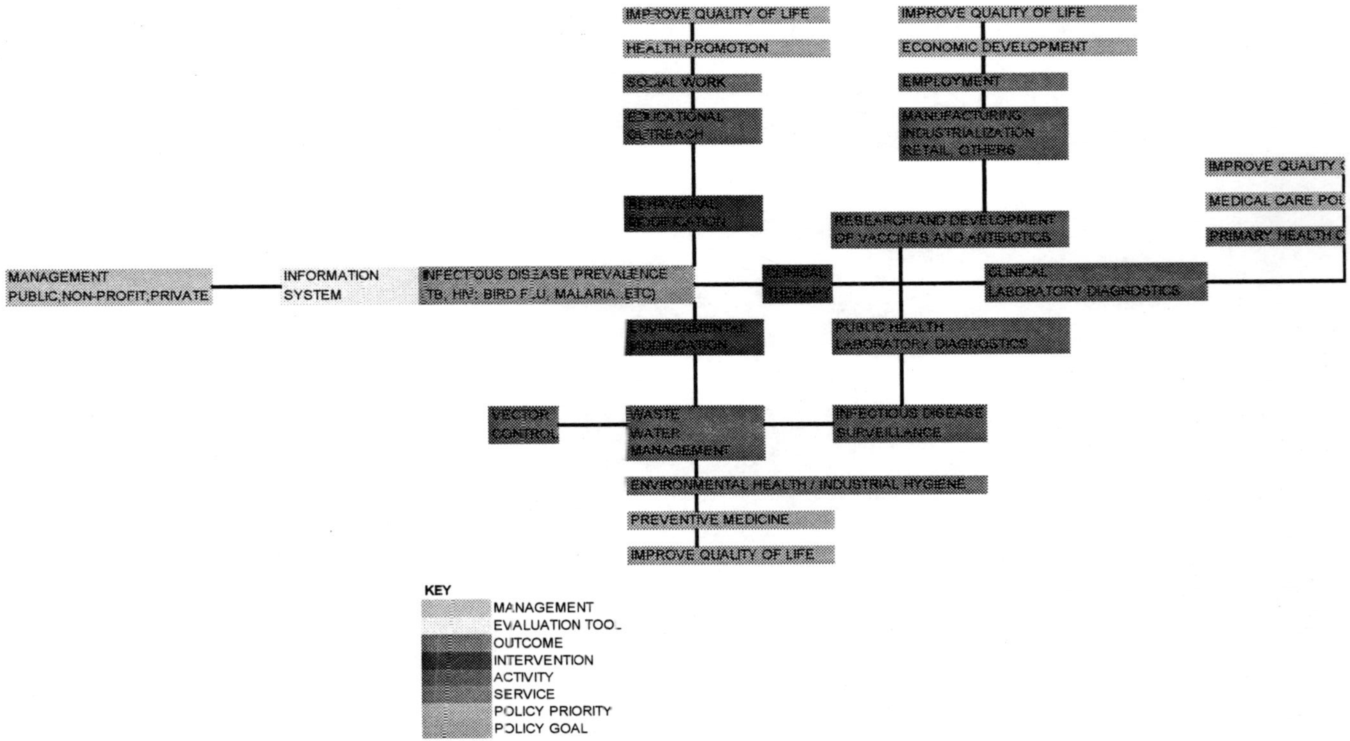

Figure 20. Conceptual model for creating an organizational chart for manpower and program outputs.

(SUPPLY)

Pandemic Bird Flu ProForma Budget

Phase	**% of Total**	**Per Capita**	**FY06**		Phase 0	Phase 0	Phase 0	Phase I	Phase II	Phase III	Phase IV	Phase V
Cycle of Pandemic	**Budget**	**Expenditure**	**Clinic Budget**		(21 days)	(21 days)	(21 days)	(21 days)	(21 days)	(21 days)	(21 days)	(21 days)
Estimated Outcome in first 21 days (biological agents index)				**1,500.00**	**level one**	***level two**	***level thre**	*	*	*	*	*
Industrial Hygiene	3%	$ 0.62	3,802.2		935.0							
Preventative Medicine	14%	$ 3.18	19,416.9		4,774.7							
Primary Care	61%	$ 13.69	83,498.0		20,532.3							
Training	4%	$ 0.98	5,974.0		1,469.0							
Laboratory	18%	$ 4.11	25,089.7		6,169.6							
Service Population 6,100.0												
Total Branch Clinic Budget per FY06			**137,780.8**		**33,880.5**							
Total Budget PerCapita		**$ 22.59**										
Total % of Budget	**100%**											

*** Dependent on Estimated Outcome (disease prevalence. See total PerCapita budget for guidance)**

Note: Outcome should be determined systematically in near real-time during pandemic

Figure 21. Budget summary (hypothetical): Sample performance based budget.

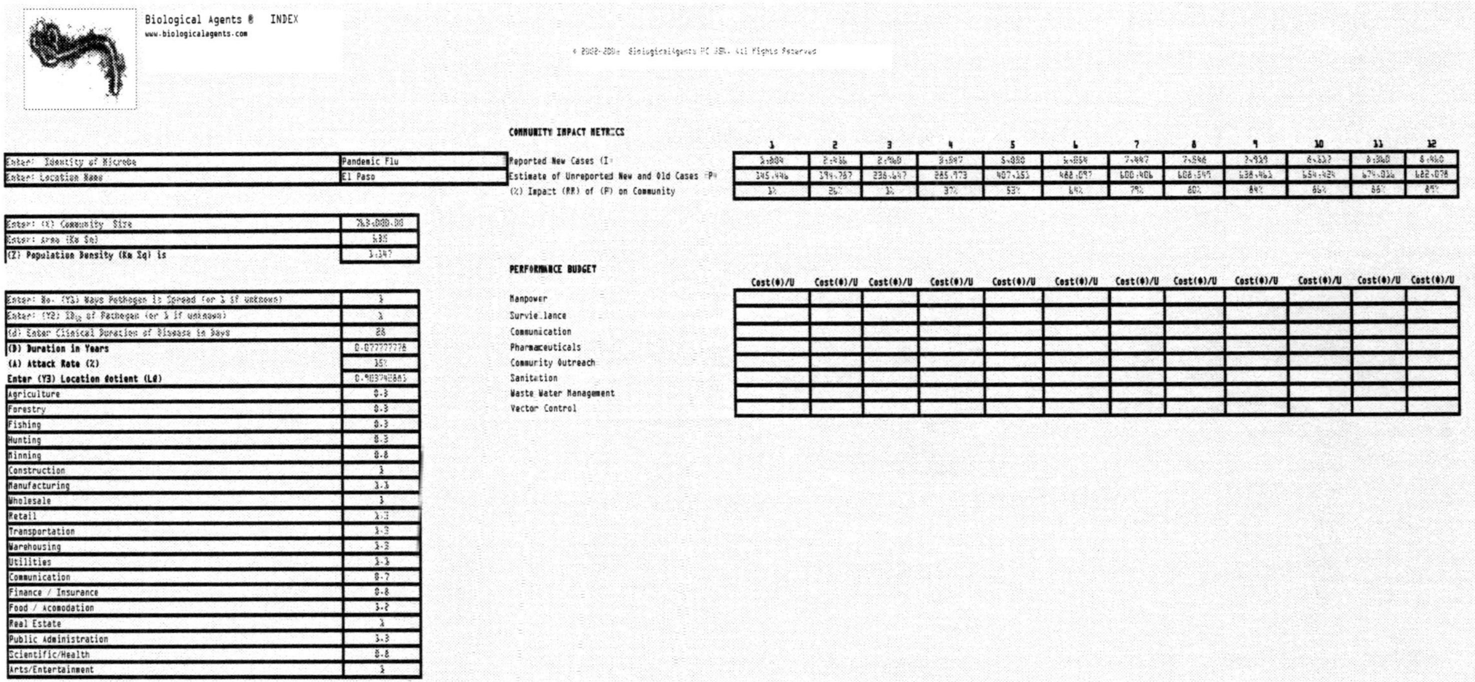

Figure 22. Mockup Screen Shot of the Biological Agents ® Index algorithms in a spreadsheet downloadable at *www.biologicalagents.com*

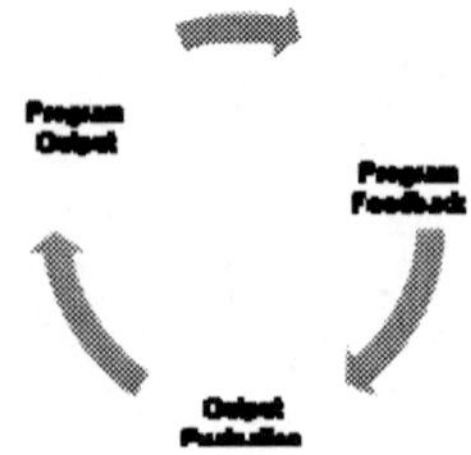

Figure 23. Continuous process for rural health advocacy

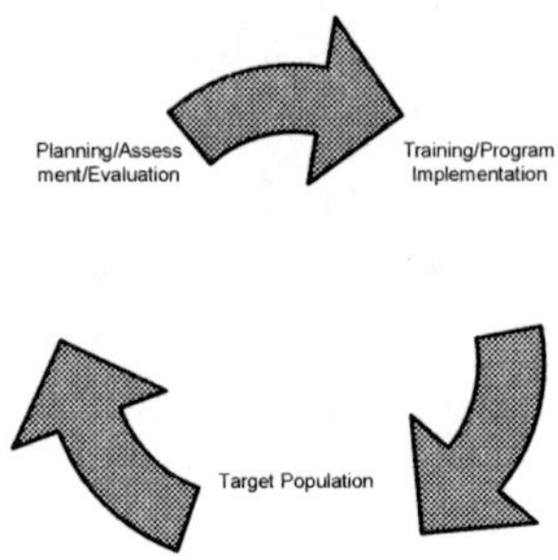

Figure 24. Continuous process for best practices training

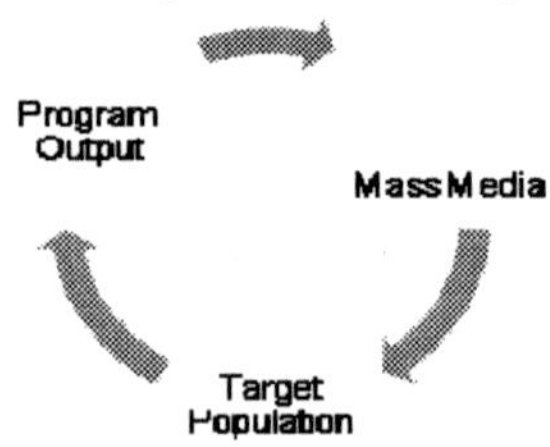

Figure 25. Continuous process for capacity strengthening

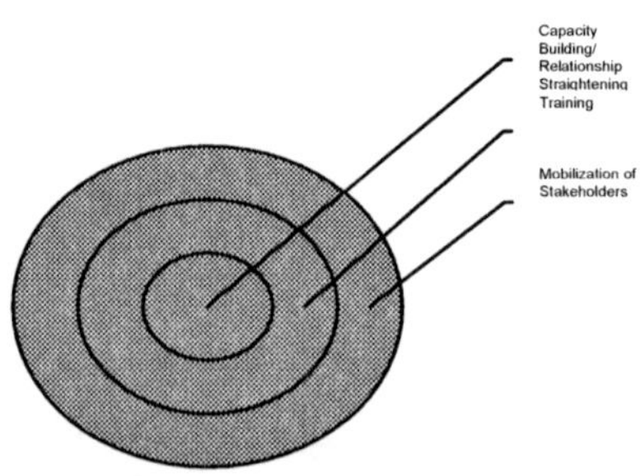

Figure 26. Continuous process for strategic goal development

TASK TWO

EVALUATE EL PASO PROGRAM IMPACT/OUTCOMES

A. STEP ONE: ANSWER THE FOLLOWING QUESTIONS

- What parameters or indicators are you going to use to determine the comparability of the groups (If using control groups)?
- What statistical techniques are you going to use to test for group equivalence (If using control groups)?
- How are you going to deal with the issues of external and construct validity?

B. STEP TWO. DEVELOP TIME SENSITIVE PERFORMANCE BUDGET TO ACCOUNT FOR:

- Medical equipment
- Non medical equipment
- Legal
- Pharmaceuticals
- Diagnostics
- Mortuary services
- Containments
- Sanitation
- Waste water management
- Animal control
- Continuous manpower training
- Continuous communication
- Continuous outreach
- Training manpower

See **Part 1; Chapter 1; Section 7; Figures 19** and **21;** and **Synopses 1,2,3,4**

STEP THREE: COMPARE YOU'RE PERFORMANCE BUDGET WITH SIMILAR BUDGETS FOR DIFFERENT YEARS OR THOSE IN DIFFERENT INSTITUTIONS (BENCHMARK).

See **Part 1; Chapter 1; Section 9; Figure 19;** and **Synopses 1,2,3,4**

STEP FOUR: PERFORM A COST-BENEFIT/ COST EFFECTIVE ANALYSIS OF BUDGET AS NEEDED.

See **Part 1; Chapter 1; Section 7, 8.9, 10** and **11,** and **Synopses 1,2,3,4**

STEP FIVE: AS A LABORATORY DIRECTOR, HOW WOULD YOU PRIORITIZE RESEARCH AND MANUFACTURING PRACTICES TO PRODUCE COST-EFFECTIVE DOSES OF IMMUNE BOOSTING THERAPEUTICS FOR USE IN VACCINES AND PROFYLAXIS AGAINST A PANDEMIC FLU STRAINS

See Part 1, Chapter 2; and Part 2, Chapter 3. Also See Figure 27

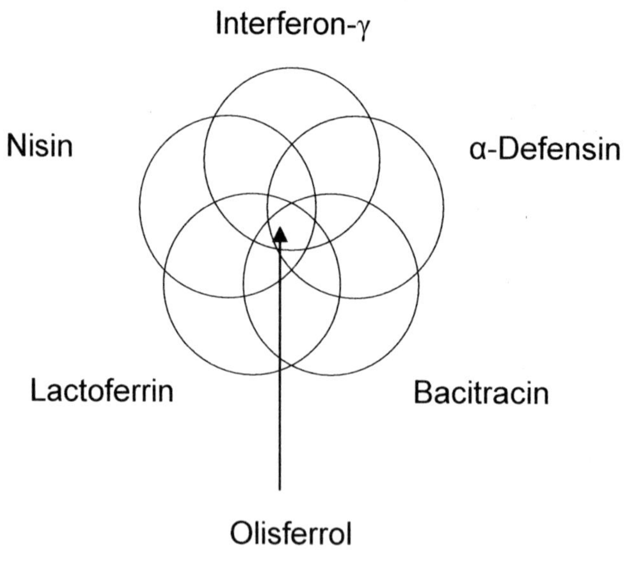

Figure 27. Similarity of Olisferrol with other human and bacterial antibiotics

REFERENCES

1. **Adams. G, Pope. John Paul II.** 2005. Politics. *Economist.* **375.**8421: 6-6.
2. **Alleyene, G.** 2002. Pan American Health Organization's first 100 years: Reflection of the director. *American Public Health Association.* **92.**12:1890-1894.
3. **Albala, C., F. Vio, and M. Yanez.** 1997. Epidemiological transition in Latin America: A comparison of four countries. *Review of Medical Child.* **125.**6: 719-27.
4. **Ament, L.** 1998. Reimbursement, employment, and hospital privilege data of certified nurse-midwifery services. *J Nurse Midwifery.* **43.**4: 305-9.
5. **Armstrong, G.L., L.A. Conn, and R.W. Pinner.**1999. Trends in infectious disease mortality in the United States during the 20th Century. *JAMA.* **281.**1: 61-6.
6. **Aziz, M., and A. Wright.** 2005. The World Health Organization: International union against tuberculosis and lung disease global project on surveillance for anti-tuberculosis drug resistance: A model for other infectious disease. *Clinical Infectious Disease.* **41.** S258-262.
7. **Bartlett, J. G.** 2006. Planning for avian influenza. *Ann Intern Med.* **145.**2: 141-144.
8. **Barnett, D.J., R.D. Balicer, D.R. Lucey, G.S. Everly, S. B. Omer, M.C. Steinhoff, and I. Grotto.** 2005. A systematic analytic approach to pandemic influenza preparedness planning. *PLoS Med.* **2.**12:359.
9. **Behn, R.** 2005. The magical performance system. Public management report. **2.** 5:1-2.
10. **Behn, R.** 2005. Adrenaline rush. Public management report. **2.**6:1-2.
11. **Behn, R.** 2005. Resistance to measurement. *Public Management Report.* **3.** 3:1-2.
12. **Bingham, R.D, and C.L. Felbinger.** 2002. *Evaluation in Practice. A Methodological approach.* (2nd. Ed.). New York. NY, USA: Chatham House Publishers.
13. **Braddock. C.H., K.A. Edwards, N.M. Hasenberg, T.L. Laidley, and W. Levinson.** Informed decision –making in outpatient practice: Time to get back to basics. *JAMA.* **282.**24: 2313-20.
14. **Brook R.H., C.J, Kamberg, and E.A. McGlynn.** 1996. Health system reform and quality. *JAMA.* **276.**6:476-80.
15. **Brass, W.** 1980. Policies for the reduction of mortality differentials. *Population Bulletin ECWA.* **19:**3-27
16. **Carroll, K, and G. Malefoasi.** 2004. Comparison of outcomes from a district tuberculosis control programmes in the Pacific: before and after the implementation of DOTS. *Trop Doct.* 34.1:11-14.
17. **Clarke, M., J. Dick, and L. Bogg.** 2006. Cost-effectiveness analysis of an alternative tuberculosis management strategy for permanent farm dwellers in South Africa amidst health service contraction. *Scand J Public Health.* **34.**1:83-91.
18. **Currie C.S., K. Floyd, B.G. Williams, and C. Dye,** C. 2005. Cost, affordability, and cost-effectiveness of strategies to control tuberculosis in countries with high HIV prevalence. *BMC Public Health.* **5:**130.
19. **Deber, R.B.** 1994 .Physicians in health care management: The patient-physician partnership, decision making, problem solving, and the desire to participate *CMAJ.* **151**.4:423. Review.
20. **Desjardins, K.S., S.S. Cook, M. Jenkins, S. Bakken.** 2005. Effect of an informatics for evidence-based practice curriculum on nursing informatics competencies. *Int J Med Inform.* **74:**11-12; 1012-20.
21. **Donley, R.** 2006. *Challenges for nursing in the 21st Century.* Med Scape. Retrieved on May, 2006. *http: www.medscape.com/viewarticle/521379*
22. **Dasgupta, K, and D. Menzies**. 2005. Cost-effectiveness of tuberculosis control strategies among immigrants and refugees. *Eur Respir J,* **25.**6:1107-16.
23. **Department of Health and Human Services**. 2005. *Federal planning and response activities. HHS Pandemic Influenza Plan.* Retrieved in August 5, 2006. *http://pandemicflu.gov/plan/tab1.htm*l **Department of Health and Human Services. 2005.** *Planning assumptions HHS Pandemic influenza plan.* Retrieved in August 5, 2006. http://pandemicflu.gov/plan/pandplan.html.
24. **Department of Health and Human Services**. 2005. *State and local government planning and response activities. HHS pandemic influenza plan.* Retrieved in August 5, 2006 *http://pandemicflu.gov/plan/tab2.html*

25. **Department of Health and Human Services.** 2005. *State and local government planning checklist.* Influenza Plan. Retrieved in August 5, 2006 *http://pandemicflu.gov/plan/statelocalchecklist.html.*)
26. **Department of Health and Human Services. Centers for Disease Control and Prevention**. Facts about tuberculosis. Retrieved November, 2006. *http://www2.ncid.cdc.gov/travel/yb/utils/ybGet.asp?obj=tb.htm&section=dis*
27. **Department of Health and Human Services. Centers for Disease Control and Prevention**. TB Program Evaluation Plan Retrieved in August 5, 2006 *http://www.cdc.gov/NCHSTP/tb/Program_Evaluation/*
28. **Dick J., S. Lewin, E. Rose, M. Zwarenstein, and H. Walt.** 2004. Changing professional practice in tuberculosis care: an educational intervention. *J Adv Nurs.* **48.**5:434-442.
29. **Dye, C., C.J. Watt, D.M. Bleed, S.M. Hosseini, and M.C. Raviglione**. 2005. Evolution of tuberculosis control and prospects for reducing tuberculosis incidence, prevalence, and deaths globally. *JAMA,* **293.**22:2767-75.
30. **El Paso City-County Health & Environmental District Service Directory**. Retrieved in 2005. *www.elpasocitycountyhealth.com.*
31. **El Paso City & County Fire Department. Emergency Management Department** 2004 *Basic Emergency Operations Plan.*
32. **Elias, C.A, and B.S. Tan.** 1990 Infectious disease control in a long-term refugee camp: The role of epidemiologic surveillance and investigation. *American Journal of Public Health.* **80.**7: 824-828.
33. **Epidemiologic Transition Theory Exception**, Retrieved in 2006. *www.demogr.mpg.de/Papers/workshops/020619_paper40.pdf*
34. **Fairchild, A.** 2004. Policies of inclusion. *American Journal of Public Health.* **94.**4: 528-539.
35. **Fox, J., B. Coffey, J. Mintert, T. Schroeder, L. Valentin**. 2005. The response to BSE in the United States. *The Magazine of Food, Farm, and Resource Issues.* **20.**2: 103-107.
36. **Garrette, L.** 1997. Infectious disease pathogens knows no borders, surveillance will be key tool in coming battle. *Nations Health.* **27.**1: 20.
37. **Giesecke, J**. 1996. Surveillance of infectious disease in the European Union. *Lancet.* **348.**9041: 1534.
38. **Gosnell, D.J.** 2006. Pandemic flu planning: get informed, be prepared, and work together. *Ohio Nurses Rev.* **81.**3:13.
39. **Gust, I.D, A.W. Hampson, and D. Lavanchy.** 2001. Planning for the next pandemic of influenza. *Rev Med Virol.* **11.**1:59-70. Review.
40. **Guzman, M.** 2005. Deciphering dengue: The Cuban experience. *Science.* **5740:**1495-1497.
41. **Halter, M J., C.A. Kleiner, R.F. Hess**. 2006. The experience of nursing students in an online doctoral program in nursing: a phenomenological study. *Int J Nurs Stud.* **43.**1: 99-105.
42. **Hatry, H.P.** 2004. *Public and private agencies need to manage for results, not measure them. Urban Institute* Retrieved in August, 2006. http://www.urban.org/url.cfm?ID=900731 pp. 1-3
43. **Hughes, R.B., H. Cummings, R.V. Allen.** 1993. The nurse extern practicum: a new Partnership between education and service. *J Nurs Staff Dev.* **9.**3: 118-21.
44. **Institute of Medicine.** 2001. *Crossing the Quality Chasm: A New Health System for the 21st Century.* pp. 1-7.
45. **Institute of Medicine**. 1999. *To err is human: building a safer health system.* pp. 1-6
46. **Krieger N., P.D. Waterman, J.T. Chen, M.J. Soobader, and S.V. Subramanian**. 2003. Monitoring socio-economic inequalities in sexually transmitted infections, tuberculosis, and violence: geocoding and choice of area-based socioeconomic measures--the public health disparities geocoding project (US). *Public Health Rep.* **118.**3.240-260.
47. **Kuiken, T.** 2005. Pathogen surveillance in animals. *Science.* **309.**5741: 1680
48. **Liebler, J, and C. McConnell**. 2004. *Management principles for health professionals.* (4th Ed.). Sudbury, MA: Jones and Bartlett Publishers. pp. 92-115.
49. **Lobato, M.N., Y.C. Wang, J.E. Becerra, P.M. Simone, K.G. Castro.** 2006. Improved program activities are associated with decreasing tuberculosis incidence in the United States. *Public Health Rep.* **121.**2:108-115.
50. **Maher, D.** 2003. The role of the community in the control of tuberculosis. *Tuberculosis. 83.*1-3: 177-82. Review.

51. **Meijer. A., M. Valette, J-C. Manuguerra, P. Perez-Brena, J. Paget, C. Brown, K. van der Velden.** 2005. Implementation of the community network of reference laboratories for human influenza in Europe. *Journal of Clinical Virology*. **34**.2: 87-96.
52. **Mikesell, J.** 2003. *Fiscal administration: Analysis and applications for the public sector.* (6th ed). New York, New York, USA: Wadsworth Publishing.
53. **Mitka, M.** 2006. National plan for pandemic flu unveiled. *JAMA*. **295.**23:2707-2708.
54. **Moore, K, and D. Biordi**. 1995. Nurses' retirement preparation. *J Nurs Adm*. **25.**6: 62-7.
55. **Mukherjea, A**. 2003. Stopping AIDS global patents, local effects, and the management of national borders. *Radical Society: Review of Culture and Politics*. **30.**2: 11-18.
56. **Murray, C.J, and A.D. Lopez.** 1997. Alternative projections of mortality and disability by cause 1990-2020: Global burden of disease study. *Lancet*. **349.**9064: 1498-504.
57. **Nelson, A., J. Tam, Y. Ly-Mee, J. Breese, C-H. Kin-Hung Poon, I. Kin-Sing, T-C. Mast, P.K. Chan, U. Parashar, F. Tai-Fai, R. Glass**. 2005. Hospital based study of the economic burden associated with Rotavirus. *Journal of Infectious Disease*. **9:** S64-S70.
58. **Nelson, A., J. Tam, Y. Ly-Mee, J. Breese, C-H. Kin-Hung Poon, I. Kin-Sing, T-C. Mast, P.K. Chan, U. Parashar, F. Tai-Fai, R. Glass**. 2005. Estimate of Rotavirus disease burden in Hong Kong: Hospital based surveillance. *Journal of Infectious Disease*. **192:** S71-S79.
59. **Neff, M.** 2004. HHS funds disease surveillance system along U.S-Mexico border. *American Family Physician*. **69.**2:254-254.
60. **Nokes, D. J, and R.M. Anderson**. 1988. The use of mathematical models in the epidemiological study of infectious diseases and in the design of mass immunization programmes. *Epidemiol Infect*. **101.**1:1-20. Review.
61. **Oberprieler, G., K, Masters, and T. Gibbs**. 2005. Information technology and information literacy for first year health sciences students in South Africa: Matching early and professional needs. *Med Teach*. **27.**7: 595-8.
62. **Ojeda, N**. 2003. Underutilization of reproductive healthcare services by women who are ineligible for employer-subsidized socialized Medicare. *International Feminist Journal of Politics*. **5.**1: 20-47.
63. **Omran, A.R**. 1977. Epidemiologic transition in the United States: the health factor in population change. *Popul Bull. May*. **32**.2:1-42.
64. **Patton, C.V., D.S. Sawicki**. 1993. *Basic methods of policy analysis and planning*, (2nd Ed.). Prentice Hall, USA.
65. **Physicians Involvement in Quality Improvement**. 2005. *Health Affairs*. **24.**3:843-853.
66. **Pio, A., F. Luelmo, J. Kumaresan, S. Spinaci.** 1997. National tuberculosis programmes review: experience over the period 1990-95. *Bull World Health Organ*. **75.**6 569-581. Review
67. **Publication Guidelines:** The beginning of a consensus project. 2005. *Quality and Safety in Health Care*. **14.**5:319-325.
68. **Raleigh, V**. 1999. Trends in world population: How will the millennium compare with the past. *Human Reproduction Updates*. **5:**500-507.
69. **Reuters Health.** *Shared decision making not always a positive patient experience*. Medscape. Retrieved June, 2006. *http.www.medscape.comveiwarticle/522895?src=mp.*
70. **Rogers, R.G, and R. Hackenberg.** 1987. Extending epidemiologic transition theory: a new stage. *Soc Biol. 34:3-4.234-43*
71. **Rossi, H. P., M.W, Lipsey, and H.E. Freeman**. 2004. *Evaluation: A systematic approach.* (7th ed.). Thousand Oaks CA, USA: Sage Publications.
72. **Ruzicka, L.T.** 1983. Mortality transition in the third world countries: Issues for research *International Union Science Study Population*. **17:** 60-82.
73. **Schneider, E., K.F. Laserson, C.D. Wells, M. Moore**. 2004. Tuberculosis along the United States-Mexico border, 1993-2001. *Rev Panam Salud Publica*. **16.**1:23-34.
74. **Scorgie, F.** 2002. Virginity testing and the politics of sexual responsibility. Implications for AIDS intervention. **61.**1:55-75.
75. **Serow W.J., Cowart, and M.E, Camezon.** 1998. Epidemiologic Transition Theory and Aging: Hispanic Populations of North America and the Caribbean. *J. Health and Human Services Administration*. **20**.3: 333-47.
76. **Smith, D.J.** 2006. Predictability and preparedness in influenza control. *Science*. **312.**5772:392-394.
77. **Simon, B.**2002. A border giveth and a border taketh away. *New York Times*. **151.**52085: 1-2.
78. **Simpson R.L.** 2005. From tele-ed to telehealth: the need for IT ubiquity in nursing. *Nurs Adm Q*. **29.**4: 344-8.

79. **Sperroff, T, and G.T. O'Connor.** 2004. Study designs for PDSA quality improvement research. *Quality Management in Health Care*. **13.**1:17-32.
80. **Spetz J and S. Adams S.** 2006. How can employment based benefits help the nursing profession. *Health Affairs*. **25.**1:212-218.
81. **Stehr, M.** 2005. Cigarette tax avoidance and evasion. *Journal of Health Economics*. **24.**2: 277-297.
82. **Texas Department of State Health Services**. 2005. *Texas State and Local Planning and Response Activities. In Pandemic Influenza Preparedness Plan*. Retrieved in August, 2006. *http://pandemicflu.gov/plan/states/texas.html* .
83. **Texas Homeland Security Strategic Plan** 2006. State of Texas Emergency Management Plan Retrieved in August, 2006 *ftp://ftp.txdps.state.tx.us/dem/plan_state/state_plan_20040211.pdf*
84. **McConnell, J.** 2006. The Lancet forum on preparing for pandemic influenza. *Lancet Infect Dis*. **6.**7:390-2.
85. **Underwood, B.R., V.L. White, T. Baker, M. Law, and J.C. Moore-Gillon**. 2003. Contact tracing and population screening for tuberculosis- who should be assessed. *J Public Health Med*. **25.**4: 390-391.
86. **Van Man, N., L-T. Luan, D. Trach, N. Thanh, P-L. van Tu, A.D. Nguyen, T. Fischer, B.Thea, B. Ivanoff, J. Gentsch, R. Glass.** 1998. Epidemiological Profile and Burden of Rotavirus Diarrhea in Vietnam: 5 years of Sentinel Hospital Surveillance, 1998-2003. *Journal of Infectious Disease.* **192:**127-132.
87. **van Rensburg H.C., H. Meulemans, L. Rigouts, J.C. Heunis, E.J. van Rensburg, S.Z. Matebesi, A. Van der Spoel, C. Timmerman, D. De Graeve, L. Pauwels, F. Portaels, B. Gryseels, J. van Houtte**. 2004, 2005. Social research as an intervention tool in tuberculosis control. *Int J Tuberc Lung Dis,* 1127-1129. *Erratum in: Int J Tuberc Lung Dis.* **9:**588.
88. **Weinberg, M, S.L. Waterman, A. Carlos, V. Falcon, P. Morales, L. Lopez, C. Peter, A. Gutierrez, E. Gonzalez, A. Flisser, R. Bryan, E. Valle, A. Rodriguez, G. Hernandez, C. Rosales, J. Ortiz, M. Landen, H. Vilchis, J. Rawlings**.2003. The US-Mexico border infectious disease surveillance project: Establishing binational border surveillance. *Emerging Infectious Disease*.**9.**1: 97.
89. **Williams S.C, S.P. Schmaltz, D.J. Morton, R.G. Koss, J.M. Loeb.** 2005. Quality of care in US hospitals as reflected by standardized measures, 2002-2004. *New England Journal of Medicine*. **353.**3:255-264.
90. **Webb R.M., M. Holcombe., M.M. Pearson.** 2003. Tuberculosis contact investigation in a rural state. *Int J Tuberc Lung Dis.* **7.**12 -3:S353-7. Review
91. **Winterfeld, A, and R. Morgan.** 2006. Preparing for a pandemic: concern over a possible avian flu pandemic is moving states, communities, and the federal government to action. *State Legis*. **32.**4:4-18.
92. **Zavala De Cosio, M.E.** 1992. The Demographic Transition in Latin America and Europe. *Notas Poblacion*. **20:**11-32.

INDEX

E

F

T